study in SPAIN

Handbook

Written and researched by
Sara Goulden

ON COURSE PUBLICATIONS

Publishers
Jeremy Hunt, Mike Elms

Managing editor
Alice Cox

Editorial team
Sara Goulden, David Pievsky

Design and typesetting
Colleen Chong, Angela Jenkins

Front cover photographs supplied by the
Spanish National Tourist Office

The publishers and editors made strenuous efforts to
ensure that the information in this guide was correct
when the publication went to press and they can
accept no responsibility for any errors or omissions.
Colleges reserve the right to make changes to their
curriculum, course content, and prices at any time.

ISBN 1 898730 25 3
© Elms Hunt International Limited 1999

On Course Publications
121 King Street, London W6 9JG UK
Tel: 0181 600 5300 Fax: 0181 741 7716
E-mail: jeremy@oncourse.co.uk
Web: www.oncourse.co.uk

Contents

USING THE GUIDE   **4**

STUDYING IN SPAIN   **5**
   Spain and the Spanish   5
   Arriving in Spain   18
   Applying to study in Spain   24
   The Spanish Education System   25
   Living in Spain   29

COURSE AREAS   **41**
   Art and Design   41
   Dance   63
   Language Schools   83
   Miscellaneous   203
   Bullfighting   203
   Acting   204
   Cooking   208
   Dressmaking and Fashion Design   213
   Teaching   217
   Music   218
   Sport   229
   Wine and Coffee Testing   233
   Cultural activities   235

UNIVERSITIES   **239**
   Studying for a degree   239
   Postgraduate studies   244
   Listing of addresses   247

INDEX   **254**

Using the Guide

Rich in tradition and one of the most romantic cities in Europe, Spain offers anyone wishing to venture there a large range of courses. Perhaps you are at university and considering options for your year in Spain. Maybe you are on a gap year looking for rewarding educational activities that could be combined with an exciting travel schedule. You might even be staying in Spain indefinitely. In any case, if you need to find out anything about study in Spain, from the best language schools to the most seductive flamenco techniques, then this guide should have all the information you need.

STRUCTURE OF THE GUIDE

On Course World Study Guides are designed to give you everything you need to make a success of studying away from home. If you are not Spanish, the Arriving in Spain section (*from page 18*) will tell you everything you need to know. It covers visa and immigration requirements, and aspects of Spanish culture with which you may be unfamiliar. If you are Spanish or live in Spain, you may want to skip this section. The subject section contains four chapters covering the main subject areas you might be considering: Art and Design, Dance, Language Studies, and Miscellaneous studies. Whether you are looking for a full-time degree course or basic instruction in disciplines with lots of Spanish character, the guide offers extensive information that will be useful for prospective students, and at the same time a relaxed and enjoyable written

account of Spain and Spanish culture. The exciting variations in Spanish life owe much to its traditions, and you will find facts about flamenco dancing and Spanish cuisine, as well as artistic and musical institutions. The chapters include practical information on courses, and contact details by phone, fax or email for all the institutions listed. There follows a section on Spanish universities. The guide covers all the main universities in Spain, including extended profiles for a selection of them. Use these to get a feel for universities you are considering applying to, and to find out key information, such as whether it is a campus or a town university, which subject areas are particularly strong, and whether the facilities meet your requirements.

Throughout the guide for reasons of consistency and brevity, certain conventions are observed. All internet addresses omit the 'http://' and start with 'www' followed by the address. All telephone numbers include the code for Spain, 34, and need to be preceded by the international code if calling from outside Spain. If you have any suggestions for the next issue of this guide, please do not hesitate to contact On Course in the UK on 0181 600 5300, 0181 741 7716 (fax) or jeremy@oncourse.co.uk (email). The writers of the best letters that we receive get a free copy of next year's edition, or indeed any other On Course guide if that is preferable.

Spain and the Spanish

SPAIN

Of all the cliché-ridden countries in Europe, there can be few that have been typecast as much as Spain. They are those familiar symbols that, to most, represent Spain and the Spanish, such as the bullfight, castanets, sangria and beaches overflowing with lobster-red tourists. Although the Spanish seem quite happy for these stereotypes to remain (a passivity that is in itself quite typically Spanish), these peeling tourist poster images cast very little light on what lies behind them.

It is hard to pinpoint any one thing that encapsulates "the real Spain" because the country itself (which forms the Iberian Peninsula, together with the chunk of land on its left hand side – Portugal) is a patchwork of different *comunidades autónomas*, each with its own very particular identity.

A *comunidade autónoma* is like a hybrid of a county (eg Yorkshire in the UK) and a state (eg Washington in the USA). The *comunidades autónomas* are self-governing, with more power than a county and less than a state, and each is formed by either a group of provinces (eg Cáceres and Badajoz are the provinces that make up the *comunidad autónoma* of Extremadura) or a single province (eg the province of Madrid is the *comunidad autónoma* of Madrid). To see how Spain is divided into her different *comunidades autónomas* consult the map on *pages 7 to 8*.

The *comunidades autónomas* that form Spain are as follows. The name in bold is the name of the *comunidad autónoma*, the names following it are those of the names of the provinces within that *comunidad autónoma*.

PAÍS VASCO: Bilbao, Vitoria (the capital), San Sebastián
CATALUNA Lérida, Tarragona, Gerona, Barcelona (the capital)
GALICIA Santiago de Compostela (the capital), La Coruña, Lugo, Orense, Pontevedra
ASTURIAS Oviedo (the capital)
CANTABRIA Santander (the capital)
LA RIOJA Logroño (the capital)
ARAGÓN Zaragoza (the capital), Huesca, Teruel
CASTILLA Y LEÓN León, Palencia, Burgos, Soria, Segovia, Ávila, Salamanca, Zamora, Valladolid (the capital)
ANDALUCÍA Sevilla (the capital), Huelva, Córdoba, Jaén, Almería, Granada, Málaga, Cádiz
COMUNIDAD VALENCIANA Castellón, Valencia (the capital), Alicante
MADRID Madrid
MURCIA Murcia (capital)
CASTILLA-LA MANCHA Guadalajara, Cuenca, Albacete, Ciudad Real, Toledo (the capital)
EXTREMADURA Cáceres, Mérida (the capital), Badajoz

Islands
ISLAS CANARIAS Sta Cruz de Tenerif, Las Palmas de Gran Canaria

5

ISLAS BALEARES Palma de Mallorca

The two Spanish outposts at the tip of North Africa
CEUTA Ceuta
MELILLA Melilla

Of course, to the outsider, the differences between these may seem negligible, but to the Spanish, the part of Spain that they come from is an integral part of their individual make-up. They are intensely proud of their regional identity; in some regions – Cataluña, for example – even more so than they are of their national identity.

Spaniards are quick to ascribe regional characteristics to one another. Recently, the country's foremost paper, El País, carried out a survey in its Sunday colour supplement. The survey, entitled *'Así somos: El retrato más completo de los españoles por comunidades autonomas'* ('The way we are: the most complete portrait of the Spanish, according to their autonomous provinces'), examines the Spanish in relation to the regions, or autonomous communities (*comunidades autónomas*), in which they live. The survey concludes, amongst other things, that those who tend to live the longest are the inhabitants of Castilla León, while those who drink the most alcohol come from Galicia (those from Madrid – *Madrileños* – are, apparently, the most abstemious).

The *comunidades autónomas* have, as their name suggests, a certain amount of autonomy. They are responsible for many aspects of their own government (eg health and hygiene, welfare, agriculture, the organisation of its institutions for self-government). The DNI – Documento Nacional de Indentidad –

is the official identification document in Spain. All Spaniards must possess one.

Although the official language of Spain is Castellano, several other languages are spoken in certain parts of the country. The most notable of these is Catalan. A language evolved from vulgar Latin, and which in some ways resembles Castellano, Catalan is spoken in Cataluña, the Islas Baleares, Valencia, and a small strip of Aragón, Andorra, much of the Pyrénées Orientales in southern France and the town of L'Alguer on the Italian island of Sardinia. It is estimated that about 6,000,000 people speak it, though it had no dictionary or rules of spelling until the beginning of the 20th century. Franco's dictatorship prohibited the use of Catalan and so it has only recently been recognised officially. A visitor to any Catalan-speaking part of Spain – Barcelona, for example – will find that signs, menus and other information are usually written in Catalan first and Castellano second. Language students should find that learning Castellano does not present a problem in Catalan-speaking areas. However, courses in both languages are run side-by-side in most Catalan language institutions. In many ways it makes more sense to study Castellano in the parts of Spain where it is the first language.

The other two languages spoken in Spain are Euskera (Basque) and Gallego (Galician). Neither of these is used on the same scale as Catalan, and both can be learnt at certain specialist institutions situated in the respective areas where they are spoken.

Having established that Spain is indeed far more than one vast tourist industry of beaches, tourists and hotels (a description really only appropriate to the famous Costa del Sol, the Islas Canarias (Canary Islands) and the Islas Baleares), the question remains, what is Spain really like?

The main facts and statistics for Spain (according to the Manual del Estado Español, 1994, edited by LAMA, SL) are as follows:

- The surface area of the country is 505,992km². Of this, 493,486km² correspond to the Peninsula, 4,992km² to the Islas Baleares, 7,447km² to the Islas Canarias, 20km² to Ceuta and 14km² to Melilla (both on the tip of North Africa), as well as the minor islands of Peñón de Vélez de la Gomera and the Islas Chafarinas.

- According to the 1992 census, the Spanish population numbers 39,085,083 inhabitants, which works out at a density of some 78 inhabitants per km².

- There are 8,077 *municipios* (cities, towns, villages, etc.) in Spain, of which six contain more than 500,000 inhabitants.

- Spain is governed by a Parliamentary Monarchy (*Monarquía Parlimentaría*) and its constitution was signed on December 27 1978.

- Castellano is the official language of Spain.

- The official national holiday of Spain is October 12. Other national holidays are: January 1 (New Year); Good Friday (*Viernes Santo*); August 15, Ascension Day (*Asunción de la Virgen*), November 1, All Saints Day (*Día de Todos los Santos*); December 6, Spanish Constitution Day (*Día de*

la Constitución Española), December 8, the Immaculate Conception (*la Inmaculada Concepción*), December 25, Christmas Day (*la Natividad del Señor*). Each *comunidad autónoma* also has its own *fiestas* (holidays), although some dates are recognised by more than one *comunidad*. These dates are, principally, January 6 (*Epifanía del Señor*, Twelfth Night – the day on which all Spanish families open their Christmas presents), Jueves Santo (Holy Thursday) and July 25 (*Santiago Apóstol*).

- Every city, town and *pueblo* (roughly translated, this means village) has its own patron saint and it is said that there is at least one holiday celebrating a patron saint for every day of the year. This means that you could spend an entire year journeying around Spain attending each one and you still wouldn't have covered them all. When in Spain you may hear the Spanish talk about a puente. Literally, this means "bridge". It also refers to the long weekends that the Spanish take, en masse, when a holiday happens to fall on a Thursday or Friday, or when two holidays fall a day or two apart. A trip to the office in the intervening day(s) is a waste of time as no one else will have bothered to turn up to work.

MADRID
In the centre of a barren plain, at the geographical heart of the country, lies Madrid, the capital of Spain. Like London, it is a spreading metropolis whose suburbs seem daily to be swallowing up the satellite towns that surround it. Its centre somewhat resembles Paris, with its wide avenues and its sculpted park (the Retiro). The buildings are mainly

FRANCE

San Sebastián

Vitoria

Pamplona

Gulf of Lion

Portbou

groño

Huesca

Figueras

Girona

Soria

Zaragoza

Lleida

Barcelona

Calatayud

Tarragona

Balearic Sea

MINORCA

Teruel

Inca

Artá

Cuenca

Castellón de la Plana

Balearic Islands

MAJORCA

cón

Palma

Utiel

Valencia

Buñol

ISLA DE CABRERA

IBIZA

Albacete

ISLA DE FORMENTERA

Alicante

Murcia

Cartagena

Mediterranean Sea

Almería

e Alborán
Spain)

ALGERIA

| 0 | 50 | 100km |
| 0 | 50 | 100mi |

turn-of-the-century or modern. Depending on the part (*barrio*) of Madrid that you happen to be in, these buildings will either be beautifully maintained (as in the area around the grand Paseo del Prado) or charmingly unkempt (the more bohemian La Latina). A visitor approaching Madrid from the North will enter the city through the twin leaning towers of the Puerta de Europa, which mark the point where the city ends and the suburbs of Madrid begin.

Madrid is a vibrant city, though quite unlike London or Paris in terms of its status as a capital city. In fact, despite the fact that it is the seat of political power and the base from which the Royal Family operate (the *Palacio Real* – the Royal Palace – is located to the west of the city centre), it has an oddly provincial, laid-back feel to it. Its most central avenues are impressive, yet it lacks a certain gravitas and its inhabitants (on the whole) simply do not possess the cosmopolitan air of city dwellers in London or Paris. Indeed, apart from those who have crossed the Atlantic from South America (Argentina, Colombia), there seem to be few resident foreigners in this city. Madrileños, it would seem, are firmly, and resolutely, Spanish.

Yet one great advantage of this (and there are many) is the fact that Madrileños will be only too happy to help if you stop them to ask for directions. Despite the fact that their English may well be virtually non-existent, they will make a genuine effort to understand and be understood. As a rule, Madrileños seem to possess none of the snobbishness of most European capital city inhabitants, who regard tourists or "visitors" as somewhat inferior beings. In Madrid, the opposite appears to be true, and Madrileños tend to be genuinely intrigued by foreigners.

There are several beautiful sights in Madrid, yet one of the most rewarding experiences for any newcomer to the city is simply to do as the Spanish do: sit in a bar on a busy square, sip your *café con leche* and watch the world go by. Almost every street, no matter how small, will have at least one bar on it, and at certain times of the day this will be overflowing with customers, from groups of men enjoying a mid morning coffee or beer to mothers grabbing a quick breakfast with their children before school. Indeed this is a phenomenon true of the rest of Spain, where bars are meeting places for everyone, of any age.

Unlike most European capitals, no river (as such) runs through Madrid. A manmade effort (the Río Manzanares) runs down the western side of the city, though its exact purpose is obscure. Certainly, it is not a significant landmark.

Madrid's major landmarks include the Retiro, the capital's main park, and three major galleries: the Prado, the Centro de Arte Moderna Reina Sofia and the Thyssen-Bornemisza. All are located on, or slightly set back from, the wide, tree-lined avenue of the Paseo del Prado (near the main train station and a few metro stops from the geographical centre of Madrid), which means that it is possible to visit them all in one day. However, to really appreciate the galleries and their content, the discerning culture-vulture should allow at least a half day for each. Of particular note is the Prado, a magnificent and vast monument to the art from the 15th to the 19th centuries. A must on any tourist checklist are the rooms devoted to the Spanish "greats": Velázquez and Goya, though these are only the icing on the cake, for the entire contents of the Prado would literally take days to view. According to popular knowledge, the gallery has in storage three times the amount that is already on display. The Centro Reina Sofía (named after Spain's present Queen) houses that which is not contained in the Prado – works from the beginning of the 20th century up to the present day. Works by Dalí, Picasso, Miró and many other leading Spanish artists of this century are displayed in spare rooms on stark white walls. The building itself (constructed around a courtyard and several storeys high), is austere and echoey, a reminder of the fact that it was once a hospital. For a view of the rooftops of south Madrid, take one of the two glass lifts featured prominently on the outside of the building to the top floor, and from there work your way down to the ground floor of the museum. The privately owned Thyssen-Bornemycza contains art spanning about six centuries over three floors, offering a choice to suit the most varied tastes.

As is probably only to be expected of a capital city, Madrid is home to the largest number of language schools in Spain. Both large organisations and smaller schools offer a range of classes catering to every need, be it Spanish for business purposes or merely Spanish for pleasure. From the point of view of language, Madrid is probably one of the safest options for any foreigner wishing to learn Castellano, as the type of Spanish spoken here is considered to be correct in terms of grammar and pronunciation. The "best" Spanish, allegedly, is spoken in a city in the north called Valladolid. Madrid and its environs are host to a number of state universities (Universidad Complutense de Madrid – UCM and the Universidad Autónoma de Madrid being the most well-known) and some private institutions.

Considering that it is a capital city, living in Madrid is not expensive, though it is pricier compared to the rest of the country. It is possible to live well on about 100,000ptas per month as basic living costs are not too great. The price of renting a better-than-average piso (apartment) will come to a maximum of about 50,000ptas and food costs are relatively low. There are a number of covered markets in Madrid, where it is possible to buy delicious, fresh produce at a low price. Supermarkets are also good value. A

few tapas and a couple of glasses of wine in a bar will probably leave you with change from 1,000ptas.

There are a number of American and British expats living in Madrid and the recent publication of a newspaper written in English ('In Madrid') catering to these residents, is testament to the fact that their numbers are growing. In Madrid is free and can be picked up at any number of establishments, including the dozen or so Irish bars around the capital. For anyone feeling homesick and a bit weary of Spanish food, these offer a reassuring pint of Guinness or Murphy's (depending which pub you happen to be in), pub grub and the dulcit tones of English and Irish voices. On St Patrick's Day these are invariably impossible to get into, as the English, Irish and American communities jostle to get in alongside the *pijos* (Spanish yuppies). If, on a regular basis, you choose to frequent these bars and mix in these circles, then it is likely that you will not speak a great deal of Spanish. It is, however, easy to socialise outside these spheres and to make friends with Spanish people who would rather you spoke to them in broken Spanish (they will probably be very encouraging) than speak to you in (probably more broken) English.

The Spanish love the Irish and their *cerveza negra* (black beer – ie Guinness and Murphy's) but are rather less enthusiastic about the British. Those Spanish school/college kids who have visited either the UK or Ireland, or both, will profess to an undying love of all things Irish and a violent dislike for the English and their unfriendly ways. Of course, these assumptions are usually based on little more than a fortnight spent in some grotty youth

Irish pubs in Madrid

Bo Finn, Velázquez, 97, (Metro Diego de León); tel +34 91 411 4079

Finnegans, Plaza de las Salesas, 9 (Metro Alonso Martínez); tel +34 91 310 0521

The Irishman, Santísima Trinidad, 32 (Metro Iglesia); tel +34 91 448 0104

The Irish Rover, Avenida de Brazil, 7, Metro Lima; tel +34 91 597 4811

Moore's, Felipe III, 4 (Metro Sol); tel +34 91 365 5602

O'Donnells, Barceló, 1, (Metro Tribunal); tel +34 91 532 6331

O'Neill's, Príncipe, 12, (Metro Sevilla); tel +34 91 521 2030

The Quiet Man, Valverde, 44, (Metro Gran Vía); tel +34 91 523 4689

Triskel Tavern, San Vicente Ferrer, 3 (Metro Tribunal); tel +34 91 523 2783

hostel in London, where the fact that they go round in noisy and slow-moving packs makes them the bane of any regular London Underground user's life. However, there is probably much about the Irish way of life and the Irish inclination to relaxation and conversation, with which the Spanish youth (and the Spanish people as a whole) can identify.

There is a large and growing band of American students who come to live in Madrid for the year on one of their university's semester or year-long "Spanish Abroad" schemes. Their yearnings for home are catered for at Taste of America, a wildly expensive (by Madrid standards) shop selling America's favourite comestibles.

Because of its location, Madrid is the ideal place from which to explore the country. So, if you tire of the bars and nightlife, the cafe life and the museums, you can always jump on a bus, train or even, a plane, to anywhere else in Spain. Depending on your chosen form of transport, journeys will take anything from an hour (eg the plane to Barcelona) to an overnight trip (eg the train down south to Almería).

Around Madrid
For a fast escape from city life, there are several destinations in the immediate environs of Madrid. On a Saturday or Sunday it is not uncommon for *Madrileños* to drive out into the countryside of the Comunidad de Madrid, to places such as Aranjuez, Toledo, El Escorial, El Valle de los Caídos, the Sierra and Puerto de Navacerrada and Segovia. Here, they will often stay for no more than a few hours to enjoy a long lunch, go for a stroll and then return to the city. Aranjuez is famous for its beautiful gardens and

strawberries and cream. Toledo, a town once dominated in turn by Moors, Christians and Jews deserves a whole day or even an overnight stay. It contains some wonderful churches, mosques and synagogues, as well as the house of El Greco (1540-1614) containing some of his elongated and haunting portraits. El Escorial, the vast 16th century monastery-palace of Felipe II that lies to the north of the capital, requires comfortable shoes and plenty of patience. El Valle de los Caídos is the eerie and imposing monument to Franco that is located not far from El Escorial. Beneath an immense cross, visible for miles around, lies an underground basilica. In the winter skiers can spend the weekend (or longer) at the Puerto de Navacerrada in the Sierra Madrileña. Finally, Segovia is a handsome town renowned for its enormous aqueduct – a legacy left behind by Spain's Roman invaders

SPAIN BY ITS COMU-NIDADES AUTÓNOMAS
With the *comunidad autónoma* of Madrid (whose capital, Madrid, is also the capital of Spain) at its geographical centre, Spain is neatly divided into north and south.

As outlined above, the differences between the Spanish depend less on this relatively clean partition and more on the region from which they come. Having said that, a Spaniard speaking to a foreigner in a bar was once heard to say that those who come from the north, although they seem cold at first, will soon open up to you. In the south, however, although people appear very friendly at first, the better you try to get to know them, the more closed they become. As with most overheard information, this is probably a very unreliable, and probably entirely erroneous, rule. Nonetheless, it gives an idea of the two basic Spanish national stereotypes.

The North

Aragón

Situated in the northeast of Spain, the northernmost edge of Aragón touches the south west of France at the Pyrenees. This area is popular primarily for the outdoors activities offered by the Pyrenees, particularly trekking. The major city of Aragón is Zaragoza, a large, thriving town, which is the focus of this region's biggest annual festival (October 12), in honour of the Virgen del Pilar. Places of interest include the Parque Nacional de Ordesa (a national park), the medieval architecture of Mudèjar and the Aljafería Palace in Zaragoza.

Asturias

The principality of Asturias (the heir to the Spanish throne is known as the Príncipe de Asturias) stretches along one section of the northern coast of Spain. The only part of Spain that was never conquered by the Moors, it is characterised by old-fashioned seaside towns and resorts.

Cantabria

Cantabria, which shares a part of the northern coastline together with Galicia and Euskadi (Basque country), is a destination popular for 'turismo rural', the term used to describe walking, trekking, mountaineering, and any other similar sport that takes place in the open air. The Picos de Europa, which act as a sort of dividing line between Asturias and Cantabria, are the glorious backdrop for most such pastimes, as well as for skiing in the winter. Santander, capital of Cantabria, is a tourist resort well known amongst

the Spanish (particularly the well-heeled *madrileños*). It is also the setting for a Jazz and International Music Festival in July and August.

Castilla y León

Valladolid, Salamanca and Ávila are probably the best known towns in this *comunidad autónoma*. As Spain's most famous university town, Salamanca's reputation ranks with Oxford, Cambridge, Harvard and Yale, and like its British counterparts, this has bred a large community of language schools second only to that in Madrid. On the basis of the fact that if you're going to learn the language and culture of a place, you might as well learn it in the most academically renowned part of the country, Salamanca teems with foreign students both at the height of summer (when no Spanish students are in sight) and throughout the academic year. It is somewhat ironic that Valladolid, supposedly the town in Spain where the best Spanish is spoken, although in the same region, hosts nothing like the same number of foreign language students as Salamanca. The University of Salamanca runs its own official language classes, but there are many other language schools to choose from. The town itself is very beautiful. With its enormous *Plaza Mayor*, narrow cobbled streets and ornate architecture, it imparts a true sense of gravitas.

Ávila, supposedly Spain's only remaining walled city whose wall is still intact, rises from the plains of Castilla y León like a medieval fortress. Its quiet winding streets and cathedral are well worth a visit.

Cataluña

If such a thing as the capital of northern Spain existed, then the title-holder would probably be Barcelona, Cataluña's most famous city. This could be due to its geographical location (a port on the east coast of Spain – the Costa Brava) or its economic weight (it is home to a thriving business community). In truth, however, it might have more to do with the fact that it exudes an importance that makes it appear more stately, at times, than Madrid. There is something about it – its groomed streets, its polished inhabitants, and its general air of wealth and sophistication – that makes the visitor feel as though they have arrived in a sort of Paris-on-Sea. The marked lack of warmth in the attitude of many Barceloneses towards visitors to the city only compounds this impression.

The city is characterised by the architectural influence of one man in particular – Antonio Gaudí. His unfinished (and roofless) church of the Sagrada Familia is Barcelona's principle landmark, and the city itself is a showcase for his art and his style. The Parc Güell, peopled by fantastical Gaudí creations and shapes covered in mosaics of multicoloured pottery, is a wonderful place to sit and contemplate the city, above which it stands.

Barcelona tries, and in some ways succeeds, to make itself as unlike the rest of Spain as possible. As the capital of Cataluña, a region that craves its own independence from the rest of Spain, it is intensely proud and fiercely protective of its own identity. The first language spoken here is not Castellano (i.e. Spanish – the language that is spoken in most of the rest of Spain), but Catalan. This is a language that resembles Castellano but which is most definitely not a dialect of it (never even suggest this to a Catalan – they would most probably never speak to you again, in Catalan or any other language!). Do not be surprised to hear a Barcelonès wishing a visitor from another part of Spain a safe journey "back to Spain" when they go home – Cataluña simply does not consider itself to be a part of Spain.

Outside of Barcelona, the beaches of the Costa Brava, which are considered to be some of the loveliest in Spain, offer the visitor an alternative beach holiday to the crowded sands of the Costa del Sol. Further up the coast from Barcelona is Figueres, home to the legendary Dalí museum. A unique creation in itself, the building houses a variety of Dalí memorabilia and art.

Galicia

Galicia, which sits at the top left-hand corner of Spain, looking out over the Atlantic above Portugal, is probably most famous for Santiago de Compostela the destination of one of the most well travelled pilgrimage routes in the world. Said to be one of the most beautiful cities in the whole of Spain, Santiago has been deemed a national monument. It has been nominated the European Capital of Culture for the year 2000.

La Rioja

La Rioja not notable for much other than its wine, for which it is very well known.

Navarra

Pamplona, the capital of Navarra, is best known for the Fiesta de San Fermín which takes place annually between the July 6 and July 14 and which has, as its *pièce de rèsistance*, the running of the bulls. Essentially, this involves any number of tourists and locals running in front of six bulls. The fiesta has inspired other towns and pueblos throughout Spain to put on their own version of this, one of Spain's best known and most internationally renowned fiestas.

País Vasco (Euskadi)

The majority of people have probably heard of the País Vasco primarily through the acts of the terrorist group ETA ('*Euskadi ta Askatasuna*' – 'Freedom for the Basques'). Like the Catalans, many Vascos consider themselves to be apart from the rest of Spain, a feeling based on their long history of ruling themselves as an independent republic. As a result of the terrorist tactics employed by ETA it is, unsurprisingly, not a particularly popular destination for tourists. However, the recent inauguration of a new Guggenheim museum in the industrial town of Bilbao may change this somewhat. A magnificent structure that appears to rise like a vast titanium ship from the river by whose side it has been built, the Guggenheim museum alone is a good enough reason to visit Bilbao. With its vast rooms and "spaces", all devoted to modern art, it is hard to tell whether the greater attraction is what the building contains or the structure itself. The town, surrounded by green hills, suddenly glimpsed at the end of streets, offers excellent food and shopping. In short, it has all the makings of a successful European short-break destination. An already well known part of the País Vasco is the elegant seaside resort of San Sebastian, whose beautiful beaches are still a predominantly Spanish tourist attraction.

The South

Andalucía

Of all the provinces of the south of Spain, in fact, of all the provinces in Spain as a whole, the one with the most easily distinguishable image is Andalucía. Flamenco, sunshine, chilled gazpacho, oranges – these are all distinctly Andalucian characteristics rather than Spanish ones, yet to outsiders they have become some of the international symbols of Spain. It could be argued that there are three principle cities in Andalucía – Sevilla, Granada

and Córdoba. Of all the cities in Spain, these bear one of the strongest imprints of the Moorish presence in and influence on Spain, particularly with regard to their architecture. Even the name, Andalucía, is derived from the Moorish *al-Andalus*. In Sevilla famous Moorish monuments include the Alcázar and Giralda tower; in Córdoba there is the Mezquite; and in Granada is the Alhambra. This last is a magical Moorish palace with a beautiful garden (El Generalife) surrounding it. It stands against the awe-inspiring backdrop of the snowy peaks of the Sierra Nevada and below it lie the winding streets and picturesque charm of Granada's old Arabic quarter, the Albaicín.

Other parts of Andalucía will be familiar even to the traveller who has not yet visited Spain. There is the town of Málaga (Picasso's birthplace) and the famous Costa del Sol, which is lined with such towns as Torremolinos and Fuengirola. Algerciras in the very far south virtually touches the northern tip of Morocco, which is accessible by boat. The most famous fiesta in the area is probably Sevilla's Semana Santa (Holy Week) and its Feria, which take place in April.

Castilla-La Mancha
The legendary backdrop against which the fictional Don Quixote rode out his surreal adventures is that of Castilla-La-Mancha. Studded with olive groves and vineyards, the landscape is otherwise bare and rocky. The windmills for which Castilla-La Mancha is famous (Don Quixote famously "fought" a group of windmills, believing them to be attacking giants) are in evidence in the town of Valdepeñas. (Much of the everyday wine drunk around Spain comes from Valdepeñas). Also known

for its fields of sunflowers, Castilla-La Mancha is home to Cuenca, noted for the houses that hang perilously from the side of cliffs.

Extremadura
Situated to the west of Madrid, Extremadura has yet to really be discovered by tourists, partly because there seems to be little to attract them to it. The principal sites are the conquistador towns of Trujillo and Cáceres, the Roman remains at Mèrida and the Monastery of Guadalupe.

Murcia
Murcia, which is situated diagonally across the country from Galicia, in the south east corner of Spain, looking out onto the Mediterranean, is renowned for its beaches. It is perhaps the least exploited and most unspoilt part of the Spanish coast, though the area known as Torrevieja and towns such as Alicante are gaining in popularity among Spanish and international tourists alike.

Comunidad Valenciana
The Comunidad Valenciana, which is situated between Cataluña and Murcia on the east coast of Spain, and home of that most famous of Spanish dishes – paella – is another popular summer holiday destination. One of the most important festivals in Spain – the Fallas de San Josè – take place in Valencia between the March 12 and March 19. The fallas are famous for the creation, procession and then burning of the enormous papier maché figures and caricatures that have been worked on all year long by each barrio (district). These are judged during the week of March 12 and are then burned one after the other, on the night of March 19.

Arriving in Spain

Once you have made a decision as to where you would like to go, what you wish to study and how long for, you will need to make certain arrangements before leaving for Spain. If you have any doubts or queries, then it is probably best to contact the Spanish embassy or consulate closest to you. Alternatively, you may wish to consult the foreign office of your own country.

VISAS AND IMMIGRATION

To be admitted into Spain, you must have either a valid passport or a valid DNI (*Documento Nacional de Identidad*, the Spanish ID card – all Spaniards must carry one). It is important to ensure that you have all the necessary documentation well before leaving for Spain. Again, check with the Spanish embassy or consulate closest to you for exact details pertaining to your country of origin.

Those in possession of British or American passports do not usually have any difficulty in getting through customs. Do not expect the Spanish police to be particularly friendly – they will take your passport, check your photo (and, where relevant, visa) and will then allow you through with either a nod of the head or a wave of the hand. They will probably not smile at you.

If you are a citizen of the European Economic Area (EEA) (this includes all countries of the EU, Norway and Iceland) you have the right to live, study and work in Spain without a permit. If you are one of these, and you decide to work in Spain, you will be entitled to the same rights as Spanish nationals with regard to pay, working conditions, access to housing, vocational training, social security and trade union membership. Your family and

Embassy addresses in Madrid

Australia, Paseo de la Castellana, 143, 28046 Madrid; Tel +34 91 579 0428

Canada, Núñez de Balboa, 35, 28001 Madrid, tel: +34 91 431 4300

United States of America, Serrano, 75, 28006 Madrid, tel: +34 91 577 4000

Ireland (Eire), Claudio Coello, 73, 28001 Madrid, tel: +34 91 576 3500

New Zealand, Pl. Lealtad, 2, 28014 Madrid, tel: +34 91 523 0226

United Kingdom, Paseo de la Castellana, 15, 28046 Madrid, tel: +34 91 319 8400

South Africa, Claudio Coello, 91, 28006 Madrid, tel: +34 91 435 6688

British and Northern Irish Consulate, Marqués de la Ensenada, 16, 28004 Madrid, tel +34 91 308 5201

immediate dependants are allowed to join you and have similar rights.

Anyone coming to study in Spain from outside the EEA will need a visa. Students from America, Canada and Australia can remain in Spain for 90 days without a visa, but will need to obtain a visa at the end of that period in order to remain in Spain.

TRAVEL

When you first arrive in Spain, you will have to get from the airport, port or railway station to you destination. Madrid has one main airport – Barajas, which is located on the outskirts of the city.

Travel from Madrid-Barajas airport

You can access the city by bus. A special bus service runs from the airport to the centre of Madrid – Plaza de Colón – stopping several times en route. It costs about 380ptas and is convenient and safe.

The Madrid Metro

Once in the centre, you will probably have to take the Metro to your destination within the city. There is also a bus network running throughout Madrid, but unless you know which bus you wish to take and where from, the Metro is probably more user-friendly. The Madrid Metro is clean, efficient and relatively easy to use. However, if you are carrying heavy luggage, the journey to your platform may be quite arduous as there may be several sets of escalators to travel up or down and, in some stations, long corridors to walk through. There is a single tariff – 130ptas for a single

ticket- no matter what your destination. If you are planning to use the Metro frequently, you can either get hold of a 10-journey ticket, a *Metrobús*, which will cost you 670ptas or you can apply for an *Abono Transportes* (a travel card). Both of these options are valid for travel by bus. The *Abono Transportes* is undoubtedly the most economical option and is a very worthwhile investment if you will be in Madrid for a month or more. Depending on the area(s) of Madrid in which you will be travelling, you can choose the zone(s) that will be covered by your *abono*. To apply for an adult *abono* all you have to do is to go to your nearest *estanco* (tobacconists) with a photo of yourself and your passport. There you will be asked to fill in a form and you will be given your abono on the spot. The form costs about 200ptas. You will be charged accordingly for a whole month or for the entire year (whatever you choose) and you will be given a coupon entitling you to unlimited travel for the whole of that month. The set tariffs (for one month only) range from 4,275ptas for Zone A (central Madrid) to 7,800ptas for the furthest zone (C2). If you are a student or a senior citizen, and you have the documentation to prove your status, you will be eligible for either an *Abono Joven* (Youth Travel Card) or an *Abono Tercera Edad* (Senior Citizen's Travel Card), respectively. Senior citizens pay a flat monthly fee of 1,230ptas, regardless of zone, and students, depending on their zones, pay from 2,965ptas to 5,225ptas.

You can buy a new monthly travel permit for your *abono* between the twentieth day of the previous month and the tenth day of the new month. If you miss these dates, you will be unable to obtain your pass for that month. Should this occur, your *abono* will not become invalid, you will simply have to wait to buy next month's.

Unlike the underground or subway systems in some major cities, the Madrid Metro is relatively safe. Unless you happen to be in or live in a particularly insalubrious neighbourhood (there are a few of these, mainly to the south of the city), you can travel on it until quite late at night. The length of time between each Metro stop is relatively short (usually no more than a minute or two) and stations are generally quite close together, so if you do miss your stop, the walk from the next station will normally not be too long.

Finally, the distance between train and platform on the Metro can be vertiginously wide. Unlike the London Underground, however, there is no sign

Finding your way around Madrid

If you will be living in Madrid for some time, it may well be worth your while investing in the *Atlas de Madrid*. This is available from most newsstands and is published by Almax. It costs a pricey 3,200ptas, but not only does it contain very detailed maps of the city (and its outskirts), it also carries a highly comprehensive directory of important/useful numbers and addresses in Madrid. These include embassies and consulates, transport information lines and several pages of hotels (in all categories) with contact numbers.

or recorded announcement to warn you. Watch out.

Taxis in Madrid

You can travel to the centre of Madrid from the airport by taxi. For those used to living in a city where exorbitant taxi fares are the norm, taxi journeys in Madrid are a pleasant surprise. The journey from the airport to Plaza de Colón should cost no more than 1,620ptas. The cost to certain other destinations within the city should be as follows: 1,740ptas to the Puerta del Sol, 1,870ptas to the Plaza de España, 1,900ptas to Atocha station, 1,500ptas to Chamartín station and 1,920ptas to Norte-Príncipe Pío station. Depending on the time of day you arrive and the amount of luggage that you are carrying, there may be a surcharge added on to that basic fare. The surcharge for tariffs should be displayed within the taxi and is as follows:

Initial fare: 180ptas
Airport surcharge: 350ptas
Bus and railway station surcharge: 150ptas
Surcharge for the Campo de las Naciones (a fair complex): 150ptas
Public holidays surcharge (6am to 11pm): 150ptas
Night service surcharge (11pm to 6am): 150ptas
Charge for each suitcase: 50ptas.

Always insist that the driver start his meter as soon as you get into his car. Otherwise you may find yourself being charged double the normal fare.

Trains in Spain

If you need to take a train from Madrid to your next destination, you will first have to work out where you wish to travel to. There are two main stations, in Madrid. As a general rule, Atocha is for trains going south (Toledo, Granada, Almería, etc) and Chamartín is for trains going north (Salamanca, Zaragoza, Barcelona, etc), although it is possible to depart from Atocha and return to Chamartín on some trains (and vice versa). Some services leave from Príncipe Pío, a station to the west of the city. A fast train – the AVE – runs from Madrid to Sevilla and Córdoba. This costs more, but it effectively cuts time of travel by at least half. Depending on where you wish to go and when, the rest of the service will either be fairly regular or medievally infrequent.

The cost of travelling by train varies according to the type of train you are taking, what class you will be travelling and when you will be travelling. As an example, a second class return ticket (with youth card discount, see below) to Bilbao on a Talgo, leaving on a weekday afternoon/evening and returning on a Saturday will cost 3440ptas. You can contact RENFE (the national train company in Spain) for general information and bookings: tel: +34 91 328 9020.

Buses in Spain

A number of bus companies run services across the country, usually varying according to region. As a rule, buses run regularly, on time and are air-conditioned and they often go to places that are not accessible by train. However, do bear in mind that on Sundays and holidays, the bus service slows down considerably and becomes much less regular. Wherever you are planning to go, it is worth finding out not only national holidays, but the holidays for that particular region or town. These dates could have a considerable effect on your travel plans.

If you are heading out of Madrid by bus, you must be warned that rather than being gathered together under one roof, the different bus companies (which all serve different parts of the country) are scattered around the centre. They are mainly concentrated in the square mile around Atocha station, but do make sure that you know exactly which bus company you need. The *Plano de los Transportes del Centro de Madrid* (Map of Transport in the centre of Madrid), available from most Metro stations and newspaper vendors, lists all these companies, with their addresses and telephone numbers.

Arriving by plane in other parts of Spain

If you will be studying in the north or south of Spain it is advisable, if you can, to fly there directly. The main airport in the north is Barcelona and if you are heading south, you will probably land in Málaga. There are other regional airports, such as the one at Bilbao in the north, which may be even closer to your destination. However, there might not be any direct flights to these places from your point of departure. If this is the case, you will have to fly to the nearest airport and then take a train or bus (or combination of both) to your required destination. As a general rule, wherever you are in Spain, it is probably best to take a taxi into the city from the airport as it is unlikely to be very far away or very expensive and it will save you getting lost. If you are on a budget, however, do find out how much a taxi will cost. In some of the smaller places, a taxi may be your only option. If you need to take a train or a bus to reach your next destination, ask your driver to take you to the train station (*la estación RENFE*) or bus station (*la estación de autobuses*).

Youth cards and travel discounts

Anyone wishing to take advantage of their student/under 26 status should be aware that ISIC (International Student Identity Cards) cards will not make you eligible for discounts on trains in Spain. In order to qualify for what can be substantial reductions, you will have to be in possession of an Under 26 card (also known as a *Carnet Joven* in Spain). If you don't already possess one, you will need to show your passport or identity card; you will also have to have a passport-sized photo of yourself. The card will cost you about £5, or the equivalent of. You can get hold of one of these in your country of origin, or at certain designated offices in Spain (such as TIVE in Madrid), though it is probably worthwhile arriving with one already.

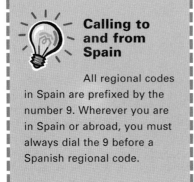

Calling to and from Spain

All regional codes in Spain are prefixed by the number 9. Wherever you are in Spain or abroad, you must always dial the 9 before a Spanish regional code.

Travel etiquette

It is advisable to buy your train tickets in advance, if you can. You can call RENFE's central reservations office in Madrid (+34 91 328 9020) or you can go to one of the stations and buy your ticket there. It is not an offence to wait until you are on board a train in order to buy a ticket. However, having a reserved seat will mean that you avoid the embarrassment of getting comfortable for half your journey only to find, at some station in the middle of nowhere, that you are in fact sitting on someone's reserved seat.

The Spaniards are natural conversationalists and they are not afraid to engage in animated discussion with complete strangers. Do not be alarmed if a fellow passenger on a bus or train (or even the Metro) starts talking to you. They will not be remotely offended if you are not very forthcoming, but this will probably not deter them from speaking to you. If you wish to be left in peace, just tell them that you do not speak any Spanish, and they will refrain at once. However, such conversations can not only be excellent for your Spanish, they may also be quite enlightening as well.

Smoking is prohibited on trains (a few carriages excepted), on buses and in the Metro. However, as the Spanish are both a nation of smokers and a nation who tend to make the rules up as they go along, don't be surprised to find people lighting up everywhere and anywhere. Just ignore them – as the police do.

The presence of beggars and buskers in the Madrid Metro, not only in the stations but in the actual carriages themselves, may come as a surprise to some. They can be a bit intimidating, but they are generally harmless. *Madrileños* tend to be quite generous to beggars, so you may feel compelled to donate a small amount as well.

Madrid is a city of long roads that can sometimes stretch out for several miles (such as the Paseo de la Castellana). As a result of this, finding the right address can be difficult as you may be on the correct street, but at completely the opposite end to that which you are meant to be. Therefore, it is always best to make sure that you know not only the number of the building that you want, but also how far up or down the street it is. Visitors to Barcelona may also experience a similar problem.

Tourist Offices in Madrid
Plaza Mayor, 3,
Tel: +34 91 366 5477/
588 1636
Open 10am to 8pm except Sundays, holidays and Saturday afternoons.

Madrid-Barajas Airport,
International Arrivals,
Tel +34 91 305 8656
Open 8am to 8pm
(Saturdays 8am to 1pm) except Sundays and holidays.

Mercado Puerta de Toledo, Glorieta Puerta de Toledo, Tel: +34 91 364 1876
Open 9am to 7pm except except Sundays, holidays and Saturday afternoons.

Chamartín Station,
Tel: +34 91 315 9976
Open 8am to 8pm

(Saturdays 8am to 1pm) except Sundays and holidays.

Duque de Medinaceli, 2,
Tel: +34 91 429 4951/4487
Open 9am to 7pm (Saturdays 9am to 1pm) except Sundays and holidays.

Teléfono 010, 8.30am to 9.30pm, Monday to Friday. English and French spoken.

Turismo de Castilla y León-Sotur,
Espronceda, 43,
Tel: +34 91 554 3769
Open 9am to 2pm and 4pm to 7pm, Monday to Friday.

Useful telephone numbers in Madrid:

Barajas Airport: +34 91 305 8343

Ambulances: 092

Buses: +34 91 401 9900

Fire Brigade: 080

Postal Service: +34 91 537 6494

Chamartín Station: +34 91 328 9020

Atocha Station: +34 91 328 9020

AVE (High Speed Train): +34 91 328 9020

Main bus station: +34 91 468 4200

Metro: +34 91 552 5909

Lost Property: +34 91 588 4346

Police: 091

Local Police: 092

Railway (RENFE): +34 91 328 9020

Lost Credit Cards: +34 91 581 1811

Applying to Study

Application and entrance requirements vary according to where you will be studying and what you wish to study. It is unlikely that there will be stringent entrance requirements, unless you are applying for a degree-type course (eg *bellas artes* or fine art), you wish to study in a professional capacity (eg to become a dancer) or you are applying to a university. For those wishing to study at a Spanish university, there is a special entrance exam, *selectividad*, which is explained in the university chapter *(see p239)*.

LANGUAGE SCHOOLS

Most language schools will require you to fill in an application form and send a deposit for the course (between 10,000ptas and 20,000ptas), when you enrol. On arrival at the school, you will normally be expected to pay the remainder of the course fees and you will probably have to sit a test so that the school can gauge your level of Spanish and place you in the appropriate class.

DANCE SCHOOLS

An application form will normally be required at most dance schools and this can usually be filled in on site. You will normally have to pay for your classes in advance. If you are taking a course with a fixed duration (eg one or two weeks), you will be expected to pay for the whole course before you start. If you are planning to take classes for an indefinite period of time, you can either buy a set of lessons (usually at a discounted rate

from the price of a single lesson) or you can pay as you go. You will probably be asked to attend a preliminary class so that the school can see which would be the class most suited to you. If you are applying to become a professional dancer, there may be more stringent entrance requirements, with your acceptance depending on how accomplished a dancer you are.

ART SCHOOLS

If you are applying to study for a degree, there will be a selection process – *selectividad (see p240)* and some schools, such as Arcade in Madrid, specialise in preparing students for the *selectividad* exams. Whether or not you are accepted will depend on how competent you are in the particular field that you are applying for.

If you are applying simply for a non-degree course, you will probably be accepted regardless of your level. For pottery/ceramic courses (not at degree level), the only requirement seems to be the desire to get your hands a bit dirty and explore your creative side.

MISCELLANEOUS

Most of the schools in the miscellaneous section will have a simple application procedure (fill in a form, send a deposit), though for some of the music courses whether or not you are accepted may depend on how good a musician you are. The requirements for each school are usually outlined in their individual profiles.

The Spanish Education System

The Spanish education system is not easy to work out. There are rules that govern the system, yet there always appear to be exceptions to these rules. At the basic level – primary and secondary education up to the age of 16 – the system is fairly straightforward. Once that age is passed, however, the student is open to the considerable vagaries of a system which is currently undergoing reform and which still, confusingly, operates through both the old and the new structures. Yet despite this apparent disorganisation, since the end of Franco's dictatorship and the introduction of democracy in Spain, the country's educational level has increased considerably, with 35 per cent of the population (in 1995) having had at least the benefit of a secondary school education.

PRIMARY SCHOOL

The Spanish education system at non-university level has recently undergone drastic reforms. After less than 30 years, the *Ley Orgánica de Ordenación del Sistema Educativo* (LOGSE; Organic Act on the General Organisation of the Education System) has replaced the *Ley General de Educación* (LGE; General Act on Education). The basic change is that, under the new system, compulsory basic education involves 10 years of schooling, starting at the age of six and ending at the age of 16. The old system involved eight years of compulsory schooling, ending at the age of 14. Parents now have the option of sending their children to school earlier, at three years of age. This stage is known as *educación infantil* (infants). At the age of six, children begin stage one of the *primer ciclo* (first cycle) of educación primaria (primary education), which lasts for a year. Following this is stage two of the *primer ciclo*, which ends when the child is eight years old. Thereafter, both stages of the *segundo ciclo* (second cycle) last until the child is aged 10, after which the two final stages (*tercer ciclo*) of *educación primaria* take place.

SECONDARY SCHOOL

Educación secundaria obligatoria (ESO – compulsory secondary education) begins when the child is 12. This also is characterised by two-stage cycles (of which there are two in this case) – the *primer ciclo* and the *segundo ciclo* – which end when the student is 16 years old. On successful completion of this stage of their education, students receive their *graduado en educación secundaria* (secondary education graduation certificate). Having carried out reforms up to this point, the education system following this stage still operates using both the old system (LGE) and the new system (LOGSE). The old system employs the *bachillerato unificado y polivalente* (BUP; unified polyvalent baccalaureate), followed by the *curso de orientación universitaria* (COU; university guidance course). BUP is the equivalent to the last two years of compulsory education under the new system, followed by the first year of the new *bachillerato* (see below). COU is the equivalent of the last year of the new *bachillerato*. The *bachillerato* (baccalaureate) is an innovation of the LOGSE. It lasts two years, beginning when the student has completed their *graduado en educación secundaria*. It involves continuous assessment on a subject-by-subject basis and grades are given on a scale of one to 10, with five out of 10 considered the basic pass mark. The *bachillerato* diploma is awarded once all subjects have been passed successfully. In addition to the *bachillerato*, those students wishing to pursue a university career must take part in *selectividad* – the university entrance exam (for more information on *selectividad see p240* in the University chapter).

VOCATIONAL TRAINING

For students with a less academic leaning who are not necessarily planning to apply to university, there is an alternative to the *bachillerato*; this is known as *formación profesional* (vocational training) and *formación profesional específica* (specialist vocational training). Again, depending on the institution, in question either the new system (LOGSE) or the old system (LGE) will be in place. The old system is divided in to FPI (*formación profesional I*; vocational training I) and FPII (formación profesional II; vocational training II). FPI was designed as an alternative to the first two years of BUP; while FPII corresponds to the three years following that. The new system involves *formación profesional de base* (basic vocational training), which lasts two years and is an alternative option to the new bachillerato. Following this is *formación profesional específica* (specialist vocational training) which lasts for one year. *Formación profesional*, in whatever form it is undertaken, is designed as a way of equipping

students with the necessary qualifications to work in a specific field or trade. To this end, there are schools, known as *centros de formación profesional* (vocational training centres), where students can learn a specific trade such as hotel and catering or travel and tourism.

ARTS SUBJECTS AND LANGUAGES

The above are all categorised as *enseñanzas de régimen general* (standard education). Art education and language education are classified under *enseñanzas de régimen especial* (specialised education) and as such are treated as separate entities. The formalisation of education in arts subjects has resulted in the establishment of the following categories: music and dance; dramatic art; design and the plastic arts; conservation and restoration of artistic objects; design. Studies in these subjects take place in institutions such as conservatoires and art schools. Where language teaching is concerned, provision under the new education system has already been made for compulsory education (i.e. school age students). As well as this, there are state-run language schools (usually known as *Escuela Oficial de Idiomas*) which cater for students who are no longer in formal education.

UNIVERSITY

University education, also categorised as an *enseñanza de régimen general* (see above) is currently undergoing certain reforms. These coincide with the reforms of education at a lower level, and have been designed to keep up with the changing requirements of the job market, as well as EU requirements. Under the *Ley de Reforma Universitaria* (LRU; Organic Act on University Reform), universities have been granted a great deal of autonomy with regard to their individual administration and management, academic organisation and research. There are both private and public universities in Spain. For more detailed information about the university sector in Spain, see the University chapter on *p239*. Education, at both compulsory and non-compulsory level, is financed through both public and private means. A parent in Spain can choose to send their offspring to one of two types of school: public or private. According to recent statistics, 73.7 per cent have chosen the former and 26.3 per cent the latter. Tuition at state schools is free, though parents have to cover additional costs such as school lunches and transport service. Private schools in Spain are similar to those in the UK in that, as a general rule, a private education equates to a better education than the one available in the state sector. Private schools include foreign language schools (such as French lycées or schools run on the English system) and will often require students to wear a school uniform. In the state sector, school uniforms are not required. University tuition fees are not paid by the state and university revenues come from a variety of sources including pupils, subsidies from the appropriate *comunidad autónoma*, private endowments and so on. Private schools complying with certain standards are also entitled to some public funding. State scholarships and study grants are available to those who wish to continue their education in the non-compulsory section (ie post 16 years of age) but who do not possess the means with which to do so.

ADULT EDUCATION

The underlying message behind adult education is an emphasis on continuing education and the acquisition of skills on top of those already acquired. As a result of this, MBAs are currently a very popular option in Spain and many universities (generally private ones) advertise themselves on the strength of their MBA provision. The provision for adult education has been decentralised and is now the concern of each *comunidad autónoma* (autonomous community). As a result, standards of provision of adult education will vary throughout the country. Adult education is available to those who possess the relevant schooling. Those who do not will first have to sit the relevant basic exams. Those over the age of 25 wishing to enter university must also make special arrangements. The presence of so-called "mature" students in Spanish universities is far less evident than in British universities. Distance learning is a more popular option and one that is encouraged by the Ministry of Education and Science, which has created the *Centro para la Inovación y Desarollo de la Educación a Distancia* (CIDEAD; Centre for Innovation and Development in Distance Learning). The type of courses available include academic training, basic training, literacy training, work-oriented training, language training and socio-cultural courses (which embrace anything ranging from yoga to cooking). It is possible to take courses in both private and public institutions. In the former, the student will probably have a wider range of topics to choose from, with greater flexibility and more "frills" added on to the course. Foreign students will find that even if English is not spoken very well at these institutions, they will be more geared up to overseas students than the public sector institutions. However, it does cost more to "go private". Public sector institutions such as *centros culturales* (cultural centres) will have less to offer but at a considerably lower cost. Foreign students tend to gravitate towards private institutions.

STRUCTURE OF THE SPANISH EDUCATION SYSTEM UNDER THE LGE AND THE LOGSE

LGE (1970) – The Old System				Age	LOGSE (1990) – The New System			
Compulsory	Stage	Grade / Track	Cycle		Grade	Cycle	Stage	Compulsory
	Middle Schooling	F.P.II 3°		18 yrs	Advanced F.P.		Secondary Education	
	Middle Schooling	F.P.II 2° · COU		17 yrs	Bachillerato 2°	Intermediate F.P.	Secondary Education	
	Middle Schooling	F.P.II 1° · BUP 3°		16 yrs	Bachillerato 1°	Intermediate F.P.	Secondary Education	
	Middle Schooling	F.P.I 2° · BUP 2°		15 yrs	4°	Second Cycle	ESO — Secondary Education	Compulsory Education
	Middle Schooling	F.P.I 1° · BUP 1°		14 yrs	3°	Second Cycle	ESO — Secondary Education	Compulsory Education
Compulsory Education	General Basic Education	8°	Advanced Cycle	13 yrs	2°	First Cycle	ESO — Secondary Education	Compulsory Education
Compulsory Education	General Basic Education	7°	Advanced Cycle	12 yrs	1°	First Cycle	ESO — Secondary Education	Compulsory Education
Compulsory Education	General Basic Education	6°	Advanced Cycle	11 yrs	6°	Third Cycle	Primary Education	Compulsory Education
Compulsory Education	General Basic Education	5°	Intermediate Cycle	10 yrs	5°	Third Cycle	Primary Education	Compulsory Education
Compulsory Education	General Basic Education	4°	Intermediate Cycle	9 yrs	4°	Second Cycle	Primary Education	Compulsory Education
Compulsory Education	General Basic Education	3°	Intermediate Cycle	8 yrs	3°	Second Cycle	Primary Education	Compulsory Education
Compulsory Education	General Basic Education	2°	Initial Cycle	7 yrs	2°	First Cycle	Primary Education	Compulsory Education
Compulsory Education	General Basic Education	1°	Initial Cycle	6 yrs	1°	First Cycle	Primary Education	Compulsory Education
	Pre-school Education		Nursery School	5 yrs		Second Cycle	Infant Education	
	Pre-school Education		Nursery School	4 yrs		Second Cycle	Infant Education	
	Pre-school Education		Kindergarten	3 yrs		Second Cycle	Infant Education	
	Pre-school Education		Kindergarten	2 yrs		First Cycle	Infant Education	
				1 yrs		First Cycle	Infant Education	
				0 yrs		First Cycle	Infant Education	

Living in Spain

Depending on where you are studying, what you are studying and how long for, your accommodation requirements and possibilities will vary. If you are planning to enrol at a Spanish university, you may be able to find a place in university accommodation for your first year. The great majority of Spanish students live close enough to their university of choice to be able to live at home for the duration of their course, which means that such university accommodation may not be as plentiful as it is in many British and American universities. It is indeed unusual for Spaniards to leave their parents' home until they are married.

COLEGIOS MAYORES

Spanish halls of residence are called *colegios mayores* and they usually incorporate a bar, a refectory (self-service) and single rooms with or without washbasin. Communal shower facilities will usually be located on each corridor. Meal times in the refectory will work around the normal Spanish timetable: breakfast at 8am, lunch between 2.30pm and 3.30pm and dinner between 9pm and 10pm. It will probably be possible to live in university-owned accommodation for your first year, after which it is normal to look for private accommodation, normally a *piso* (apartment).

For students on language courses, accommodation options will vary.

Students on courses run by a university will probably find themselves in a room in a *colegio mayor* (the more expensive option) or living with a Spanish family (homestay) which is usually the cheaper possibility and certainly the one choice worth considering if you are serious about learning the language. Good as your intentions may be, if you are staying in a *colegio mayor*, or any other arrangement involving cohabiting with other foreign students, you are likely to end up speaking either very flawed Spanish (there will be no one to correct your mistakes) or non at all. Most foreign students speak English, and although the first few days of the course may be filled with stilted conversations in Spanish, most people find it hard (and feel idiotic) speaking a language that they hardly know to others with whom they share a more fluent common language. It is surprising how tiring it can be to have to speak a foreign language all day long, particularly when you are a beginner, so there is a temptation to think that you have "done your bit" by simply having attended all your lessons. Don't kid yourself – post-lesson conversation, be it with your host family or fellow students, or even the man behind the bar, is probably the most fruitful part of the experience as it will allow you to put into practise all that you have just learnt. It will also show you just how much you have absorbed during class hours, which is often less than you think.

The smaller private language schools can normally offer either one or both of the above accommodation options. They might also own their own apartments in town, which they rent out to groups of their students on a monthly or weekly basis. These are known as flatshares, and the same theory applies here as it does to living in a *colegio mayor* – if you want to really make strides with your Spanish, it is probably best to try and avoid this.

Homestays

Homestays involve living with a Spanish family. This means that you will either have your own room or that you will be sharing with one of the family's offspring (should there be any). Sometimes, the "family" will be a little old lady in a big old flat, with only a canary for company. Foreign students, no matter how briefly they pass through, are in these cases a welcome intrusion, not only in terms of companionship, but also financially. The amount that you pay will usually vary according to the area of Spain that you happen to be in and whether you have chosen bed and breakfast, full board or lodgings only. The opportunity to sit down to at least one meal a day with your host family will be extremely rewarding linguistically and highly enlightening culturally. So it is worth enduring the initial humiliation of having the family's youngest offering (smugly) to lend you his language primer for five year olds when you sit down

to your first meal. Remember that you will have to reset your body clock to eating a late lunch, possibly taking a siesta and then eating a late dinner; you may also have to adjust to the culinary vagaries of whoever does the cooking in the household (which may not be representative of Spanish cooking as a whole).

The Spanish tend to stay up late – an English couple who had just moved to Madrid was amazed to find their neighbour washing his car at midnight. So it will not be taken amiss if you return from a night out in the early hours of the morning, as long as you don't disrupt the rest of the household. Unless, of course, they return from their night out after you do. On the whole, the Spanish are fairly relaxed about rules and regulations and prize enjoyment above all else. If your family see you getting into the party spirit, and staying out a bit later than you might usually do,

they will probably be pleased that you are settling in so well. That having been said, it is impossible to generalise about what a family will be like, and it is not inconceivable that you will end up with an uncharacteristically strict or unwelcoming host. If this is the case, and you really are unhappy about staying where you are, it is generally not a problem to find an alternative arrangement. Most schools are used to such situations.

Renting a flat

For language students planning a longer term stay in Spain, renting a flat is probably the most sensible (and the best value) option. Renting a flat in Madrid will cost anything from 25,000ptas to 55,000ptas per month. The cost of renting elsewhere (except for Barcelona) will almost certainly be lower. To find out where such accommodation is available, it is best to consult the daily paper of the town/area in which you are based. On Sundays, El País, one of Spain's main national newspapers, carries a middle section (distinguishable by the salmon-pink colour of the pages) with small ads for rentals, courses and anything else pertaining to the region that you happen to be in. Thus, the El País reader in Madrid will find the section relevant to Madrid, and no other region, in the middle of his/her paper. You may find information about flat rentals here. Alternatively, ads for flats that are available to rent often appear on university notice boards. Even if you are not attending a course at a university, it may be well worth a visit to check out the general notice board of the university in the town that you happen to be in. A bonus of doing this is that you could end up sharing with a group of Spanish students, which will do wonders for your Spanish.

In Madrid, the main mouthpiece for those with a flat to rent is *Segundamano* (literally, Secondhand). This flat-hunter's bible has pages of flats, listing them according to area and price. The section entitled *Pisos Compartidos* (shared flats) will probably be the most useful. This contains ads for shared student-type accommodation, specifying, in many cases, whether the flat in question is for women only or men only. The paper costs 275ptas, comes out at least once a week and is available from most newsstands around Madrid. You can consult Segundamano on the web before you leave for Spain; the address is www.segundamano.es. All the information is written in Spanish, which may be a bit daunting at first, but armed with a dictionary and a few of the basics of the language you should be able to work your way around it.

An alternative channel for finding accommodation in the capital is: RoomMadrid (C/Conde Duque, 7 Tel: 00 34 91 548 0335 Website: www. fondos.net/room/piso Email: roommadrid@redestb), a service that specialises in matching up like-minded people in flats/houses around the capital. If you plan to enrol on the service, you will have to fill in a form giving basic details about yourself. It costs 10,000ptas, which is a lot of money by Madrid standards. However, the entire amount will be discounted from your first month's rent once you have been placed in suitable accommodation. Bear in mind, however, that your enrolment has a fixed time limit – it only lasts for up to a month, which means that if you are not satisfied with the solutions that they offer by the month end, you will have to pay a further 10,000ptas to re-enrol. Another possibility is to contact:

ForOcio International Friends
C/Mayor, 6-4∞B;
Tel: 00 34 91 522 5677, a group that organises events and get-togethers for international students in Madrid. Although they don't specifically cater for accommodation-seekers, they may be able to put you in touch with other students looking to share an apartment.

When renting a flat, it is normal to put down one month's deposit in addition to your first month's rental. This will be repaid to you when you leave, provided no damage as been done to the flat during your stay. Often, if all has gone smoothly, your last month's rent will be waived and your landlord will keep the deposit instead. You may also be asked to sign a contract stating what you can and cannot do in the flat. This is unlikely to be particularly draconian. However, if you are sharing an all-women apartment, it is possible than you may have to ask for permission when inviting people to stay over (this could even include members of your own family) and you may not be allowed to let men into the flat. Whether or not you are permitted to have parties, and how often, will depend entirely on your landlord.

As with accommodation anywhere, the cost of living will differ from region to region. Madrid, Barcelona and the more tourist-aware places will be amongst the most expensive in terms of rent and day-to-day living expenses. Yet even these prices will be markedly lower compared to their UK equivalents.

For students on courses other than language programmes, the provision of accommodation will depend entirely on how geared up for the needs of foreign students your school/organisation is. Some may offer all, or a combination of, the above, others may only be able to provide help in finding you a room – they might have lists of places where students have stayed in previous years or they may have some agreement with a nearby *hostal* or *pensión*. Otherwise, you could be on your own.

Hostales and pensiones

If you are only planning to stay in Spain for a few weeks, then finding a room in a *hostal* or *pensión* may well be your best option. In Madrid or Barcelona, these are usually apartments converted into guesthouses. They will normally be spotlessly clean and fairly inexpensive. You may find that you will have to share a bathroom with the occupants of some of the other rooms. Your room will be made up every day and breakfast may be included in the daily room rate.

ADDRESSES

To the uninitiated, Spanish addresses may seem to make little sense, particularly if you are still in the elementary stages of learning the language. You will see that many addresses look something like this: "*C/Jaén, 100 3ʃ A izda, 28020 Madrid*". The "*C*" is an abbreviation of the word *calle* (street), *Jaén* is the name of the street, *100* is the number of the building, *3°* is the floor number and *A* is the letter of one of the apartments on that floor. You may find that some addresses appear to have no number and instead bear the rather cryptic lettering "*s/n*". This means *sin n'mero* (without a number); often large or important buildings have this, presumably because they are easy enough to find without a number. *Izda* (an abbreviation of the word *izquierda*, meaning left; it can also be abbreviated to *izqd*), refers to the side of the building (the staircase) that the apartment is on. Large apartment blocks are usually divided into *izquierda* (left) and *derecha* (right, usually abbreviated to *dcha*) and, sometimes, *central* (middle). This means that there could be up to three apartments called A on the third floor of any given building, but there is only one apartment 3A on the left hand staircase of that building.

BULLFIGHTING

Seen by the majority of non-Spaniards as a cruel and barbaric ritual (to call it a sport would be slightly misleading), bullfighting is widely practised all over Spain and most towns have their own *Plaza de Toros* (bullring). The bullfight is a social event, attended by smart women in dark glasses and scruffy students alike. Bullfighters tend to become national heroes and school-girl pin-ups, their every move documented in the gossip press (see below).

BUREAUCRACY

Spain is a very bureaucratic country. To send a parcel anywhere, or to receive official permission to do anything, you will need time and plenty of patience. The reason for this is obscure, though it is probably a legacy of Franco's regime. It usually involves much to and froing between different offices and a great deal of paper shuffling. Official documents normally need to be signed by at least three people before they can be declared valid. Stamps can only be bought from *estancos* (tobacconists) or from the post office itself. When sending a parcel anywhere, you will need to get hold of some brown paper and string with which to wrap it up – you will only be allowed to send your parcel once it has been covered in this way. The Spanish postal system is very slow and can be quite unreliable – the Spanish do not seem to correspond very much with one another.

When paying for anything with a credit/debit card and when withdrawing money from a bank, you will need to show your passport (the Spanish have to show their DNI). The process of sending anything abroad is expensive and frustratingly bureaucratic – you have to sign a variety of forms and can only pay with plastic if you have an account with Argentaria (the bank which runs the postal service).

ETIQUETTE

When you are introduced to someone for the first time in Spain on a social basis, they will probably lean forward and kiss you twice on both cheeks. To those who are used to having virtually no contact with people unless they happen to be family or very good friends, this may seem slightly intimidating. Although you will offend no one by extending a hand to shake, rather than a cheek to kiss, your behaviour will only succeed in underlining the fact that you are foreign. If you want to blend in, you know what to do.

Interestingly, however, for a nation of people who seem to become familiar with one another on an almost immediate basis, the Spanish are not accustomed to inviting each other into their own homes. Rather than having dinner parties at home or inviting friends round for a drink, they will normally meet up in a bar or a restaurant. It is generally only family members who are ever invited round to each other's homes.

Punctuality is not a Spanish forte, so when you arrange to meet someone, either be prepared to wait, or arrive about fifteen minutes late yourself. If you happen to have kept someone waiting, they will look at you in wonder and amusement if you begin to apologise profusely. Lateness is part of the Spanish lifestyle – no one expects anything to begin on time.

The Spanish are passionate about expressing their beliefs and will often raise their voices in conversation when trying to make a point. To many non-Spaniards, what Spaniards consider to be harmless discussions will appear to be full-blown arguments. As well as being argumentative, the Spanish are also honest and very direct. They do not employ euphemisms, as the English do, so for anyone used to receiving veiled criticism rather than direct reproof, you would do well to grow a thicker skin in Spain.

Patience is a virtue and none more so than in Spain, where things just happen a lot more slowly than in most English speaking countries. A product of this is the fact that it is also a very inefficient country – something that most Spaniards will freely admit. They will often say, with a shrug of their shoulders and an air of resignation, that Spain has all the raw material to be a truly great and prosperous country, if only they could be bothered to exploit that potential. The paradox is that what makes the Spanish so innately *Spanish* is the fact that they are so relaxed and unbothered about so many things involving hard work. Spain simply would not be Spain if it were more efficient.

The Spanish do not eat on the street, in the Metro or while walking – they don't need to, as there will always be a bar nearby where a quick shot of coffee or a small beer and a little something to eat (a *pincho*) will ease any hunger pangs. Even takeaway outlets such as the ubiquitous Pans & Co have generous seating arrangements. If you are in a hurry to go somewhere and grabbing a sandwich or a bar of chocolate to eat en route is your only option, people will probably give you strange looks and you may even attract some sarcastic comment such as *"Había hambre?"* ("Feeling hungry were you?").

FOOD

The Spanish are extremely proud of, as well as being intensely critical of, their food. They can, and will, talk at length about the merits of last night's *gazpacho* (chilled tomato soup – an Andalucian speciality), *tortilla española* (a cake-like omelette made with potatoes) or whatever else happens to have been on the menu. Yet although they take their food very seriously, little is known about it outside Spain.

The Spanish are great meat-eaters, and although vegetarianism is becoming increasingly widespread, the majority of Spaniards, particularly those living in pueblos (small towns), will exhibit mild amusement and slight concern if you tell them that you will not partake of their *jamón serrano/gambas a la plancha* for dietary reasons. As a result of this, a typical Spanish menu is somewhat limited for non meat-eaters. For the rest, however, the choice is great and delicious: *paella, rabo de buey, boquerones con vinagre, patatas ali oli*... the list is extensive and mouthwatering, though certain palates may take some time to accustom themselves to it. Much of the food is fried, but the overwhelming impression is one of freshness. The food that you will see beneath glass cases in bars will almost always have been prepared that morning on the premises. If this means it looks less attractive than the processed and prepared foods that have become the norm in many other European countries, it is also fairly certain that it will taste more delicious. Indeed it is interesting to note that the Spanish do not seem to have cottoned on to the idea of pre-packaged meals in the way that other nations have. Supermarkets carry a good deal of fresh fruit, vegetables, fish and so on, but there is a marked lack of tinned food and a noticeable absence of heat-in-the-microwave prepared dishes.

On a typical day, breakfast in a bar, which will set you back no more than about 250ptas, will consist of coffee (usually *café con leche* – a shot of strong coffee with hot milk) and a *bollo* (a pastry such as a croissant). Mid-morning, there will be a break for another coffee or a small glass of wine, and a *tapa*. *Tapas* consist of small portions of food, which can be eaten alone or in combination with each other. This food can be anything from a bowl of olives to a plate of prawns. Tapas are usually eaten either as snack food during the day and for dinner at night (the main meal of the day is lunch). On ordering anything that is not coffee in a bar, you will be served a complementary handful of olives, crisps or a small serving of whatever happens to be on the counter that day. Lunch will be a three course affair and usually takes place at 3pm (sometimes later at weekends).

Although bars are frequented by all and sundry, they are generally the domain of men, who will stand around in groups drinking and "opinionating". A TV will usually be on constantly in some corner, and occasionally late at night it will be broadcasting programmes that some may find offensive (namely mild pornography). As a result of these factors, a foreign woman entering a bar on her own may feel slightly self-conscious. However, although she will probably attract a few stares she will usually be left alone.

THE GENERATION GAP
The leap in lifestyle from dictatorship to democracy has generated a marked generation gap between those who lived through the Franco years, those born at the end of it and those born once Spain was already a democratic country. The usual generation gap brought about by age alone is compounded by the fact that there are tremendous social differences between these generations, often within the same family. The Franco regime encouraged, demanded even, austerity and modesty. Women covered up and

people went to church. While the rest of the Western world was enjoying a new found sexual freedom in the 1960s, Spain was hidden from such "revolutions" and traditional values prevailed. In the mid-seventies, when finally it was freed from the dictatorship and its eyes were opened, Spain experienced a belated sexual awakening that was only to be expected, under the circumstances. There was much catching up to do.

The reaction to Franco can still be felt and seen today. Pornography is displayed on newsstands explicitly, at eye level. Young girls who were not even born when Franco died often dress provocatively in the extreme and their attitude towards their sexuality is brazen and showy. They are forward and confident in a way that makes the older generation blush. Public displays of affection are frequent and explicit. Girls and boys in their mid to late teens will often kiss openly and unselfconsciously on a crowded Metro carriage. Yet couples living together, rather than getting married, is a fact that is still not easily accepted, particularly in the smaller towns. The younger generation seems to enjoy behaving in a way that shocks the older generation. Disapproval from their elders is something that seems to encourage them and somehow validate their behaviour. The very fact that this behaviour still has the power to shock is proof enough that Spain has some way to go in catching up with many of the other countries in Europe.

It is only recently that English has been introduced in schools as a second language. Up to that point, French was the second language taught in Spanish schools and English was barely taught at all. As a result, the younger generations have a much better grasp of the English language. The older generations therefore now find that they have to take extra English lessons, mainly for professional reasons. This has given rise to a major surge in the teaching of English, and the establishment of English language schools everywhere. There are advertisements all over the Metro in Madrid enticing travellers to learn "the language of business" quickly and painlessly. This also means that a lot of Spaniards speak very little English at all – be prepared.

THE GOSSIP PRESS

One of the most popular magazines in Spain is the ubiquitous Hola!, a publication so successful that it has spawned a British version of itself (Hello!). Hola! is essentially a weekly scrapbook featuring snapshots from the lives of the rich and famous. It is a fascinating read – or rather, it is fascinating to look at: it is rare for anyone to bother reading its bland, slightly sycophantic prose and fawning interviews. Those featured include Spanish matadors, film stars, rock stars and anyone else who happens to have achieved some sort of fame (or notoriety) in Spain, with the odd famous non-Spaniard thrown in for good measure (South Americans also feature). Like the French, who are committed to preserving their famous-people for ever on the pages of Paris Match, the Spanish do not forget those who have had their 15 minutes of fame, even once those 15 minutes are well and truly over. If the latest edition of Hola! is looking a little thin, they can always find someone to wheel out from the archives.

Aside from these, the other faces that grace the glossy pages of the magazine are those who inhabit the upper echelons of Spanish society. In the aptly named Cóctel de Noticias (News

Cocktail), coiffed ladies and besuited gentleman beam out from photographs taken at gallery openings, charity dinners, and other social functions. Also featured in this section are announcements of recent marriages (usually among the minor aristocracy), all illustrated by stiff, posed photographs of a dark-haired/swarthy couple standing uncertainly in the centre of a family grouping.

HEALTH AND WELFARE

If you have a health problem, the best person to go to is probably your landlord, as they may be able to direct you to a doctor, possibly their own, or the local pharmacy. Pharmacies in Spain are allowed to dispense a wider range of drugs without a prescription than in the UK and America. If you have an emergency contact either your local hospital or your nearest embassy or consulate.

THE LOTTERY

ONCE is an acronym that you will see frequently in Spain, particularly on random cabins dotted along the streets in any major city. ONCE stands for *Organisación Nacional de Ciegos de España* (Spanish National Organisation for the Blind), a charitable institution that coordinates the biggest lottery events in Spain, in particular the Christmas lottery known as *el Gordo* (literally, the Fat One), which 96 per cent of the population (allegedly) play. Tickets for ONCE are sold on the street by sight-impaired people and the popularity of this particular lottery may stem from the fact that the Spanish are very superstitious about blind people - they believe that they bring good luck.

MUSIC AND NIGHTLIFE

The Spanish are renowned for their love of enjoyment, and music and going out are central to this. There are even two terms to describe the nightlife scene – *La Marcha* and *La Movida* – which are usually applied to Madrid in particular (you may hear people referring to *La Movida Madrileña*). Despite the fact that the younger generations have embraced American culture and are well versed in music beyond that which is written and performed in Spanish, Spanish pop music (sometimes called "roots-rock") is still hugely popular. Groups such as Mecano, Presuntos Implicados and Heroes del Silencio gain as much (if not more) chart recognition as do groups and performers with international reputations. Of course, the music that is native to Spain and for which it is best known is that of the guitar and, more specifically, the flamenco guitar. Few Spanish groups within this genre have managed to make themselves known beyond the Spanish-speaking world, apart from The Gipsy Kings in the late 1980s (and even they are Spanish-speaking French). Latin American music, and artists, easily make the transition across the Atlantic to Spain because language is no obstacle.

Nightclubs tend to play dance/house music from around the globe, which is referred to as *bacalao* (which also means cod). The growing popularity of Ibiza (one of Spain's Balearic islands) as a destination for dance music fanatics has made it an important centre for this type of music. Annually, famous clubs and clubnights from other countries decamp to the island for a few weeks or a couple of months on a sort of summer rave pilgrimage.

NEWSPAPERS AND THE PRESS

As befits a nation that is fanatical about sport (especially football), the newspaper with the highest circulation in Spain is Marca – a sports paper. In these pages, on a daily basis, Spanish males (women never appear to read it) can fuel their obsession for Real Madrid, Atlético Madrid, Barça (as FC Barcelona is known in Spain) or whichever team they have pledged their lives to support. The main non-sporting papers are El País, ABC and El Mundo. El País is probably the most highbrow of the three, and everyday it offers a broad range of stories from the world over. ABC offers a more pictorial account of world and Spanish events, while El Mundo sits somewhere between the two.

If you want to find out what's going on around town, from cinemas to restaurants and even courses, most major cities will have a Guía del Ocio (Leisure Guide), costing about 250ptas and available from most newsstands. There are also tourist oriented publications (such as 'Qué hacer? En Madrid' – 'What's On?') that are distributed by tourist offices and which feature information and articles in English and Spanish.

POLITICS

From the end of the Spanish Civil War (1939) until 1975 Spain was ruled by the dictator, General Francisco Franco. When he died, on November 20 1975, the country entered a period of political uncertainty known as La Transición (The Transition), during which it prepared itself for its first democratic election in 36 years. Spain elected its first government in 1982 and the party that came to power was the PSOE – Partido Socialista Obrero Español (Spanish Socialist Workers Party) –

headed by the charismatic Felipe González. In the general elections of 1996, having been in power for fourteen years and under crippling charges, and proof, of corruption at the highest levels of government, the PSOE lost to the right-wing PP – Partido Popular – fronted by the mustachioed José María Aznar.

The fact that the Spanish population has veered to the right of its own accord after almost 40 years under a right-wing dictatorship and only 14 under a socialist government, points to its intolerance of corruption (or "sleaze" as the English would have it). Already some Spaniards, generally the older generation that lived much of their lives under Franco, hark back to the "good old days" of his dictatorship, when no such scandal ever existed (or, at least, ever came to light).

After two years in government, the PP still curries favour with the majority of the Spanish population. This is partly due to the fact that the present government has been more effective in dealing with the Basque problem than the PSOE ever was.

The Basque problem is not unlike the situation between Britain and Northern Ireland. The region of northern Spain known as Euskadia (Basque country) belongs to Spain but would like independence from it. The main spokespeople for this are ETA (Euskadi ta Askatasuna – Freedom for the Basques), a terrorist movement not unlike the IRA which, over the years, has used many similar tactics to make their point and express the lengths to which they will go to achieve independence (car bombs, etc).

Spain is currently in the process of decentralising its administration. The implications of this mean that different powers and responsibilities are being distributed between the state and its 17 *comunidades autónomas.*

RELIGION

During its history, Spain has been ruled by the Moors and has hosted a major Jewish population. Both cultures, but in particular the Moorish culture, have left a deep and lasting impression on the country. Toledo, a small city to the south of Madrid, was once home to Spain's most important Jewish community, until the expulsion of the Jews in 1492. The Moors at one stage had conquered the whole of Spain, apart from the region in the north that is known today as Asturias. Granada in particular, with its magnificent Alhambra (a Moorish palace) and Albaicin (the city's Arab quarter), still bears a heavy Moorish influence. The impact of Moorish culture remains within the language (Castellano), which carries a number of words whose etymology is either directly or indirectly Arabic (for example, the name *Andalucía* comes from the Moorish *Al-Andalus*). Today, Spain is a predominantly Catholic country, though it is only the older generation that seems to practise its faith with any seriousness.

THE ROYAL FAMILY

The Spanish have a healthy respect for, and interest in the lives of, their Royal Family. Unlike their British counterparts, the *Familia Real* are fairly informal and are frequently pictured in the pages of Hola! (see the Gossip Press, above) aboard some yacht, in casual dress. The Spanish seem to regard them with a familiar affection, rather than the complicated mixture of reverence/irreverence with which the British regard their own First Family. At present, the Spanish royal family consists of King Juan Carlos, Queen Sofia and their children: the Infantas Elena and Cristina and Prince Felipe. Having witnessed the weddings of both infantas in the past five years, the nation now awaits the good news that Felipe (a handsome, good-time boy) will also be settling down. The gossip press regularly pictures him, always with a different beauty (Spanish or otherwise) on his arm, so it may be some time before the Spanish are treated to yet another Royal Wedding. In the meantime they will mildly speculate, though without wasting too many column inches on the subject.

SMOKING

To say that Spain is a nation of smokers is to exaggerate only slightly a fact that most Americans and many British people may find somewhat surprising. Many Spaniards smoke and there are few places in Spain where it is not permitted to do so. This is evident on arrival in the baggage hall at Madrid's Barajas airport. Smoking here is not only allowed, it seems positively *de rigueur*, as smokers recently disembarked from non-smoking flights can be seen to take long, hungry drags on their first cigarette (of many) on Spanish soil. Even on the Metro in Madrid, the 'No Smoking' signs are blissfully disregarded as smokers of all ages casually light up while waiting for the next train. For those who come from countries where smokers are virtual pariahs, the presence of smokers wherever you go (particularly in bars and restaurants) may be hard to get used to. It is useless to ask them to blow their smoke elsewhere, as any such request will be met with a mocking glance and, probably, even more fumes blown deliberately in your direction.

TIME

On arrival in Spain, the traveller would do well to forget entirely their usual timetable. Spanish time *is* different. The weekday begins at about 8am, during which the tedium of work is interspersed by various coffee breaks. This is enough to keep the Spanish going until about 2.30pm, when they break for lunch. After lunch, they retire for a *siesta*, a cultural phenomenon that may seem almost too clichéd to be true to non-Spaniards, but which is very much a way of life in Spain. At 5pm, they emerge from their siestas to go back to work. A few hours later, it is time to return home, in time for dinner (9pm is considered early to eat dinner in Spain). Shops and services operate in line with this way of life, and most shut at 2.30pm in order to re-open at 5pm to 5.30pm. Shops are usually open from Monday to Saturday. They close on Sundays, except for on the first Sunday of the month.

At weekends, socialising and clubbing begins after midnight on Friday and continues well into the early hours of Saturday morning. It is quite normal for a night out to end at 8am the following morning, when jaded revellers end the merry-making with *chocolate con churros* (fried pastry dipped in thick hot chocolate), before climbing into bed and sleeping all day in order to prepare for the next night's fun.

WEATHER

Famed for its sunshine, it comes as quite a surprise to most people to find that the Spanish weather can actually be quite cold. A visitor to Madrid any time between November and March will need a heavy overcoat, hat, scarf and gloves to ward off the chill winds (and, sometimes, snow) that sweep through it in the winter. Beyond Madrid, the lush greenness for which the north of Spain is famed (particularly the far north, such as Galicia and Asturias) is due to the rain that drenches the region for a good part of the year. Think Ireland and you'll have some idea of what it's like.

In the summer, however, the whole country is bathed in sunshine. On a daily basis, between May and September, the weather reports on television present a Spain covered entirely in glowing golden orbs of sunshine.

Spain is hottest in the South, where it is possible to catch a few rays of warmth even in the darkest winter months. Many English retirees, fed up with sharing most of their lives with an umbrella, have chosen to settle here. Some *pueblos* in the south (Denia, for example) have been virtually taken over by a growing band of ageing expats.

Because the weather in the South is virtually guaranteed to be good, it is the country's most popular tourist destination. It is here, in resorts such as Torremolinos and Benidorm that sun-starved Northern Europeans bake annually on overcrowded beaches. Their presence has made a deep impression. Their desire for a home away from home is catered for by menus incorporating eggs, bacon and chips, and pubs serving, not the modest *cañas* that are consumed in most Spanish bars, but pints and litres (or *minis* as they are also, rather curiously, known) of beer. Although this is the Spain known best to tourists, it is indeed far removed from anything really "Spanish".

Art and Design

Picasso, Goya and Velázquez are three of the most famous artists in the entire history of art in the western world. They were also all Spanish. Spain has a rich artistic tradition, and the three major museums in Madrid (see Spain and the Spanish *p5*) attest to this, their walls crowded with works of art from all over Europe, many of them painted by Spanish artists. Barcelona is equally prosperous where art is concerned – just walking down the street you are likely to encounter the inspired designs of Antonio Gaudí on a building or a lamp post.

Museums and galleries throughout the rest of Spain are considered a national treasure not merely reserved for the privileged few. Spaniards of all walks of life make it their business to visit the latest artistic innovation – from the recent liberation of Picasso's Guernica from behind protective glass at the Centro de Arte Reina Sofía in Madrid, to the magnificent, recently unveiled Guggenheim museum in Bilbao. For these reasons alone, taking a short course in ceramics or studying for a full-blown degree in art in Spain, particularly in such "art-rich" cities as Madrid and Barcelona, could be very rewarding.

WHERE TO GO

The schools profiled in this chapter are a mixture of the professional and the non-professional, the majority of them private schools or colleges. Some are large, such as the *Escuela de Artes*

Decorativas de Madrid (private) and the *Escuela Oficial de Cerámica* (state-run). Others are tiny – schools that take up only one or two studios, such as Taller Fang and Arte Hoy. Some provide degree-type courses geared towards those who wish to make their livelihood from art, others provide classes for those in search of a satisfying hobby. From the individual profiles in this chapter it should be clear what sort of student the school is geared towards.

Despite the government's recent reforms of the Spanish education system, there is a deep sense of dissatisfaction with the provision of education in general provided by the state, particularly in the arts. As a result, people are setting themselves up privately in order to fill the gap in the market for the type of service that the general public is asking for. A general complaint is that there is inadequate provision for people who wish to study certain subjects, such as interior design and decoration, to degree level. As a result, there are many private schools in Spain (not just art schools) none of which are controlled by any central government body. Below is a list of art faculties within universities throughout Spain and design schools in Barcelona, where there is probably more activity in art education than in any other part of Spain.

WHAT TO STUDY

The subjects that can be studied within the arts in Spain are varied. Those looking for something genuinely

Spanish will probably find that the ceramics classes/schools offer what they are looking for. The arabic influence in particular can be felt in this subject, with students decorating tiles and pots with elaborate designs inspired from the sort of Islamic art that can be seen at the Alhambra Palace in Granada. One school – Taller-Escuela "Camille Ceramistas" – offers the opportunity of learning to speak Spanish "while you pot", and even advertises classes in this way in Madrid's English language paper, InMadrid. A school offering a slightly more unusual provision (though one that is not particularly Spanish) is the Escuela Superior de Dibujo Profesional in Madrid, where you can study for a degree in what is, essentially, the art of cartoon-drawing. Very few schools in Europe offer this subject at degree level.

TERMINOLOGY

You will find that one or two terms crop up frequently in art school/class prospectuses. These are: *taller*, which means "workshop", and *curso monográfico*, which refers to a monothematic class, in other words, one in which you study only one thing, or a specific aspect of something, such as a method for painting or baking ceramics or a drawing technique.

MASTERS COURSES

A number of Masters in art subjects (mainly restoration) are mentioned in the University chapter *(see p239)*.

For further information contact:

Ministerio de Educación y Cultura, Oficina de Información, C/Alcalá, 36, 28014 Madrid, Spain, Tel: +34 91 701 8000.

Information on the worldwide web

For non-regulated (i.e. private) education in Catalunya, INCANOP (*Institut Catalá de Noves Professions, Catalan Institute for New Professions*) offers links to 900 schools in that area, offering more than 7,500 courses, with a wide provision in art and pottery/ceramics schools. Go to www.xtec.es/incanop/guia.htm for the list of subjects with centres affiliated to INCANOP. For lists of the centres in each category, click on the category itself.

SPANISH ART SCHOOLS

Facultad de Bellas Artes de San Jorge (design, sculpture, engraving painting and restoration) Universidad Central de Barcelona, C/Pau Gargallo, s/n, 08071 Barcelona
Tel: +34 93 334 5004

Facultad de Bellas Artes
(audio-visual techniques, conservation and restoration, design, sculpture, photography, painting and graphic techniques) Universidad del País Vasco, Ciudad Universitaria de Lejona, 48071 Lejona (Vizcaya)
Tel: +34 94 464 7700

Facultad de Bellas Artes
(miscellaneous), Universidad de Castilla-La Mancha, C/Astrana Marín, 4, 16071, Cuenca
Tel: +34 969 211 752

Facultad de Bellas Artes (painting, sculpture, design, restoration (painting and sculpture), Universidad de Granada, Campus Universitario de Cartuja, 18071 Granada
Tel: +34 958 243 819

Facultad de Bellas Artes de San Fernando (design, sculpture, engraving, painting, printing and restoration) Universidad Complutense, Ciudad Universitaria, 28071 Madrid
Tel: +34 91 549 5063

Facultad de Bellas Artes (painting, sculpture, design and audio-visual techniques) Universidad de Salamanca, Ctra. Fuentesauco, s/n, (E. Claretianos), 37071 Salamanca
Tel: +34 923 258 363

Facultad de Bellas Artes (sculpture, engraving, design and painting), Universidad de la Laguna, Camino del Hierro, 4, 38071 Santa Cruz de Tenerife Tel: +34 922 214 722

Facultad de Bellas Artes Santa Isabel de Hungría (conservation and restoration, sculpture, engraving, design and painting) Universidad de Sevilla, Laraña, 3, 41071 Sevilla
Tel +34 95 421 7506

Facultad de Bellas Artes de San Carlos (drawing, sculpture, engraving, painting, conservation and restoration) Universidad Politécnica de Valencia, Camino de Vera, s/n, 46071 Valencia
Tel +34 96 362 6611/2.

Student Story

"My husband was sent here by his firm on a "temporary" posting which was extended from six months, to a year, to 18 months and we've now been here for almost two years. I used to work as a chartered surveyor in America but as I can't work legally here, I'm currently unemployed. I needed to fill my time, so I found out about classes. As well as pottery at Camille, I attend a tae kwon do class three times a week. My husband and I are rock climbers, so Spain is like heaven for us! Every weekend we go somewhere new and we've made friends through that. It's not easy getting to know people here if you're of a certain age. Although the Spanish are very open, they won't let you get too close to them. My husband and I both took the winter and summer Spanish courses at the Complutense, which we thought were very good. Before that we had taken classes at Sampere International and had a mixed experience there. I reckon if you have a 50 per cent success rate with your teachers you're lucky and at the Complutense our success rate was definitely above average. I had never done any pottery before I started taking classes at Camille and I chose to come here because I felt it was very low key. I liked the fact that you can pay for the amount of times that you attend (I usually pay after eight lessons) rather than for a number of months. You have plenty of freedom here to do what you want to do — almost too much freedom, and the point of being here is to be creative, as opposed to working towards an exam."

Jennifer Rosner, Spain

DESIGN DEGREES IN BARCELONA – COLLEGES AND SCHOOLS

Escola Superior de Disseny (ESDI), C/Marqués de Comillas, 79-83, 08202 Sabadell
Tel +34 93 727 4819

Escola Superior de Disseny Elisava, Via Augusta, 205, 08021 Barcelona
Tel +34 93 200 1133

Eina I Escola de Disseny I Art, Pg de Santa Eul‡lia, 25 (torre), 08017 Barcelona
Tel +34 93 203 0923

Escola d'Alts Estudis de la Imatge I del Disseny, Avda Diagonal, 401,
Tel +34 93 416 1012

Dissenyadors, Interioristes I Arts de Catalunya, Avda Diagonal, 433 bis, 5Ë, 08036 Barcelona
Tel +34 93 200 1553

Lai. Escola-Taller Disseny, C/del Caire, 2, 08023 Barcelona
Tel +34 93 417 7744

CERAMIC SCHOOLS IN MADRID

Escuela Oficial de Cerámica, Francisco y Jacinto Alcántara, 2, 28008 Madrid
Tel +34 91 542 3241

Escuela Madrileña de Cerámica de la Moncloa, Francisco y Jacinto Alcántar, 2, 28008 Madrid
Tel +34 91 247 8589

Federación Española de Universi-dades Populares, Modesto Lafuente, 63-2∫, 28003 Madrid,
Tel +34 91 533 8374

Estudio de Cerámica Lucette Godard, Virgen de Lourdes, 8 posterior, 28027 Madrid
Tel + 34 91 405 5745

Escuela de Cerámica con Torno, Gladiolo, 1, 28039 Madrid
Tel +34 91 311 7203

Escuela de Artes Aplicadas y Oficios Artísticos, Palma, 46, 28004 Madrid
Tel +34 91 521 6232

The following addresses may also be useful

Gremio (*union*) de Artesanos de **Madrid,** Palafox, 23, 28010 Madrid
Tel +34 91 447 0055

Fundación de Gremios, Cardenal Herrera Oria, 378, 28035 Madrid
Tel +34 91 358 2159.

ART SCHOOLS

Arte Hoy
Pza Humilladero, 4, 28005 Madrid
Tel: +34 91 366 6936
Established: 1996
Level: Basic
Nearest Station: La Latina
Contact: Pedro León

You will find Arte Hoy in the old part of Madrid, near the Plaza Mayor and the Royal Palace and around the corner from Madrid's famous flea market, the Rastro. It is conveniently ensconced between two trendy bars which, on a sunny day, were filled to overflowing with bohemian twentysomethings, all smoking and wearing shades. It may take you a moment or two to find the Plaza Humilladero as it is really more a funny shaped street than a square and it runs off Plaza Puerta de Moros.

Arte Hoy is a pottery (*ceramica y torno*) school and comprises two large spaces – the front and back studios, and a bathroom. You walk into the first studio, as you come off the street which seems to serve a variety of purposes: shop, exhibition space (for friends of Pedro Leon), studio and office. The back room is another workspace and houses the kiln as well as shelves bearing the fruit of recent student labour.

Pedro León studied at the Moncloa school and when he left, decided to set up on his own rather than join an already established workshop, as he wished to remain his own boss. Arte Hoy thus allows him both to create and to teach and he is the school's sole teacher. Enthusiastic and relaxed, he is clearly stimulated by what he does. He formed the school only two years ago but has already organised a one-day festival for adults and a one-day workshop for the neighbourhood children. Both are free and take place in the summer; the adult festival – the Festival Solsticio – accordingly takes place on the day of the summer solstice. He chose to set himself up in this part of Madrid because of its history and culture – he felt that it would be an appropriate backdrop for the school.

He has a link with a language school in Madrid, which has already sent him a handful of students eager to add something to their schedule of grammar and conversation classes. The other students at the school range from children (10 at the moment) to OAP's (there are about 30 adults attending classes) and the level of expertise varies from absolute beginners to professional. There are intensive courses in the summer (the school closes for a couple of weeks in mid-August), which allow you to do 12 hours a week over three weeks and during the rest of the year the maximum number of weekly hours is six (the minimum being two).

There is an enrolment fee of 3,500ptas, and prices range from 5,200ptas per month for two hours a week to 11,000ptas per month for six hours a week. The school is open 10am to 1pm Tuesdays and Fridays, 10.30am to 2.30pm on Saturdays, 5pm to 9pm on Mondays and Wednesdays and 6.30 to 10pm on Tuesdays and Thursdays. The children's workshops take place on Tuesdays and Thursdays from 4.30pm to 6.30pm, Fridays from 5pm to 9pm and Saturdays from 11.30am to 1.30pm.The cost for these ranges from 3,200ptas per month for one hour a week to 5,000ptas per month for three hours a week. Students may begin their set hours whenever they wish to within these hours.

Class sizes are no bigger than seven or eight. For enrolment details please contact the school.

Arcade

Sotomayor, 9-11, 28003 Madrid
Tel: +34 91 553 5625
Established: 1985
Level: Basic to Intermediate
Nearest Station: (Metro)
Guzmán el Bueno
Contact: Inocente Aguilera

Inocente Aguilera founded Arcade 13 years ago. A graduate from the Faculty of Fine Arts at the Universidad Complutense de Madrid, he had been somewhat disillusioned with the way in which his course had been taught and he set up the school in a bid to do things in his own way. He admits that it hasn't always been possible to do things precisely as he had planned, but

Arcade

essentially the ethos of the school is to allow students absolute freedom of expression, without imposing any technique or style on them. His job, he says, is to guide them, thus allowing them to discover their true artistic selves. With his bushy beard and round glasses, Snr Aguilera bares a striking resemblance to a French impressionist painter. He talks with the rapidity and clarity of someone from the north of Spain and speaks no English, (neither do any of the other three teachers at the school). In fact the students, who come mainly from Madrid and the surrounding areas, probably speak better English and might even be called upon to interpret when necessary. The school is two flats knocked together and the sense that you are standing in someone's private studio is reinforced by the fact that every time the doorbell rings Snr Aguilera jumps out of his chair in order to let in another student.

Over the years the school has been attended by a variety of overseas students. At the moment, a Japanese girl, the friend of a previous Japanese

student at Arcade, is studying there. The students are aged mainly between 16 to 21, though people of all ages attend classes. The younger students tend to be those preparing for the entrance exams of the Fine Art Faculties at universities such as the Complutense (this is a sort of foundation year). There is also the possibility of doing a full three-year course, rather like the equivalent of doing a degree at university (except that it won't be validated by an official body such as a university). Alternatively, you can simply stay on to do classes for as long as you want to, with no goal in mind other than improving your skills.

The walls of the school are covered with examples of student's work – exercises in colour, charcoals, sketches and so on. Each classroom is dedicated to a particular subject, such as painting or technical (architectural) drawing. The charge for lessons is calculated according to the number of hours that you do per week, and once you sign up, you can turn up to classes at any time within the school's opening hours (9am to 2pm and 4.30pm to 9.30pm, Monday to Friday, 10am to 2pm on Saturdays). There are occasional theory lessons on a point of technique or on a particular theme, but apart from these, students can come and go as they please.

The courses available at the school are Architectural Drawing, Fine Art, Restoration, Graphic and Interior Design, theoretical classes in Aesthetics and preparation for the Fine Arts entrance examination. Only about 35 students pass through the school every day, so it is not a big school. (The average class has about twenty people in it.) Classical music is played throughout the day, creating a laid back atmosphere that students seem to enjoy working in.

Snr Aguilera can provide students with information regarding student residences. If a student has financial problems, there is the possibility of paying for some of the course by spending a few hours handing out flyers for the school. Excursions are organised to places of interest such as the new Guggenheim museum in Bilbao. Courses are charged per month or per term. Fees range from 9,000ptas per month for one day (three hours) a week to 58,000ptas per term for five days (three hours a day) a week. The enrolment fee is 3,000ptas. The cost for materials is about 3,000ptas to 5,000ptas per month and you can buy what you need from the school.

Escuela de Artes Decorativas de Madrid

Salustiano Olózaga, 5 dcha, 28001 Madrid
Tel: +34 91 431 7789/21
Fax: +34 91 576 2228
Established: 1963 (Under Construction)
Level: Intermediate to

Advanced
Nearest Station: Retiro, Banco de España, Colón and a number of buses
Contact: J Enrique Ovejer

Spend a few moments in the company of the Escuela de Arte Decorativas de Madrid's enthusiastic Head of Studies, Enrique Ovejer and you will find yourself being converted to the joys of becoming an interior designer. Contrary to what I had assumed prior to our interview, you do not need any previous artistic experience to do a course in Interior Design, as the basic skills (such as learning how to draw) are taught in the first year of the course. (The course usually lasts four years but can be shortened on proof of former experience in interior design or a related field.) Ovejer, himself an alumnus of the school, confided that he had seen one or two recently arrived first years whose drawings were less accomplished than those of a three year old. The school is allegedly the only one of its kind in Spain to bear the seal of approval of the IFI – the International Federation of Interior Designers. It is located off the Puerta de Alcalá and is within easy walking distance of the city's main museums (the Big Three – the Prado, the Thyssen-Bornemyzca and the Reina Sofia), ideal for finding interesting material and ideas.

According to Enrique Ovejer, many students at the school are people who tried other routes before finding "their true vocation" in interior design. He himself is one such a person (he first tried medicine and then fine art!) and he cites one example of a current student who left his law studies to pursue a career in interior design. As a result, he claims that there is a sense of fulfilment and enjoyment among students that is rarely found in other fields. Of the 300 students at the school, there are overseas students, the majority of them from South America. It is important to have attained a fairly high level of Spanish when you start at the school, particularly in view of the theoretical content of the course. Each course module lasts an hour and a half and emphasis varies between the practical (designing on computer, drawing models) and the theoretical (history of art). There is a mini-break between each module and there are two sessions (called "turnos") daily: 9am to 2.30pm and 4pm to 9pm. (You have to sign on for either one or the other - it isn't possible to alternate between am and pm classes.)

The principal course offered by the school is Arquitectura de Interiores; this lasts four years, each of which includes a set of modules – six in the first three years and four in the final year – for which students can receive credits (between five and 25 for each module). The course covers all aspects of interior design, from the basic technology of construction to landscape gardening. There is a matriculation fee of 42,000ptas and thereafter you have to pay and 73,000ptas every month (nine instalments every year). The school year runs from October to June and in the months of July and September there are occasional courses in Landscape Gardening and Computer Assisted Design. There are also classes for children in Drawing and Painting.

The employment prospects for graduates of the school are excellent. Every year about 80 students graduate form it and most of them walk straight into jobs as the school has an excellent reputation and therefore its graduates are in high demand. In fact, so great is the demand that the school does not have sufficient numbers of students with which to feed it. At the end of your course you will receive the title of Graduado Superior en Arquitectura de Interiores, (Graduate in Interior Design) which is recognised by the International Council of Design Schools (of which it is a member). This qualification means that you will be able to work internationally, as well as in the rest of Spain. Most alumni of the school have tended to stay on in Spain. The school has a list of student residences, hostals and so on. The cheapest option is to stay with a Spanish family (from 30,000ptas per month). For enrolment details contact the school.

Escuela Oficial de Cerámica
Francisco y Jacinto Alcántara, 2, 28008 Madrid
Tel: +34 91 542 3241/6322
Fax: +34 91542 3241
Email: eafac000@teleline.es
Established: 1911
Level: Intermediate
Nearest Station: (Metro) Príncipe Pío
Contact: Isabel Anasagasti

The Escuela Oficial de Cerámica is situated around one half of a courtyard (complete with a lovely garden of historical interest), which it shares with another pottery school, the Escuela de Cerámica del Ayuntamiento de Madrid. Until recently the two schools were one, but a quarrel between the Ayuntamiento and the Ministry of Education has resulted in this division. To get to the school, you have to walk from Príncipe Pío station over a bridge across the railway tracks and Calle Francisco y Jacinto Alcántara begins at the base of the bridge. The school is on your immediate left. The area is very quiet and has a slightly desolate feel to it, inside however, the school is a hub of activity and the atmosphere is industrious and friendly. The building is large and lets in a lot of light. A beautiful sweeping stone staircase (which must once have been very grand) leads from the administration area and the kiln on the ground floor to the workshops and classrooms on the first and second floors. A focal point is the open area at the top of the staircase with vending machines, tables and chairs.

Founded in 1911 by Francisco Alcántara Jurado, an intellectual of the period, with the aim of recovering traditional methods of pottery making, this was both a school and a factory producing new works. From the top floor of the school you can still see the enormous outdoor kiln that used to serve it. Today, it preserves its commitment to the traditional art of Spanish pottery and ceramics and is one of a group of schools under the jurisdiction of the Ministry of Education's Department for the Teaching of the Plastic Arts and Design. Four courses are taught here. The Ciclo Formativo de Grado Medio (training to Intermediate Level), in either Pottery or Decorating Ceramics, involves two years of study and the production of a work of art at the end of your course. The Ciclo Formativo de Grado Superior (training to Superior level), in either Modeling and Moulding Pottery or Artisitic Ceramics, involves two years of study and the production of a final project. Modules in all four include: drawing, the history of pottery, basic computing and practical work experience.

The school participates in the Leonardo da Vinci programme and operates an exchange with the School of Pottery at Faenza in Italy. These Italian students do monothematic courses in traditional Spanish pottery, which can also be organised for overseas students who do not wish to do the full course. Certain basic materials are also provided; the least expensive materials such as pens and paper, you must purchase yourself. You will be required to sit an entrance exam. Students up to 20 years of age must have GCSEs (or the equivalent) and will be tested on drawing, modelling and the history of art; those over 20 years of age, without these basic requirements, will have to sit a basic general knowledge test.

There are 180 students at the school of whom about 10 are from overseas. Language is not a problem as long as you have a genuine interest in pottery. English classes, where students learn technical terms, are an obligatory element of every course. Every year, at springtime, the school organises a Cultural Week. This is attended by various well-known figures in the world of Spanish pottery who give lectures and demonstrations.

To apply for a place you must contact the Ministry of Education at: Subdirección Territorial Madrid Centro, Asesoria de Alumnos, Francos Rodriguez, 106, 28071 Madrid (tel: +34 91 459 0150 extn 212/213).

Escuela Superior de Dibujo Profesional
Santa Engracia, 129-1 dcha, 28003 Madrid
Tel: +34 91 399 4639
Fax: +34 91 399 4815
Established: 1978
Level: Intermediate to Advanced
Nearest Station: (Metro) Iglesia
Contact: Emilio Luján

One of the first schools of its kind in Spain, and one of very few in Europe, the Escuela Superior de Dibujo Profesional (a school specialising in the teaching of cartoon art) is located on the first and second floors of a building on Santa Engracia, a wide and busy street that runs north from the centre of town. The atmosphere as you walk into the school is calm and studious, with students either working alone or in pairs. The walls of the school are covered with cartoons of fantastical creatures and impossibly built humans, all of which seem slightly incongruous amidst the décor of the place: clean white walls and a pale green carpet. The atmosphere at the school is friendly and intimate: people come here because they share a passion: drawing.

Of the 280 students (average age 18 to 25) currently studying at the school, there are about six from overseas and all speak Spanish. However, according to Emilio Luján, the founder and present director of the school, you do not need a particularly high level of Spanish to take part in the courses. The only pre-requisite is that you should love to draw and you will be asked to show some examples of the work that you have already done when you apply to the school. This is purely a formality to make sure that you are genuinely interested in the subject.

There are six courses at the school: Infografía (Advertising Graphics), Aerografía (Spraypainting), Diseño Gráfico Publicitario (Graphic Design in Adveritsing), Ilustración y Cómic (Illustration and Comic Illustration) or Dibujo Animado (Cartoons). At the end of your courses you will be presented with a diploma that endows you with the qualification of Técnico de... (Specialist in...) whichever course you attended. The courses last from four months (Aerografía) to three years (Dibujo Animado). The qualification of Técnico de Dibujo Animado was created by Emilio Luján, who himself has a great deal of experience in drawing and animation. Job prospects for graduates of the school are excellent. There is very little unemployment and some graduates have reached the vertiginous heights of Disney and Warner Bros in the States, though the majority of them tend to stay in Spain.

To complete the course you must attend the school for two hours daily. There are five two-hour slots throughout the day, between 10am and 10pm. It costs 27,000ptas per month to study here, in addition to which there is an annual 29,000ptas enrolment fee. The cost of all materials is included in the fees. The courses run from September to June.

Contact the school for enrolment details.

Escuela Teresa Muñiz

Los Vascos, 5- 1 izda, 28040 Madrid
Tel: +34 91 554 5467
Established: 1970
Nearest Station: (Metro) Guzmán el Bueno; Buses: 44, 45, 2 and Circular
Contact: Teresa Muñiz

Teresa Muñiz runs this school, which is situated north of the centre of the city, and believes that her greatest assets are the fact that she has had 28 years of teaching experience and that she is an active painter herself. The ethos of her school is not to impose a style onto students, but to encourage and guide their own personal approach. Of maximum importance is the individual's own way of expressing themselves. There are about 40 to 50 students in the school, the maximum num-ber of students being 11 at any one time as she wants teaching to be as personalised as possible.

It is possible to study painting, drawing, architecture and po-ttery at the school and there are courses to prepare students for the entrance exams for Fine Art degree

Escuela Teresa Muñiz

courses. There are also short printing courses as well as biannual weekend outdoor landscape painting courses. These are organised to coincide with fiestas in Madrid and take place over several days in areas outside Madrid. For example, from March 19 to March 24 last year a trip to Rioja was organised. The cost for this is 26,500ptas and includes three nights and four days full-board, including the workshop itself.

Teresa Muñiz has a degree in Fine Art as do the other two teachers who also give classes at the school (one of whom speaks English; Teresa Muñiz does not). Teresa Muñiz's daughter works for a company that brings American students to Madrid (some of whom have attended classes at the school), so she is probably more clued up than most about helping overseas students. Student's ages range from late teens (those preparing for the Fine Art degree exams) to people who are considerably older and who simply want to learn how to paint. An exhibition of student's work is

organised every two years (in the autumn) and takes place in a nearby cultural centre.

The cost of classes is: 7,500ptas for two hours a week, 9,500ptas for four hours a week, 11,000ptas for six hours a week and 12,500ptas for eight hours a week. The workshop costs 9,700ptas and includes a monthly class with a live model. Those students who do not take part in the workshops but who wish to participate in this class must pay a monthly supplement of 2,000ptas. The workshop plus two hours a week of classes per month costs 12,000ptas; for the workshop plus four hours a week per month the cost is 13,700ptas. There is an enrolment fee of 2,500ptas. Sessions are from 10am to 12pm on a Monday and Thursday, from 5.30 to 7.30pm from Monday to Friday and from 7.30pm to 9.30pm from Monday to Thursday. Prices do not include materials (apart from easels), which students must provide themselves. However, materials are provided on the printing course. A special discount rate for groups of six or more can be arranged.

The school is on the first floor of an assuming building round the corner from the metro. It comprises a small hall/office, the painting studio and the printing studio. You will be given a few excercises to do on your first session in order to assess your level. For enrolment details contact Teresa Muñiz.

Estudio de la Bola
La Bola, 3-bajo dcha
Tel: +34 91 559 4681
Established: 1993
Nearest Station: (Metro) Santo Domingo
Contact: Ana Montejo Pernas

This school is run by three women, all graduates in Fine Arts, and classes have only been running in its present location (in the old part of Madrid near the Royal Palace) since January 1998. Ana founded the school five years ago with the aim of teaching those who have no faith in their artistic abilities that yes, they can paint, draw, do photography, etc. Ana is in fact so convinced of this that she will return their money to anyone who has not managed to realise some sort of potential within two months of starting a course (so far, this hasn't been necessary). Essentially, the aim is to take the "scariness" out of art and to make it accessible to whoever wants it. As a result, pupils at the school range from working women who only have the time to study on a Saturday, to bored Spanish housewives who feel that they need to do something with their lives in order not to be left behind by the rest of society.

The studio is on the ground floor of a typical *Madrileño* building, situated opposite a cosy tapas bar frequented by employees from offices next door and students from a nearby equivalent of a sixth form art college. As you walk through the front door of Estudio de la Bola, you walk straight into the studio itself, a large high ceilinged room with tiled floor and white walls. There is also another 'space' for classes, in the basement directly beneath this room. This main studio gives onto three smaller rooms, one next to the other, each belonging to one of the three partners and crammed with examples of their own work. The feminine influence is clearly palpable throughout all of the rooms and in every detail, including a stilllife set up in one corner of the studio, featuring delicate, curved objects and colourful drapes.

The idea of the studio came to Ana after years spent as an art student herself. She was dissatisfied with the way the subject was taught, sensing that people who did not possess any obvious talent just weren't given a fair chance. She felt that most teachers were in it simply for the money, which, she claims, is precisely what she and her partners are against. They are more interested in simply enjoying the job than making money from it, and to this end they charge a very modest 1,000ptas per hour. As classes are kept small (eight people maximum because, according to Ana, "You can't teach 20 people well."), there is certainly no danger of them cashing in on oversubscribed classes. For drawing, painting and photography, two hours of lessons a week per month cost 8,000ptas. The fee is reduced the more hours you subscribe for, so eight hours a week for a month works out at 20,000ptas. Four hours of engraving per week for a month cost 12,000ptas and there are classes for kids (materials included) which cost 8,000ptas per month for two hours a week. Classes are offered according to demand, which means that they will teach what students want to learn. From the March 15 three workshops, run by Ana, will be on offer: these will cover engraving, gilding and polychroming (very typically Spanish) and mosaic (a technique originally brought to Spain by the Arabs). The fee for these is 15,000ptas per month for two hours of classes per week. Classes take place every day of the week (including Saturday and Sunday), from 10am to 12pm and 5pm to 9pm on weekdays and from 11.30am to 2pm and 5pm to 9pm at the weekend. All materials must be paid for by the students themselves, except for those attending the workshops.

All three partners speak English so language, should you have a very limited knowledge of Spanish, shouldn't be a problem. In fact, one of the partners used to work as a guide for English speaking tourists at the Prado museum and two series of tours of Madrid's museums are also on offer (one for modern art and one for classical art).

Fundación de Arte y Autores Contemporáneos – ARAUCO

Paseo de Recoletos, 21-2 izda, 28004 Madrid
Tel: +34 91 521 6229
Fax: +34 91 523 3970
Email: 100714.1315@ compuserve.com
Established: 1996
Level: Basic
Nearest Station: (Metro) Atocha or Recoletos
Contact: Toñeta Sauco

Located next to Café Gijón, one of Madrid's most legendary watering holes and restaurants, on one of the city's grandest avenues, ARAUCO is ideally situated. It is but a short walk away from the Prado, the Centro Reina Sofia and the Thyssen museums, as well as the Biblioteca Nacional (the Spanish equivalent of the British Library). The Fundación was formed two years ago with the aim of promoting the teaching of the plastic arts and providing a meeting point for all those involved in different aspects of the arts, be they artists, promoters or specialists in a particular field. The centre is open to everyone, from whatever background and there is a wide provision here. Be warned, however, that you will be expected to take your studies seriously – as one of the partners of the Fundación commented, somewhat strictly: "Don't come here expecting to have fun."

The Fundación's headquarters are in Madrid but it also has a base in Chinchón (a small town about 50km southeast of Madrid that is best known for being the home of the liqueur anís). This is a 17th-century building – Casa Dusmet – that is currently being restored and when repairs are completed it will also provide residential facilities.

There are workshops in Drawing and Painting , Framing and Mounting (four classes a month – 10 hours – 20,000ptas) and Theatre (Performance or Scriptwriting), for which there is a 3,000ptas enrolment fee. Prices for Drawing and Painting vary according to whom is giving the class: with Guillermo Muñoz Vera as your teacher the price will be 20,000ptas (15,000ptas for under 21s) for four classes – eight hours – per month and 35,000ptas (25,000ptas for under 21's) for eight classes – 16 hours – per month. With any of the other teachers at ARAUCO, these courses cost: 15,000ptas

(10,000ptas for under 21's) for four classes – eight hours – per month and 25,000ptas (15,000ptas for under 21's) for eight classes – 16 hours – per month. Courses in Sculpture and Landscape Painting (every Saturday from 10am to 2pm, 5,000ptas per session) take place in Chinchón. From April 1998, there will also be courses in Singing (three months to a year, 5,000ptas per session if there are three students in the class, 10,000ptas for a one-to-one lesson), Icon (three months, 15,000ptas per month), Marbling (three months, 15,000ptas per month) and Restoration (three months, 15,000ptas per month).

The people who attend courses here are mainly professionals and the teachers are not teachers per se, but artists and professionals who also happen to want to teach. Pupils also include people who work and who have taken up painting as a serious hobby. Grants are available and prices of courses are reduced for people under 21 years of age.

The Fundación can provide information about food and accommodation on request. There are intensive courses in the summer and, if there is enough demand, they will provide courses in August. You can buy materials from ARAUCO. There is a language school – Garrett Escuela de Idiomas (+34 91531 8898) – in the same building as the Fundación, which provides classes in Spanish as well as other languages. For more details and a copy of the Fundación's prospectus in English, contact the school.

IADE (Institución Artística de Enseñanza)

Claudio Coello, 4, 28001
Madrid
Tel: +34 91 577 1728
Fax: +34 91 577 1730

Website: www.iade.es
Established: 1957
Level: Very basic
Nearest Station: Metro Serrano
Contact: Diego Peréz de Castro Méndez

You will find this school in the posh part of town, behind the expensive and very central shopping street called Serrano. It occupies an entire building and the décor is stark: white walls (all the better to show off examples of student's work) and black floors. Classes take place on the top floors, either in large workrooms with long tables and stools (for Fashion, Interior Design, Window Dressing) or in the computer rooms, where students sit at individual computers facing the walls. The general atmosphere is hard-working but relaxed and friendly: teachers and pupils seem to enjoy an easy going relationship involving plenty of idle banter and jokes. Indeed, Diego Peréz de Castro Méndez is keen to stress that the teachers know students as names rather than numbers. This relationship is consolidated during the Mediterranean cruise that takes place every two or three years.

The school offers a variety of courses in the Applied Arts. Most of the 300 students attend the Interior Design course (three years). Other courses include Fashion Design, Graphic Design (both three years) and the Masters in Graphic Design. Communicating is not a problem as the teachers at the school all speak English as well as a variety of other languages. IADE has experience of non-Spanish speaking students and Diego Peréz de Castro Méndez pointed out that it is actually a wonderful way to learn the language as the majority of your fellow students will be Spanish. All courses last three years, except for the Graphic Design course, which you can do in two years. The Masters in Graphic Design involves 15 students working with five teachers and is focused on professional work only. Students are often given commissions from companies, for which they sometimes get paid. At the moment, for example, they are working on the design of a wine label for a new wine that will is to be brought out next year.

The school also offers short courses for ex-students or anyone with an interest in the subject. Subjects include designing exhibition stands and window dressing. Last year they lasted from mid-November to early February and cost 80,000ptas (materials included), for three hours a day, three times a week.

A combination of practical experience and studying is fundamental to the ethos of the school, with an emphasis on the practical rather than the theoretical. This year, for example, IADE is taking part in Casa Décor (similar to the Ideal Home Exhibition), for which students will be decorating one room of the exhibition's show house. IADE is also very interested in exchanges with other design schools; it already has links with Central St Martin's in London and Marangoni in Italy, among others, as well as its sister school in Lisbon (also called IADE). The school has links with companies that can provide work placements for students during their course, it also has links with the Centro Reina Sofia (the capital's main modern art museum). Well-known alumni include Miguel Muñoz and Rafael Gonzalez Sichez. A more recent graduate is currently working with Spain's most sought-after new designer, Amaya Arzuaga.

There is an annual matriculation fee after which you pay for the course per month. It will cost you about 5,000ptas (around £25) to set yourself up with the basic materials, and thereafter you will have to buy materials according to when you need them. There are posters on the notice board in the administration department giving details of shops offering discounts to students at the school. The school is open to students from 10am until 1pm and from 4pm to 7pm.

The average age of students is about 20 and you will need to have done GCSE's and A levels (or their equivalent). There is an entrance test. An English prospectus is available on request.

Taller Fang
**Esparteros, 11-2 dcha,
28012 Madrid
Tel: +34 91 528 6893 (Mobile: 904 205 944)
Established: 1988
Level: None
Nearest Station: Metro Sol
Contact: Pedro Llobet Porta**

Situated on the second floor of an office block a stone's throw away from the Puerta del Sol, (said to be the geographical mid-point of the capital and the country itself), it would be hard to find a more central place to study. If you can ignore the tackiness of the tourist shops and the slight sleaziness of the surroundings (think Leicester Square and you have the exact British equivalent), there is something exciting about Sol. It is also incredibly convenient, as it is accessible via three different lines on the metro and several bus routes.

The name of the workshop (fang), means mud in Catalan (it is charmingly misspelt – Taller Fagn – on the sign by the door) and is a reminder of the fact that Pedro is himself originally from Catalunya. He came to Madrid en route to the States, but was seduced by the capital and so his journey ended there. Barcelona, he claims, is definitely prettier, but you live better in Madrid! The Taller (workshop) itself is just a room where students sit at work tops lining the walls and Pedro is the only teacher. The space is not large, but there is room enough for about six students not to get in each others way.

There is no exam to sit and you are free to learn whatever you wish and to attend classes for as long as you want to. Some students have been coming for years while others come for a few months to learn a specific technique and then leave once they feel they have mastered it. Pedro, an alumnus of the Moncloa school of pottery in Madrid, is well versed in the many different skills of his art. He is particularly knowledgeable about those with a Spanish basis (eg Arab influenced designs and techniques) and he also has a keen interest in experimenting with the more complex techniques such as Raku (a Japanese varnishing technique) and crystallisation, a baking method. He organises special day-long workshops in the country where he, his students and friends can experiment with these techniques in the open air (weather permitting!). He has also organised trips abroad with his students. Recently, for example, a group of them went to Florence where a student who is also a painter was exhibiting her work.

The philosophy of the workshop, if there is one, is to create things for the sake of art and not in order to produce useful everyday objects. Pedro himself is a prime exponent of this - a glance at the photo album that he keeps of his work is enough to prove it. He is also very keen for students to enjoy themselves. He and his students often go out for dinner and the idea of the day-long workshops is not simply to work but, in Pedro's words, "hablar, comer, reir" (to talk, eat and laugh). Sessions take place twice a week and last for three hours. These are not fixed hours and can begin at any time within the hours that the workshop is open (Monday to Thursday, 4pm to 10pm). The cost is 9,000ptas per month for two three-hour sessions a week. There are no intensive classes and the school is closed in August, so these classes are probably most suitable for people who are already in Madrid attending a language course. However, Pedro has had students who spoke not a word of Spanish and who came to his classes to learn Spanish in an alternative way. He speaks no English but understands a great deal.

The atmosphere in the workshop is easy-going and friendly, with classical music playing in the background. Students are mainly working people looking to do something creative in their spare time and there is an air of concentration as students get on with their projects. There is a pottery wheel and a variety of other facilities at the student's disposal, such as a small library (a few shelves really) of books on pottery and different techniques, which students are encouraged to refer to. There is also a kiln in the workshop.

Contact Pedro for enrolment details.

Taller-Escuela "Camille Ceramistas"

Conde de Vilches, 7, 28028 Madrid
Tel: +34 91 361 2514
Established: 1994
Level: Basic. It's an opportunity for you to use and learn Spanish while learning pottery.
Nearest Station: Metro Diego de Leon
Contact: Nuria Magaña Limón

Although Camille Ceramistas is based in one of the least exciting areas of Madrid, do not be deterred from coming here on that basis: this really is a special school. It is named after Rodin's mistress, Camille Claudel, who was posthumously credited with a number of sculptures wrongly attributed to her famous lover. The studio is owned and run by Nuria Magaña Limón, a charming and intelligent woman who speaks a bit of English and is keen for overseas students to see the studio not only as a place to pot, but as somewhere to practise their Spanish. She is happy to help out if you have any questions about the language. There are three other permanent teachers, all of whom were trained at the Escuela de Cerámica de Moncloa. In the summer these are joined by others from the same school, who give classes in particular techniques.

The studio is a single space – a large, light room, not unlike a greenhouse, that stands beside a block of flats. Children and adults work together and there is a maximum of about eight students at any one time. Each class lasts two and a quarter hours and sessions take place between 10.30am and 2pm and 5pm and 8pm. In addition to classes, students can come to work on their oeuvres outside of their class hours, as long as they pay a fee for the space and take heed of various conditions. As space is limited, this may not always be possible.

Nuria runs intensive monothematic summer workshops and in 1998, for the first time ever, the school will remain open in August. The workshops include restoration of ceramics, raku (a Japanese method of varnishing pottery) and silkscreen printing. All last 20 hours and cost between 19,000ptas (Decorating Techniques) and 35,000ptas (Restoration and Silkscreen printing). The school has about twenty students annually. This number rises to 80 in September, when Nuria organises a special programme of classes with the CECE. These courses are closed to overseas students.

Hours are flexible as many students work and can't always make the classes every week. In these cases, lessons are spread out over an indefinite period of time so that these people are not penalised. Courses can be tailor made to suit an individual or a group's requirements.

The price for the basic year round courses (pottery, modelling and techniques for decorating ceramics – all based on traditional Spanish techniques) is 10,000ptas per month for five hours a week. You will have to pay approximately 2,000ptas extra per month for clay. The school/workshop can provide you with a certificate at the end of your course. The school is approved by the Escuela Oficial de Cerámica de Moncloa *(see p44)* which sends students there on work experience. Refresher courses for pottery teachers are available (prices to be arranged with individual institutions) and "therapeutic" pottery courses are currently being planned.

For more information, contact the school.

OTHER SCHOOLS THAT MAY BE OF INTEREST

BARCELONA Acadèmía Racó Mágic
(drawing and painting)
Cros, 22, Tda 2a, 08014 Barcelona,
Tel: +34 93 296 7666

Academia Raco Magic

restoration, jewelry-making, gemology, sculpture, ceramics, framing, tracing and various single modules such as drawing, painting and glass. Students are Spanish, Japanese and German and candidates must attend an interview.

BARCELONA Escola Massana
(art and design)
Hospital, 56, 08001 Barcelona
Tel: +34 93 442 2000
Fax: +34 93 441 7844
Email emassana@mail.bcn.es
Website: www.bcn.es/massana

L'Argila Escuela de Cerámica

BARCELONA L'Argila Escuela de Cerámica
(pottery and ceramics)
Nápols, 94, 08013 Barcelona
Tel: +34 93 231 0417

BARCELONA Escola D'Arts I Oficis Diputació de Barcelona
Urgell, 187, 08036 Barcelona,
Tel: +34 93 321 9066
Fax: +34 93 419 0063
Email: asantper@pie.xtec.esf

This, a state institution, offers courses in picture conservation and restoration, archeological conservation and

BARCELONA Escola Taller de Relligat **(framing)**
La Nau, 3 baixos, 08003 Barcelona
Tel: +34 93 310 2796

BARCELONA Escuela de Comic Joso
(cartoon art – including manga, illustration, caricatures)
Violant F'Hongria, 69, 08028 Barcelona
Tel: +34 93 490 2120
Fax: +34 93 409 1465
Email: escola.comic.joso@ sendanet.es
Website: www.sendanet .es/escolajoso

BARCELONA Escuela de Dibujo y Pintura Carment Muret
(drawing and painting)
Mayor de Gracía, 161, pral 1, 08012 Barcelona
Tel: +34 93 415 796

BARCELONA Escuela Forma
Enamorats, 78, 08013 Barcelona
Tel: +34 93 245 0050

L'Argila Escuela de Cerámica

This is a ceramics school located in the centre of Barcelona, near Gaudí's famous unfinished cathedral of the Sagrada Familia. The four main courses on offer are ceramics, sculpture, pottery wheel and drawing and painting. Facilities include five large kilns and ten pottery wheels. The academic year runs from September to June, though it is possible to join or leave whenever you wish to. It costs 12,000ptas to register

and monthly fees range from 8,700ptas to 29,000ptas, depending on the number of hours taken. All materials are included in the monthly fees. Intensive courses of 24 hours (16,500ptas) and 48 hours (29,700ptas) are also available. Students at the school come from Europe, Japan and South America.

BARCELONA L'Estudí
Els Vergos, 10, 08017 Barcelona, tel +34 93 417 2144, fax +34 93 417 2144
Email: cramos@maptel.es
Established: 1980
Level: None (they speak English), though "Spanish is always useful"
Nearest Station: Metro Tres Torres
Contact: Jette Bjerg or Carles Rames

Escuela Forma

A private art school 10 minutes from the centre of Barcelona, the course provision here is highly suitable for English-speakers as two of the three teachers trained at Goldsmith's College, University of London, and all speak excellent English. This is reflected in the nationalities of students who come from, amongst other countries, the UK, the USA and Scandinavia; the school also attracts Spanish students. Prices are given in both pesetas and pounds and the school can arrange accommodation for students. The school also organises BCN, a contemporary art workshop in Barcelona for fine art students (help for travel and accommodation is available).

BARCELONA Estudi Adelina Gaeta
(drawing and painting)
Francesc Carbonell, 35-37 bajos, 08034 Barcelona
Tel: +34 93 203 0421/1870,
Fax: +34 93 203 9200

BARCELONA Fundació Centre del Vidre de Barcelona
Comtes de Bell.lloc, 192, Barcelona,
Tel: +34 93 490 2886/1656
Fax: +34 93 490 6171
Email: vidrebcn@fcv-bcn.org
Website: www.fcv-bcn.org
Established: 1990
Level: Basic (spoken and comprehension)
Nearest Station: Metro Plaça del Centre
Contact: Pilar Muñoz i Domènech

A non-profit making cultural organisation located in the centre of Barcelona, the Fundación Centre del Vidre de Barcelona, is a centre dedicated to glass – its manufacture, its restoration and its history. Courses on offer include Escultura en Vidrio (casting) (glass sculpture), Vidrio para la Arquitectura (glass for architecture), Vidria Tradicional (traditional glass), Restauración de Vitrales y Objetos de Vidrio (restauration of windows and glass objects) and Talla Escultórica (glass workshop).

Applicants to the school have usually had prior training in the fine arts and the selection procedure involves a written application with drawing and photographs of works, an interview, a drawing exercise and the creation of a three-dimensional object. The Specialist Course (1,500 hours) involve modules in kiln techniques, cutting and engraving and cold techniques. Students from outside the EU must pay 50,000ptas per month to attend the course. On successful completion of the course, students are awarded a diploma. The majority of students at the school are Spanish, French and British. Facilities include a library and an archive specialising in material on the theme of modern glass making.

BARCELONA IDEP – Institución de Estudios Politécnicos de Barcelona
(major centre in Barcelona for graphic design, photography, film, TV, fashion, etc.),
Diagonal, 401, 08008 Barcelona,
Tel: +34 93 416 1012,
Fax: +34 93 416 0438,
Email: idep@idep.es,
Website: www.idep.es

BARCELONA Taller de 4 Pintors
(painting and drawing)
Portaferrissa, 16-3r, 08002 Barcelona
Tel: +34 93 318 3148.
Level: Lessons can be in English.

BARCELONA Winchester School of Art
(University of Southampton), MA in European Fine Art
Park Avenue, Winchester, Hants, SO23 8DL, UK,
Tel: +44 1962 842 500,
Fax: +44 1962 842 496,

Website: www.soton.ac.uk

While students on this course are affiliated to the Winchester School of Art in the UK, nine of the 12 months of the programme actually take place in Barcelona at the graduate studios. For the last three months of the course, students return to the UK to complete their MA at Winchester.

LERIDA Estudi Dibuix i Pintura Dolors Pons
Princep de la Viana, 92, pral 3a, 25008 Lerida
Tel: +34 973 236 481
Website: www.xtec.es/incanop
Established: 1965
Level: None. Teachers speak both English and French
Nearest Station: There is a train station on the street on which the school is situated.
Contact: Jaime Salla

Located in Lleida, a town situated in the comunidad autónoma of Catalunya, this school offers courses in iconography, decorative techniques (trompe l'oeil, imitation marble) and drawing and painting. The duration of the course is for the entire academic year, though prices are charge per hour for those who can only attend classes for a limited period of time. All students at the school are Spanish.

MADRID Artestudio, Hermosilla
89-2º ext. izda, 28006 Madrid,
Tel: +34 91 575 9150
Fax: +34 91 734 9748

Academic year courses in drawing and painting, intensive weekend courses in acrylic, batik, glass, chinese painting, etc. and outdoor summer courses in Navarra and the Alpujarras mountains in Granada.

MADRID Aura
(drawing and painting)
Francisco Silvela, 5-1ºB, 28028
Madrid Tel: +34 91 309 0170

MADRID Avalon
(antique and furniture restoration)
Narcisos, 9, 28016
Madrid Tel/Fax: +34 91 413 7284 UK: 17 Cats Lane, Sudbury, Suffolk, CO10 6SG
Tel: +44 1787 370 638
Email antonio.rubio36 @virgin.net

MADRID Centro de Restauración del Mueble
(furniture restoration)
Eresma, 7, 28002
Madrid
Tel: +34 91 561 3145

MADRID Escuela de Arte y Antigüedades
(antique and furniture restoration)
Conde de Aranda, 4, 28001
Madrid
Tel/Fax: +34 91 577 6713/ 523 1214

MADRID Escuela de Arte no.4 Diseño de Interiore
Camino de Vinateros, 106, 28030 Madrid
Tel: +34 91 439 0124/0000
Fax: +34 91 437 9639
Level: Correct spoken and written Spanish
Nearest Station: Vinateros
Contact: The director

This is a state-run school attended by Spanish students. It is suitable only for those who speak Spanish and is probably useful only to those who wish to pursue a career in interior design in Spain.

ART AND DESIGN

Dance

Picture a raven-haired woman standing on a stage, poised as though ready to charge, with arms stretched out above her head, hands entwined and body extended. She will be wearing a dress (probably red) with a tight bodice, plunging neckline and tiered skirts, her ears adorned with large gold hoops. One of the most enduring images of Spain this is, of course, the picture of a flamenco dancer. You may have been to a flamenco show, but had you ever thought that you too might one day be able to don that outfit and assume the same dramatic pose?

Every day, all over Spain, men and women of all ages and sizes go to flamenco classes, both at private centres and state-run adult education colleges. They will probably not resemble anything remotely similar to what you see on the stage, either in their dress or in the way that they dance. However, flamenco is extremely popular as it is an incredibly accessible dance, albeit one that many can dance though few can actually master.

Flamenco is not the only dance particular to Spain – there is *ballet clásico español* which to the untrained eye is indistinguishable from flamenco and which tends to be taken up by professionals rather than those for whom dancing is a hobby. There are also regional dances, the most famous of which are *sevillanas*, which are also similar to flamenco, though easier (the

basic difference being that the role of the male dancer is limited purely to accompanying the female dancer – it's a sort of courtship dance). There is also *baile de salón*, which English-speakers might call ballroom-dancing and which encompasses *tango, pasodoble* etc. Strictly speaking, *baile de salón* is not the same as latin dancing (*salsa, merengue,* etc), but both are often offered under the title of *baile de salón*.

The main attraction of taking dancing classes in Spain probably stems from the general Spanish attitude to most things – the emphasis is on having fun rather than taking the dancing too seriously. Many classes do not require much talent; a predisposition for enjoyment is probably the best qualification that you can possess. This is particularly true of *baile de salón* classes, for which couples and groups of friends tend to come in off the street with no prior knowledge of dancing.

LANGUAGE

The great thing about taking dance classes in a foreign country is that speaking the language is not a necessary pre-requisite for enrolment. In fact, it may prove to be a good fun way of learning the language, though you are more likely to pick up the (not necessarily accurate) grammatical vagaries of your teacher(s) and fellow dancers, than learn how to speak textbook Spanish.

Flamenco is particularly popular amongst Japanese tourists – it is even said that there are more flamenco schools in Tokyo alone than there are in the whole of Spain. As a result, your fellow students, if they do come from abroad, may well be Japanese.

If you wish to combine language-learning with serious flamenco classes, Carmen de las Cuevas school in Granada provides both. The school is profiled in the language schools section on *p113*.

ACCREDITATION AND LEVELS OF PROFESSIONALISM

There is no official accreditation for dancing schools and academies in Spain, though many teachers are highly trained, sometimes abroad. Some teachers, such as Carmen Cubillo, have qualifications from the *Real Academía de Baile* (Royal Academy of Dance) in both classical ballet and *ballet clásico español*. Often former students will come back to teach at their old school. Reputations of schools are based largely on word of mouth, and most of the founders of dance schools are dancers who first made a name for themselves on stage (photos of them in their former glory will often adorn the walls of their schools). In general, schools are named after their founders (eg *Estudios de Danza Carmen Senra*) and the staff working at each will assure you that the person for whom they work is the most famous dancer in Spain.

The one school with a reputation and a history to rival all others is the legendary Amor de Dios in Madrid, where the famous flamenco dancer Joaquín Cortés studied. It is profiled on page 68.

The students at many schools are divided between professional dancers

who take classes for several hours a day and others who dance purely as a hobby. Often the non-professional dancers will be housewives looking for something to help pass the time. On enrolment you will probably be asked to participate in a class so that the school can gauge your level. If you are an absolute beginner, such a test will not be necessary.

Despite the presence of professional dancers at most schools, the atmosphere is likely to be warm, friendly and fairly easy-going. Do not be surprised to find students and teachers in the corridors, smoking and having a chat after the class. It is surprising how many dancers at these schools do smoke.

WHAT TO WEAR

Flamenco and Ballet Clásico Español

Apart from wearing the right type of shoes – men wear cuban-healed boots and women wear similarly heeled shoes with a strap across the front to stop them from falling off – flamenco/sevillanas/ballet clásico Español students can wear whatever they like. However, if you want to look the part, there is an unofficial dress code for women requiring a long, flowing black skirt (often hitched up at the front so that the teacher can see what the students' legs are doing), a leotard and leg warmers. Castanets may also be necessary. Flamenco shoes cost between 4,000ptas and 7,000ptas, and skirts cost about 12,000ptas. Men's boots will cost more. This equipment can be obtained from: Zapatillas Coral, Cava Baja, 5, 28005 Madrid, Spain, Tel: +34 91 366 5596/365 5869, Fax: +34 91 366 5596 and Flamenco Vive, C/la Unión, 4, 28013 Madrid, Spain, (Metro Opera), which also sells other flamenco accoutrements and memorabilia.

Baile de Salón

You can go as casually or as dressed up as you like to these classes. Generally people come in off the street in their work clothes. For professional female dancers, provocative clothes such as tight skirts with dangerously high slits and heels are probably *de rigueur*. (Think Strictly Ballroom, with a bit more style.)

FLAMENCO OUTSIDE SPAIN

For those who would like to find out more about flamenco before going off to Spain, there is a group of flamenco aficionados based in London called the Peña Flamenca de Londres. They organise *juerga* nights (evenings when flamenco aficionados can practise the skills they are developing) and produce a newsletter several times a year. The newsletter acts as a mouthpiece for those involved in the Peña and contains information, flamenco course listings (both in Spain and in the UK), reviews and small ads (looking for a pair of size seven flamenco shoes?). The Peña meets on the first Sunday of every month (except August) at the Union Chapel Project Studio Theatre, Compton Avenue, London, N1 2XD UK, (Highbury and Islington underground station). Entrance costs £5 for members and £7 for non-members. Membership costs £12 for 12 months. Contact 0171 703 6893 for more information about the Peña Flamenca de Londres and courses offered in the UK and in Spain. A new Peña has opened in Reading in the UK at Rising Sun Arts Centre, Silver St. It meets on the last Saturday of every month from 7.30pm onwards.

Flamenco summer schools take place in the UK in London, Birmingham and Bath. The Peña's newsletter carries information about these nearer the time. Contact Gemma de la Cruz

(0171 485 8603), Rosi Reed (0181 968 6782), Juani Garcia (0181 879 0102), Felipe (0171 511 4892), Ana (0121 240 7828) or Emmanuelle Ginn (01225 875 522) for more details.

The Peña's newsletter lists a number of summer courses (flamenco dancing and flamenco guitar) that take place in Spain. Summer schools have taken place in Estepona (call Loretta on: 0181 968 5174 for details), Jerez (call Rosi Reed on: 0181 968 6782 for details), the Escuela de Baile "Angelita Gómez", (C/Porvera, 22, 11403 Jerez de la Frontera (Cadiz), tel/fax +34 956 168 183) and Art-Danza (C/Avenida Salvador Gallardo, 42, Urb. Mazacote, 11, Sanl car de Barrameda (Cádiz), email artdanza.flamenco @mad. servicom.es.) These courses tend to take place on an annual basis. Contact the Peña or the numbers given for more details.

FLAMENCO GUITAR

Courses in flamenco guitar are included under the chapter headed Miscellaneous. There are fewer such courses compared to the provision of flamenco dancing courses, though some flamenco schools do offer the occasional course in guitar. The annual Festival de la Guitarra in Córdoba focuses on all aspects of the guitar (classical, jazz, flamenco, etc.) and includes the provision of a few courses. For more information write to Gran Teatro, Festival Internacional de la Guitarra, Avda del Gran Capitán, 3, 14008, Córdoba or call +34 957 480 237 (fax +34 957 487 494).

BECOMING A TEACHER OF BAILE DE SALON

Orthos, a group of schools dedicated to training sports instructors, offer a course in teaching baile de salón. The course covers standard dances such as waltzes and the foxtrot and latin numbers such as cha-cha-chá and salsa. Various

aspects of each dance are studied, including the history and the music of each one. For more information, contact the central Orthos school: Córcega, 371, 08037 Barcelona, tel +34 93 207 7303.

FESTIVAL DE JEREZ

The Festival de Jerez is an annual festival that takes place in Jerez in the last two weeks of April. The main attractions are the shows that take place each night, bringing together important names in flamenco. A part of the festival is also devoted to lectures and courses in flamenco and classical Spanish ballet.

For more information tel: +34 956 329 313 (fax +34 956329 511).

Further information

A group called Amigos del Baile de Salón (Friends of Ballroom dancing) provides information about ballroom-dancing all over Spain. Contact details for ABS are: C/Las Naves, 14 C, 28005 Madrid, Spain.
Tel/fax +34 91 517 4029,
Email: abs@develnet.es,
Website: www.develnet.es/abs.

For information (in Spanish) about tango (history, places to dance it, etc.), visit the Patio de Tango website on www.gen.com/ vbforum/patiodetango.

Information about flamenco festivals in Spain can be obtained from the Centro Andaluz de Flamenco, Jerez, Tel +34 91 956 349 265.

DANCE

Ballroom dancing associations in Spain:

(NB: not everyone who answers the phone will be able to speak English

Asociación Española de Baile Deportivo y de Competición, Sant Quinti, 37-45 Esc. A entre 2a, 08041 Barcelona, Spain, Tel/fax +34 93 456 5167

Asociación Madrileña de Baile Deportivo y de Competición, C/Aniceto Marinas, 106, 5°-C, 28008 Madrid, Spain, Tel +34 91 547 2897

Asociación Aragonesa de Baile de Salón, C/Castelar, 53, 50013 Zaragoza, Spain, Tel +34 976 552 452

Asociación Cultural Aragonesa Arabaile de Bailes de Salón, C/San José, 57, 50120 Montzalbarba, Zaragoza, Spain, Tel +34 976 598 966

Asociación Española de Rock Acrobático, C/Quevedo, 7, 12004 Caste-llón, Spain, Tel/fax +34 964 245 608

Asociación Española de Profesores de Bailes de Salón, C/Torrent de l"lla, 16-18, 08012 Barcelona, Spain, Tel/fax +34 93 457 2548

Asociacio Dámics del Ball de Salo de Sant Cugat, C/Frco. Moragas, 3, 4°-1a, 08190 Sant Cugat del Vallés, Barcelona, Spain

Asociación de Tango Sabadell, C/Joan Valera, 2B, 08206 Sabadell, Barcelona, Tel +34 93 717 9843

Asociación Navarra de Amigos del Tango Argentino, C/Mayor, 8 3°D, 31200 Estella Navarra, Spain, Tel +34 948 553 274

Asociación de Tango de Cataluña Patio de Tango, Pso. Mare Dedeu del Coll, 155, 08032 Barcelona, Spain, Tel +34 93 420 9556, Fax +34 93 302 0839

Asociación Guipuzcoana de Amigos del Tango Argentino, C/Escuela, 54, Trasera, 20140 Andoain, Guipuzcoa, Spain

Amigos del Baile de Valencia, C/-Islas Canarias, 245, 46023 Valencia, Spain, Tel +34 96 331 0968, Fax +34 93 331 0978

El Paso – Asociación Guipuzcoana de Baile de Salón, C/Pinar, 5 entresuelo, 20300 Irún, Guipuzcoa, Spain, Tel +34 943 284 955

El Pisotón – Asociación de Bailes de Salón, C/Mariano Sebastian Izauel, 9, 28100 Alcobendas, Madrid, Spain

Garua – Asociación de Amigos del Tango, Muelle de la Merced, 3, 48003 Bilbao, Spain, Tel +34 94 416 3383

Tangoneón – Asociación Amigos del Tango, Tel +34 91 305 1696 (ask for Martín or Mari Paz) or +34 91 531 3840 (ask for Marcos or Rosi).

Pista 3 – Asociación Vizcaina Bailes de Salón, C/Santutxu, 40 bajo, 48004 Bilbao, Spain, Tel +34 91 433 5546.

DANCE

DANCE SCHOOLS

Academia Amor de Dios

Fray Luis de León, 13 bajo,
28012 Madrid
Tel: +34 91 530 1661
Fax: +34 91 527 4498
Established: 1950
Level: None
Nearest Station: (Metro)
Embajadores or Palos de la
Frontera

The recent explosion of interest in the world of Flamenco has leaped well beyond national boundaries. Currently the world seems to be hooked on what was once an exclusively Spanish passion. There are flamenco schools and shows all over the world and it is said that in Japan there are now even more flamenco schools than there are in the whole of Spain. It is invidious to credit a single person with having single-handedly opened the eyes of the world to a new passion like flamenco. However, there can be little doubt that the arrival of Joaquin Cortés on various stages around the globe sparked a great deal of interest among people who didn't even know what flamenco was. All great artists must start somewhere, and in the case of Joaquín Cortés, that somewhere was the Academia Amor de Dios.

Less a school and more a national institution when, in 1993, it was forced to move from its location on the calle del Amor de Dios (from which it took its name) in the historic district around La Latina, there was such a hue and cry that the protests of the school's aficionados made it into the national press. Today its setting is more prosaic: a rather ordinary looking building, to the south of the city, whose appearance belies the hive of activity going on behind its walls.

Coming here was is an experience like no other. As you walk into the reception area, your senses are assaulted by a barrage of sights, smells and above all else, sounds, in particular the rhythmic tapping of feet as dancers warm up in the corridors before the start of their classes. There's a sensation of chaos - with everyone talking and smoking. It is impossible to tell who is coming from a class and who is about to start one and there is no sense whatsoever of anyone being in charge. It is an odd place, at once utterly 'gitano' (gipsy-like) and yet very cosmopolitan - girls who look as though they could be nothing but Spanish turned out to be American and professional Japanese flamenco artists dance amongst Spanish performers.

No other flamenco school in Madrid is like this. It is unique and is without a doubt the nucleus of flamenco dancing in the capital. It has spawned generations of flamenco dancers who have either gone on to become professionals or to form schools in their own right (such as Merche Esmeralda). The raison d'eÍtre of the Academia Amor de Dios is undoubtedly its teachers. This is not a conventional school: there is no central administration, no Head of Studies who will process your application and assign you to a class. Here, you are free to choose the teacher whom you want and, conversely, teachers are at liberty to choose whether or not they wish to take you on as their pupil. Officially there are thirty teachers at the school, among them some of the most well known flamenco artists in the country: people such as Paco Romero, La Tati and Manolete. Each of these has a small sign on one wall of the entrance hall of the academy with their name printed on it together with the hours they give classes and the price they charge. (Between 5,000ptas to 8,000ptas for five classes a week, depending on the teacher.) In order to sign up with one of them you must talk to them directly. Unofficially, there are other people (including a few pupils from the academy) who also give classes. These are probably slightly cheaper than the official ones.

If you are looking for somewhere to live, the academy's secretary can try to put you in touch with other students. Apart from the classes, you will have to pay for shoes, a skirt (for the women) and any other clothing that may be necessary such as legwarmers and leotards.

The aim of the academy is not to turn out strict professionals, but to bring people to an understanding of the tradition behind flamenco. You can study here for as long as you like, with whomever you like and you can sign up as an absolute beginner or as an experienced professional. The essence of it is having the freedom to do what you want and to express yourself as you would wish to, which in itself is the fundamental philosophy behind flamenco.

This school is not an undiscovered gem. It is already famous all over the world and there are frequently more foreign dancers here than there are Spanish students. However, it is an extraordinary and exciting place, where beginners get to rub shoulders with skilled professionals. If you are looking for a quintessentially Spanish experience, whether or not you are serious about becoming a professional dancer, then this is, without a doubt, the place to come.

Centro Internacional de Danza Carmen Roche
Roble, 22, 28020 Madrid
Tel: +34 91 576 3161/579 0805
Fax: +34 91 579 3161

Established: 1984
Level: None
Nearest Station: (Metro) Tetuan
Contact: Ma Jesus Martinez

Situated on a quiet street in a residential part of Madrid, from the outside this school really doesn't look anything special. Once you walk through the door, however, a long corridor takes you to the heart of the building, which appears to have been recently redecorated. The décor is clean and modern, with blond wooden floors and good facilities. Carmen Roche is the director of the school, which she founded in 1984. Before then she was a cofounder of the Ballet Nacional and had been the prima ballerina for Maurice Béjart as well as a ballerina in Antonio's (Spain's most famous dancer) company.

There are about 250 students at the school, the majority of whom are Spanish. After that, there are a large number of Norwegian students, as the Official Ballet School of Stockholm sends pupils here. The school is divided in two as it caters both for people who wish to become professional dancers and for those who are doing it purely as a hobby, yet the same teachers teach both groups. Professional dancers attend classes every day, usually in the mornings and often, all day, whereas non-professionals come in the afternoons once or twice a week. The school can prepare students for the Conservatorio de Madrid examinations.

There are classes in classical ballet, jazz, performance, singing, flamenco and sevillanas. The more classes you do a month, the cheaper it works out. Prices start at 6,000ptas per month for only two lessons a week. There are intensive summer courses lasting 10 days in theatre, singing, classical ballet, modern

DANCE

dance, classical Spanish ballet, ballroom dancing and sevillanas. Prices vary from 10,000ptas to 20,000ptas per course depending on the topic. You don't need to speak any Spanish at all. They explain that this is because all technical terms are in French, the international language of ballet and it is always possible to illustrate what you want to say with movement rather than language. The school is evidently used to dealing with non-Spanish speakers. An interesting feature of the school's provision are the courses in Techniques for Musicals that are run by John O'Brien, an Englishman and international choreographer who teaches dance. The short week-long course that takes place a few times a year costs 10,000ptas.

Clothing such as ballet shoes, tights and the uniforms for children can be purchased from the school. There are three dance studios and three dressing rooms (two female) as well as a cafeteria. For groups of 10 or more, the school can organise a programme according to their needs. There is an all female residence across the road from the school on Bravo Murillo and boys can be given contact numbers for accommodation. Contact the school for enrolment details.

Escuela de Baile de Salón
Jorge Juan, 127, Madrid
Tel: +34 91 408 0714
Established: 1993
Level: None
Nearest Station: (Metro)
O'Donnell
Contact: Gema

The entrance to this school is beside the door to building 127 and immediately inside, a small concierge's booth serves as an office/reception. This is probably not the school to bring you to Spain for its courses alone. Rather, lessons here are the ideal accompaniment (and antidote?) to studying at a language school. Classes sound as though they are a good laugh, particularly if you go with a group of friends. Obviously there are those who take ballroom dancing seriously, but at this school, where students are mainly people who come in off the street with no prior experience, the emphasis seems to be on learning and unwinding.

Classes take place from Monday to Friday between 10am and 11pm, with the majority of classes in the afternoons. Most students come once a week, the cost for which is 5,000ptas per month. There are eight teachers (four men, four women) who always take classes in pairs. None of them are qualified ballroom dancing teachers, as such a qualification does not exist in Spain. They are all, however, qualified dancers. In July, August and September there are intensive courses. The fee is 8,000ptas for eight hours of classes per week.

There are no particular courses in specific styles of dancing. All groups are taught a bit of everything and in one and a quarter hours (the length of the lessons), you will learn one or two of a variety of techniques such as mambo, bachata, swing, waltzes, salsa, merengue, cha-cha-chá, latin rhythms and so on. There is no extra cost for kit as you can dance in anything you like, as long as you feel comfortable in it. The teachers organise outings to dance sal-ons and at the end of the academic year, the students put on a show in a theatre.

There is no enrolment fee and no prerequisites. Help in finding accommodation is available on request.

Escuela de Dansa Merche Esmeralda

O'Donnell, 4 y 6 , 28009
Madrid (entrance via Antonio
Acuña)
Tel: +34 91 575 9160
Established: 1995
Level: None
Nearest Station: (Metro)
Príncipe de Vergara
Contact: Isabel Santos

Getting to this school was a bit tricky as it located on the side of two enormous office blocks at one end of O'Donnell (the end furthest from the metro station of the same name, so don't make the mistake of going there as I did!). To access the school, take the left hand path by building number 6 and take the stairs down to the square. The school is on your right hand side at the bottom of the stairs.

At 12 years of age, Merche Esmeralda started to work with people such as Matilde Corral and at one stage was prima ballerina at the Ballet Nacional under the direction of Antonio (Spain's most famous dancer). Later she created, and became the director of, the Ballet Company of the Region of Murcia. Claims to fame include appearances in a number of films by Carlos Saura. Today she teaches, choreographs and dances all over Spain and around the world. Awards include the Premio Nacional de Ballet.

This school is dedicated to the teaching of flamenco from all levels from beginners to professionals. Flamenco classes cost 9,000ptas per month for two days a week. One-off classes cost 1,500ptas. Spanish dancing courses cost 9,000ptas per month for two days a week for beginners. At advanced level the cost is 12,000ptas a month for two days

a week and 16,000ptas a month for three days a week. (All flamenco classes last one and a half hours. All other classes last one hour.) The Escuela Bolera (Bolero dancing) costs 12,000ptas per month for two days a month and 16,000ptas for three days a month. Classical Ballet, for which there are classes for advanced students and beginners, cost 9,000ptas for two days a week and 13,000ptas for three days a week. Sevillana classes cost 9,000ptas per month for two classes a week and classes in Regional Dances cost 6,000ptas per month for one lesson a week. Ballroom dancing, also once a week, costs 5,000ptas for the month. There are also exercise classes and pre-ballet classes for little ones. In July there are intensive short courses, taken by teachers from outside the school who are specialists in their field. Usually these are attended by people at intermediate level and above, although beginners could be accepted. The school is closed in August as well as at weekends.

The school has about 150 students, with overseas students from Australia, Brasil, Puerto Rico and Italy. A couple of the teachers at the school speak English, but knowledge of Spanish is not essential as you don't need to talk if you can already dance. A number of the school's overseas students have included Japanese dancers, sent over by their schools to learn flamenco for a couple of years in order to be able to teach it back in Japan. The average age of students is between 17 and 25, though older people and those who work take part in the less professional classes such as ballroom dancing. You will have to pay about 7,500ptas and 8,500ptas for the flamenco skirt and shoes. Some kit is available to buy from the school.

Contact the school for enrolment details.

DANCE

Escuela de Danza Teatro Kainos

Office: Encomienda de Palacios, 27-1A, 28030 Madrid;
Studio: Castelló,l 43, 28001 Madrid
Tel: +34 91 772 7053
Established: 1996
Level: Basic spoken
Nearest Station: (Metro) Velázquez
Contact: Sergio Cardozo or Cristina García

Arriving at this entrance to this school you will doubtless be struck by its grandeur. Two huge wooden double doors are flanked on either side by marble columns adorned with brass plaques with the school's name engraved on them. The interior is no less impressive: walls panelled in dark wood and a beautiful stained glass window in one of the bathrooms. This must once have belonged to a wealthy family and everything about it preserves a sense of nobility. It is worth coming to the school for this alone. There are two studios here, both of them large rooms (perhaps they were once the drawing rooms of the house) with wooden floors, an exercise bar running the width of each wall and a mirror covering one wall.

The school was set up two years ago when Sergio (originally from Argentina) and a group of his friends decided to form a dance/performance collective. This, therefore, is not the only place where lessons are given, as each friend has their own school. The group is predominantly Spanish, though there is one person from France and another from England amongst them. Each one specialises in a different area of dance. Sergio, for example, is qualified in physical education (a qualification he received in Argentina) so he gives classes in Acrobatics and Physical Training. He also teaches Tango Argentino and other Bailes de Salón (styles of ballroom dancing) as well as contemporary dance. Other partners in the group teach ballet, performance, voice and jazz, as well as other techniques.

The school is geared towards both professionals and non-professionals. There is a very comprehensive three-year complete training course for professionals which has yet to get off the ground and for which they are now receiving applications. It will cover most aspects of dance and performance and will involve the diverse skills of each member of the collective. It will also include the input of visiting experts in a variety dance and performance areas. This course is geared towards dedicated professionals, with a maximum of 20 people in each class and costing about 30,000ptas for enrolment and nine monthly instalments.

Other courses are the beginners and summer courses. The beginners classes take place three times a week for three hours and costs 17,000ptas for enrolment and nine monthly instalments. The cost of summer courses (July and September) ranges from 7,000ptas to 17,900ptas. These programmes include a variety of dance styles (Classical Spanish) Ballet, Belly Dancing, Ballet, etc) and a range of theatrical techniques (mime, clowns, performance, textual analysis, etc). The special courses cost 25,000ptas and these include The History and Aesthetics of Dance and the Methodolo-gy of Ballroom Dancing. There are discounts of up to 20 per cent for people signing up for more than one course. The school also has a link with a language school in Madrid – Madrid Plus (+34 91 548 1116). It is also possible to take a single lesson once a week, the charge for this is 5,500ptas per month, which rises to 16,000ptas per month for four classes a week.

Short courses and seminars take place throughout the year. There are a limited number of grants available for dedicated students who need financial help. The teachers themselves were themselves given grants and they feel that it is only right that they should help needy students in their turn. From April 1998, they are hoping to start improvisation workshops.

Contact the school for enrolment details.

Estudio de Dansa "Pepa Guerra"

Valenzuela, 8, 28014 Madrid
Tel: +34 91 531 2085
Fax: +34 91 319 9312
Email: alvaroto@itelco.es
Established: 1973
Level: None
Nearest Station: (Metro) Banco de España or Retiro
Contact: Pepa Chacón

You will find this school in a wonderful location on a street just off the Puerta de Alcalá (one of Madrid's grandest plazas) and a few steps away from the capital's famous park, the Retiro. The street is easy to identify: at the end of it you will see what looks like a piece of modern art but which is in fact a building clad in a black and white zig-zag pattern, looking slightly out of context amidst a cluster of classic, turn of the century buildings. The entrance to the school is the next door along from the impressive and heavy wooden door of Portal 8. It's tiny in comparison (makes you feel a bit like Alice chasing the rabbit down the rabbit warren in Alice in Wonderland!) and leads down to a tiled and airy basement area with whitewashed walls

and an Andalusian feel which is in sharp contrast to the busy, commercial atmosphere outside. The walls are decorated with a couple of ageing, but rather charming Spanish tourist board posters and photos of Pepa Chacón. An alumnus of Pepa Guerra, Pepa Chacón took over from her teacher 18 years ago when Pepa Guerra began to lose her sight and decided to move to Málaga. The school was actually founded by Pepa Guerra in 1958.

It attracts a large number of American students as it has a special arrangement with TUFTS and Skidmore College in Madrid (fees are paid to the school via the universities). It also has European, Japanese and South American students, though the majority of students are Spanish and mainly female (though, allegedly, the number of male students is increasing due to the recent boom in Spanish dancing).

There are two dance studios, one of which is the original studio where the school started, the second and larger one being in the part that was later extended. There are changing rooms, showers and a handy massage room, where Pepa Chacón's husband treats people with sports injuries. There is one other teacher at the school who gives classical ballet classes, gym training and beginners ballet.

Classes are given in flamenco, sevillanas, bulerias, tangos gitanos and other Spanish dance forms. The school offers a week of summer courses in choreography and flamenco technique ($210, advanced students only), basic flamenco technique and rhythm ($210) and sevillanas ($150). You will have to pay a $70 deposit (payable by postal order or bank draft) in order to enrol. Lessons in each take place for two hours a day.

DANCE

Estudio de Danza Carmen Cubillo

Apart from university students, pupils at the school are generally working women (and men), many of whom are civil servants who work in the nearby Insalud building. The average age is about 25.

The cost for the classes is 7,700ptas a month for two days a week, 6,000ptas a month for one day a week, 9,000ptas a month for three hours a week, 10,000ptas for four hours a week, 12,000ptas for five hours a week. One off classes cost 5,000ptas and one-to-one classes cost 1,500ptas. There is a special price for groups. The school is open from 12.30pm to 6.30pm during the week and on a Tuesday and Thursday there is a class from 9pm to 10pm. Bear in mind the added cost of flamenco shoes and skirt. (See the introduction to this chapter for more information about the cost of the clothes.)

For enrolment details, contact the school.

Estudio de Danza Carmen Cubillo

Ponzano, 44, 28003 Madrid
Tel: +34 91 441 1662/399 1359
Fax: +34 91 553 9725 – mark the fax for the attention of Carmen Cubillo
Established: 1976
Level: Basic
Nearest Station: (Metro) Ríos Rosas
Contact: Ma. Carmen Martinez de Maturana

Located in a well-to-do area north of the Pueta del Sol, the entrance to this school is easy to spot: white-washed walls surround a dark door framed with ivy. The school is run and was founded by Carmen Cubillo, a Madrileña who trained in Classical Spanish Ballet, and become a professional dancer aged 14. However, realising that this would not provide enough constant work to generate a steady income or job security, she decided to set up the school with her sister, also a dancer. Today, both still teach at the school, along with nine to 10 other teachers.

The school is small and the cramped entrance hall is usually filled with people on their way to and from classes. In the afternoons, between 5.30pm and 7.30pm, there are classes for children (aged about four). The rest of the time, from 10am to 10.30pm, classes are attended by adults, from beginners to professionals. Depending on how seriously they take their dancing, students will come from an hour or two a week to several hours a day.

There are two types of courses: those that run for the full academic year and the short courses from the end of June to the end of July. These programmes include 'Spanish dancing' (sevillanas, flamenco, etc), Jazz and Ballroom Dancing and cost 16,000ptas for four hours a week. The course in Classical Ballet takes place five hours a week and costs 20,000ptas. For the full academic year courses there is an enrolment fee of 2,500ptas as well as a monthly charge, which varies according to the course you are doing. The fees range from 4,400ptas per month for one hour a week of Bolero dancing or regional dancing and 8,000ptas per month for two hours weekly of Spanish Dancing, Jazz or Ballroom Dancing to 18,000ptas per month for five one and a half hour lessons a week in 'Classical Ballet. A discount is available for groups enrolling together.

An end of year performance is usually organised for all the students at the school. Although the school is usually closed in the month of August, there would be a possibility of keeping it open then, should there be sufficient demand for classes. The majority of the school's students are Spanish, though they do get some students from a nearby language school. A Japanese girl recently graduated from the school with a qualification from the Real Academia de Ballet Español.

Facilities at the school include two studios, two female dressing rooms with toilet and showers and one male dressing room with toilet. For enrolment details contact the school.

Estudios de Danza Carmen Senra

Apolonio Morales, 11, 28036 Madrid
Tel: +34 91 345 1877/359 1647
Established: 1993
Level: None
Nearest Station: (Metro) Plaza de Castilla
Contact: Nieves or Carmen Senra

Estudios de Danza Carmen Senra is situated beneath a large office/ apartment block a few minutes walk away from the imposing Torres de Castilla. These are the enormous leaning twin towers that act as a sort of gateway as you enter Madrid from the north and which have become a modern landmark for the capital. The school is known internationally and attracts students from South America, Greece and other European countries. Carmen Senra herself is responsible for introducing Contemporary Jazz dance to Madrid in the 1970s, having previously worked with Martha Graham in New York. Until 1993 she had her own dance company and her contacts with the dance world outside of Spain mean that she can occasionally bring over well-known teachers from abroad.

The speciality of this school is contemporary dance, though classes are not confined to this. There are courses in the more traditional Spanish styles such as Flamenco, Sevillanas and Classical Spanish dancing. About 450 people attend classes at Estudios de Danza Carmen Senra (about 15 per cent of them from overseas) and ages range from children (from four years) to adults of any age. Levels are also diverse, and this is reflected in the school's slogan ("Profesión, Formación, Diversión, Salud" – which, roughly translated means: "For your career, for your vocation, for your health, for fun"). Students range from absolute beginners to professional dancers who are attracted mainly because of the Contemporary jazz classes. Contemporary jazz dance teachers who have their own schools also come to take classes here. Less professional dancers include housewives learning to dance sevillanas and groups of friends who come to learn latin and ballroom dancing (tango, salsa, cha-cha-chá).

The school year runs from mid-September to the end of June and throughout July and September there are intensive daily summer courses. There are sometimes classes in August, though the heat in the capital at that time of year often precludes any sort of movement whatsoever! The school is open from 9am to 10pm every day. There are about 15 teachers at the school. Some of them are ex-students at the school and all have been extremely well trained. Many have been trained abroad. On your first session at the school, you will be put in a class so that your level can be assessed and you will then be placed in an appropriate class. If you aren't too sure about what sort of classes you would like to take, you can try two or three classes free of charge and then make up your mind.

Prices vary. The basic cost is 8,000ptas per month for two classes a week. However, professional dancers who come on a daily basis choose the rate of 24,800ptas for 62 hours a month. Twenty-four hours a month will set you back 13,200ptas. The price for the short courses (ie when a visiting professional comes to the school) varies according to the cachet of/how well-known that particular teacher is. The summer course costs 12,000ptas (one and a half hours every day from Monday to Friday). Discounts of about 20 per cent are available for groups (15 minimum). One-to-one classes are available, as are workshops for more experienced dancers.

Extra costs depend on what course you are taking. For example, you will need to buy the appropriate shoes and skirt for the sevillana and flamenco classes. However, for contemporary jazz the only clothes that you will need are those that you feel most comfortable dancing in. The school cannot help with accommodation, but you can always put a sign up on the school notice board and someone might be able to help you.

You don't need to speak Spanish, you just need to want to dance! Contact the school for enrolment details.

OTHER DANCE SCHOOLS

ÁLAVA Traspasos Centro de Danza y Movimiento
(contemporary dance, baile de salón, afro-carribean dance)
Domingo Beltran, 61 bajo
Tel: +34 945 248 358
Fax: +34 945 279 632

BARCELONA AREA Espai de Dansa I Creació
(contemporary dance, modern jazz, ballet)

DANCE

AREA Espai de Dansa I Creació

Alegre de Dalt, 55 bis 1°B,
08024 Barcelona,
Tel: +34 93 210 7850,
Fax: +34 93 420 5660

**BARCELONA Centre de
Dansa de Barcelona**
(ballet, contemporary dance, jazz)
Nil Fabra, 5, 08012 Barelona,
Tel: +34 93 217 9020

**BARCELONA Centro
Maxime D'Harroche**
(salsa, tango, jazz, contemporary
dance)
Sicilia, 402-404 pral 1a, 08025
Barcelona
Tel/Fax: +34 93 457 9619

**BARCELONA Escola de
Ballet Isabel Porcar**
(ballet)
Escipió, 9-11 baixos, 08023
Barcelona
Tel /Fax: +34 93 211 2018

**BARCELONA Escola de
Dansa "Rosita Mauri"**
(flamenco, ballet, contemporary
dance, jazz)
La Granada del Penedés, 27
baixos, 08006 Barcelona
Tel: +34 93 217 2648/217 7850
Fax: +34 93 217 2648

**BARCELONA Escola de
Dansa Madó**
(flamenco, ballet, contemporary
dance)
Rosari, 8, 08340 Vilassar de
Mar (Barcelona)
Tel/Fax: +34 93 759 5175

**BARCELONA Studio
Isadora**
(flamenco, baile de salón,
Spanish ballet, contemporary
dance, jazz)
Ciutat de Balaguer, 60 (bajos),
08022 Barcelona
Tel/Fax: +34 93 211 9722

DANCE

Academia de Baile de Conchita Fernandez

JAÉN Academia de Baile de Flamenco Conchita Fernández

Luna y Sol, 11, 23400 Ubeda (Jaén)
Tel: +34 53 752 054
Fax: +34 53 743 100

From the age of four Conchita Fernández was learning how to dance in her mother's dance academy. At eighteen she moved to Granada where she studied for a diploma in Flamencología – studies which involved tuition in the theory and practice of flamenco under the auspices of Mariquilla and Pepe Guardia, two important figures in flamenco. Her career has brought her into contact with teachers such as Antonio Canales, Mario Maya and Matilde Coral and she has been a member of various flamenco companies. She has since formed and now directs her own flamenco group. She began teaching in her mother's

school at the age of twenty two and has participated in lectures designed to introduce beginners to Flamenco.

Three types of courses are available at Conchita Fernández's school. The Complete course lasts from September to June (one hundred and twenty hours) and offers a comprehensive survey of Flamenco dancing including footwork, how to use castanets, and a range of different routines and styles (all with guitar and singing accompaniment). At the end of the course, students take part in a show. For those who require them, theory lessons are also available. The total cost of the course is 55,000ptas, which includes an enrolment fee of 5,000ptas and monthly payments of 5,000ptas. The Cursos de Orientación (Introductory courses) are suitable for closed groups and their content can be worked out according to the needs of the group. Students on this course can start from scratch and the price depends on the number of hours of tuition. The third type – Cursos de Perfeccionamiento – are for professionals and the cost varies according to the requirements of each student.

Conchita Fernández owns a hotel in Baeza, 8km away from Ubeda and classes can be arranged in the hotel itself for organised groups of a certain size. The school remains open in August when there is sufficient demand. A special discount is available for those students who book to stay in the hotel (full board) and in these cases, complementary activities can be organised enabling students to go on guided tours of Ubeda and Baeza.

MADRID Arabesques
(flamenco, flamenco guitar)
Santiago de Compostela, 26, 28034 Madrid
Tel: +34 91 739 1659

MADRID El Karnak
(belly-dancing)
Infantas, 40-1ºIzda, 28004 Madrid
Tel/Fax: +34 91 521 9354
(Mobile 929 864 286)
Email: elkarnak@cestein.es
Website: www.fdg.es/usr /elKarnak

MADRID Escuela de Bailes de Salón "Loreto y José Ignacio"
C/Gral. Alvarez de Castro, 12/14 (patio interior local no.1), Madrid 28010
Tel: +34 91 631 9045/593 9150
(Mobile 908 217 769)

Spanish, European and American students participate in the classes held in this school where classes are given in baile de salón alone. The provision includes the range of dances categorised under this title: waltz, tango,

Escuela de Bailes de Salón "Loreto y José Ignacio"

foxtrot, pasodoble, polka, merengue, mambo, cha-cha-cha, salsa, samba, swing, rock'n'roll and so on. The teacher can speak English and the schools claims to have a "método de enseñanza infalible" (an infallible teaching method). Facilities include one studio (with air conditioning and heating) and separate male and female changing rooms (with showers).

From September to June students can take a one hour class per week, either in the whole range of dances (each dance is looked at over a two week period) or in one particular dance. Prices vary according to level, of which there are eleven, and range from 5,100ptas to 6,900ptas for four weeks. Intensive classes take place in July. These involve eight classes (in one dance only) spread over two weeks. The cost for these is 10,900ptas.

MADRID Max Latino
Povedilla, 13, 28009 Madrid
Tel: +34 91 402 7286
Fax: +34 91 401 5514

This school located in central Madrid offers a comprehensive range of courses in bailes de salón (tango, pasodoble, etc), Latin dancing (salsa, merengue, etc), and Spanish dancing (sevillanas and flamenco). Each course involves three levels and the student must pass the relevant tests in order to graduate to the next level. On successful completion of each level, students are issued with a diploma. The academic year course lasts from mid-September to the end of June and July 1 and August the school offers intensive and refresher courses. It costs 5,000ptas per month to undertake one course in any one of either baile de salón, latin dancing and Spanish dancing. This includes four

Estudio de Danza Rodolfo Otero

Centro de Danza Ana Roca-Monzo

theory classes and one purely practical lesson. If you wish to take another two courses simultaneously, the cost for both will come to 8,000ptas per month. The programme for teachers costs 20,000ptas per month and includes five classes per week. It also organises extra curricular activities (excursions to the theatre, museums, dance halls, trips outside the city). The majority of students at the school are Spanish, Italian and American.

MADRID Relevé Escuela de Arte y Danza
(Spanish dancing, baile de salón)
Arturo Soria, 98, 28027 Madrid
Tel: +34 91 407 7414/367 2280
Fax: +34 91 741 3162

SEVILLA Academia de Juan Triana
(flamenco)
Quevedo, 7, 41003 Sevilla
Tel: +34 95 438 1902
Fax: +34 95 434 3360

SEVILLA Academia Almoraima
(sevillanas, rumbas, flamenco, flamenco guitar)
Tel: +34 95 443 0900/490 6910

TARRAGONA Artemis Escola de Dansa
(classical ballet, classical Spanish dancing, contemporary dance)
Passatge Cobos, 5, 43001 Tarragona,
Tel/Fax: +34 77 218 626/ 217 564

VALENCIA Centro de Danza Ana Roca-Monzo
(ballet, Spanish dancing, jazz)
Calixyo III, 11 y 13 bajos, 46008 Valencia
Tel/Fax: +34 96 385 8054

VALENCIA Centro de Danza Mari Cruz Alcala
(ballet, Spanish ballet, contemporary dance)
Alginet, 8 y 10, 46010 Valencia
Tel/Fax: +34 96 362 2779
Tel: +34 96 362 9706

VALLADOLID Estudio de Danza Rodolfo Otero
(classical Spanish ballet, flamenco)
Paseo Isabel la Catolica, 22-23, 47003 Valladolid
Tel: +34 983 256 536/397 480
(between 2pm and 3pm)

DANCE

Language Schools

Spain has language schools in abundance. The problem is which one to choose? If you are looking for official lists and accreditation to help inform your decision, you will find that the only official, universally-recognised accreditation given to language schools comes from the Spanish Ministry of Education. Its list of three hundred or so language schools (published on an annual basis), includes many courses that take place either at universities or at official language schools. Yet there is a far greater choice available and many of those schools not included on the ministry's list are certainly not to be avoided. The schools profiled in this chapter include a mixture of those accredited by the Ministry of Education and those that are not. The full list of accredited schools can be found at the end of this chapter.

WHERE TO START?

Before you even think about choosing a school, the wisest course of action would be to take a look at what you want from your language school. In this way, when you are ankle-deep in prospectuses, you will at least have some way of narrowing down your search and eliminating what really doesn't suit you. The problem is that although language schools offer essentially the same product, the differences between individual schools can be enormous.

The language schools that form part of a chain – either in Spain (eg the don Quijote group of language schools), in Spain and South America (eg Estudio Internacional Sampere, which has a centre in Ecuador) or Europe-wide (eg Eurocentres) – are usually located in the larger cities. These organisations often have a good track record for high quality teaching, though teaching groups can be large (12 to 16). If you are looking to escape from the crowd and want a rather more personalised service, there are numerous one-centre schools, often in slightly more off-beat places, where classes tend to be smaller.

If you want a holiday as much as a way to learn the language, one particularly unusual school is Sierra y Mar *(see p123)* in Granada, where the school is also a remote hotel tucked away in the mountains around the city of Granada. If you want to gain a skill other than Spanish, you could try Carmen de las Cuevas, also in Granada, which offers flamenco dancing and guitar lessons in tandem with language classes, in the breathtaking surroundings of the Albaicin (the Arab quarter of Granada).

Remember that *when* you choose to go is as important as where you go. In the summer, for example, Madrid is a furnace and is probably the last place anyone would want to be stuck in a classroom for several hours a day. It is to be avoided, particularly, in August when everyone leaves town to go on holiday. Find out in advance about the local holidays of the area that you are going to – it could greatly enhance your stay if you are present to witness the annual holiday of the town that you are based in. It might even make the difference between a functional language-learning break and a truly memorable cultural experience.

Below is a checklist with the main questions that you should ask yourself when choosing a school.

Language schools – what to look for:

1 Where would you like to be based? A lively and funky city (e.g. Barcelona or Madrid), an historical town (eg León or Santiago de Compostela), a typical university town (eg Salamanca or Granada) or are you looking for a beach holiday combined with language learning (eg Málaga, Tarifa or Islas Canarias)?

2 Start dates: can you take part in the course at a time of year to suit you? Students with some prior knowledge of Spanish will find that start dates for intermediate and advanced classes are more flexible than start dates for absolute beginners.

3 Does the language school cater to your level of Spanish? Some schools may specialise in classes that are more oriented towards beginners, or the provision could be more suitable for very advanced learners.

4 Does the school offer DELE ('Diploma de Español como Lengua Extranjera')? Do you want to take DELE, or at least have the option to do so? (For more information about DELE, see below)

5 Extra courses (eg culture, history, cooking): does the school offer these? If so, will you have to pay an additional amount to take them, or are they included in the overall cost of the course?

6 How varied are the courses?

7 Accommodation – is accommodation available via the school? If so, what kind of accommodation is it? Where is it located? Whom would you be staying with (homestay, other students, colegio mayor, etc – *see p29*), Living in Spain, for more detailed information about accommodation. Some schools will offer the opportunity to actually live with one of your teachers and/or their family for the duration of your course.

8 Does the school teach other languages? If so, will you be attending school at the same time as Spanish students learning other languages? If this is the case, how big and how important, is the Spanish as a foreign language provision at the school? Will there be an opportunity to mix with the Spanish students?

9 Where is the school located (central location/very remote)? How far is it from the town centre/the nearest town?

10 How big is the school itself? Does it have any sister schools in the same town, in other towns in Spain or in South America? Is there any possibility of changing centres at some point during your course, so that you get to see more of the country?

11 Type of school – does it attract professionals and business people or is it more student-oriented? The clientele may be more varied, including a mixture of the above as well as others, such as holidaying couples.

12 What is the minimum age group accepted by the school?

13 How much will it cost? What is and is not included in the price? Be aware of this, as choosing a more expensive programme with everything included (accommodation, food, excursions) may, in the long run, turn out to be cheaper than paying for the cost of the course only, with everything else (including accommodation) extra.

14 Will extra-curricular activities be organised for you or will you have to arrange any excursions/trips/outings yourself?

15 Are teaching materials/textbooks included in the price of the course?

16 Are there any perks? At Escuela Hispalense in Tarifa, for example, students receive a discount when renting surf equipment at the local Surf School Spin Out.

17 How well established is the school? Do you want to go to a school that's been around forever or do you want a new set up? (You will find that every school entry in this book shows the date when each school was founded).

OFFICIAL RECOGNITION

The teaching of Spanish as a foreign language in Spain is largely unregulated. Some schools do carry accolades, though these do not seem to appear anywhere else. For example, ACE Consultores de Idiomas, was awarded the European Training Quality System seal of approval, but no other school in Spain seems to have received this qualification.

University courses tend to be fairly simple and straightforward, with one type of course available at various different levels. At the higher levels, there will be some provision of classes on cultural themes such as Spanish literature and films.

The two most widely-recognised qualifications in Spanish as foreign language are those from the Escuela Oficial de Idiomas *(see below)* and the Instituto Cervantes. You do not have to attend an Escuela Oficial de Idiomas to take their exams. Preparation for the Instituto Cervantes' DELE *(see below)* exams is available at many schools throughout Spain.

ESCUELA OFICIAL DE IDIOMAS

When a school is termed *Escuela Oficial de Idiomas* it is an official, state-run and regulated school. The courses offered at these schools concentrate purely on language and grammar and offer absolutely no frills whatsoever. Wherever you go in Spain, the EOI offer the identical course provision. The courses are based around two cycles, the *Ciclo Elemental* (Elementary Cycle) and the *Ciclo Superior* (Superior Cycle). The first takes place from October to February and is composed of three modules; the second takes place from February to June and is composed of two modules. In 1997/98, at the *Escuela Oficial de Idiomas* in Salamanca, the fee for the first cycle was 9,350ptas and for the second cycle it was 16,130ptas.

The courses are entirely language based, with an element of Spanish culture and literature at the higher levels. The courses include topics such as practicalities (telephone formalities, conventions when writing letters), grammar, phonetics and phonology (listening and speaking).

Students are evaluated at the end of every module in each cycle. Then, at the end of each cycle, students are tested on aural comprehension (15 minutes, 10 points), reading comprehension (30 minutes, 10 points), writing skills (one hour, 25 points), grammar (one hour, 15 points), vocabulary (20 minutes, 10 points) and oral expression (15 minutes, 30 points). In order to pass the exam, students must achieve a minimum of 60 points, having achieved a minimum of 50 per cent of the pass mark in each module. Up to the highest level (i.e. from levels one to four) the tests involve exercises intended to demonstrate grammatical and communicative competence. At the highest level (level five), students have to complete a piece of written work under timed conditions and take an oral examination, which involves summarising, analysing and commenting on a piece of literature or journalism from the 20th century in the presence of a panel.

The precise content of each course is outlined in the information sent out by the individual *Escuela Oficiales de Idiomas*. The *Diploma del Ciclo Elemental* is awarded to students who have successfully completed the first three modules. The *Diploma del Ciclo Superior* is awarded to students who have successfully completed the last two modules.

If you are planning to take part in a course at an *Escuela Oficial de Idiomas*, bear in mind that the main provision of the school will include a range of languages taught to Spaniards (such as English, French, Russian and Arabic). There is a tendency for class sizes at these institutions to be larger than at other schools.

DELE

Preparation for DELE (*Diploma de Español como Lengua Extranjera*, Diploma in Spanish as a Foreign Language) is offered at many of language schools in Spain. It is an exam prepared by the Instituto Cervantes (see below) and the qualification has been approved by the Ministry of Education and Science in Spain. There are three categories of exams: *Certificado Inicial* (Beginner's Certificate), *Diploma Básico* (Basic Diploma) and *Diploma Superior* (Advanced Diploma). The exams take place twice a year, usually in May and November, and language schools tend to offer preparatory courses up to about two months prior to those dates (no earlier). As a rule, when you enrol at a language school you do not immediately have to specify whether or not you will be taking the DELE. It is possible to choose to take the exam during the course of your programme when you have a clear idea of the progress that you are making. Obviously, if your stay in Spain will in no way be coinciding with the exam dates (e.g. you are taking a summer course), you will not be able to sit the DELE.

TEACHERS

With official rules as to who can and cannot open a language school in Spain being so few and far between, anyone can set up and teach Spanish in Spain. Although this leaves the market open to cowboys, we have heard of no one who has encountered any. Teachers tend to be graduates in *filología*, which means that they have studied Spanish language and literature at university-level. Courses in teaching Spanish as a foreign language are available and, as you will see below, it is possible to take a Masters in the subject. Some schools try to make it their policy to recruit staff who have taken the courses on offer at either International House or the Instituto Cervantes. With fierce competition raging amongst Spanish language schools all over Spain, it is not in their interest to employ teachers who simply cannot teach, so you are unlikely to end up with someone who is unqualified for the job.

MAKING A DECISION

Reading through prospectuses can be like looking through a bewildering array of menus from restaurants of varying degrees of quality. Some are more expensive but offer less value for money, while others may be cheaper but turn out to be real finds. Cost doesn't always equal quality, but it can be a good indication of what you will get.

If you want to learn Spanish for business and/or professional purposes and you need to learn as much as possible in a very short time (such courses are usually called Intensive courses), a big city such as Madrid or Barcelona may be the best place to go. Not only will the atmosphere and location be more conducive to learning the sort of Spanish that you need, the schools will be very geared towards students like you. A handful of schools (such as ACE Consultores de Idiomas in Madrid) specialise purely in teaching Spanish for business purposes.

If you are more interested in having fun and cultivating a tan, with the aim of learning the language quite low down on your list of priorities, then it may be best to head south for the coast (particularly in the summer). The way of life there is very easy going and lessons may take place out of doors at some institutions.

Ultimately, every school has something

that separates it from the rest, but if they're all beginning to look like clones of one another, maybe you should pay attention to the small details. Take, for example, the Eurocentres schools where they have a policy of accepting no more than 15 per cent of students of the same nationality at any one time, in any one centre. Sometimes factors such as these can swing a decision.

INSTITUTO CERVANTES

Created in 1991, the Instituto Cervantes is a public institution funded by the Spanish government with branches all over the world. It provides cultural information about Spain and Latin America and organises Spanish language courses. It is basically the Spanish equivalent of the Institut Françis and the Goethe Institute. IC headquarters are based at the following address in Spain: Instituto Cervantes, Libreros, 23, 28071 Alcalá de Henares, Spain, Tel +34 91 883 0277 Website www.cervantes.es

The library at the Instituto Cervantes in London *(see below)* has a CD-Rom, which can be consulted free of charge, containing a wealth of information about language schools and courses in Spain. Other ICs may also have the same CD-Rom facility.

INSTITUTO CERVANTES
Centres around the world
Email address: informa@cervantes.es

ABIDJAN. Marble Coast
Instituto Cervantes (Centro de Recursos),
Impasse Ablaha Pokou
Cocody Danga Nord,
08 BP 876
ABIDJAN 08
Tel: 225 - 44 57 20
Fax: 225 - 44 26 64

ALEXANDRIA, Egypt
Instituto Cervantes
101, Avn. El Horreya
21514 ALEJANDRÕA
Tel: 20 - 3 - 492 02 14/459 20 94
Fax: 20 - 3 - 494 16 94
icalej@dataxprs.com.eg

AMMAN, Jordan
Instituto Cervantes,
Mohammad Hafiz Ma'ath St, nʃ 10,
B.P. Box 815467,
AMMAN 11180
Tel: 962 - 64 - 61 08 58
Fax: 962 - 64 - 62 40 49
icamman@go.com.jo

ALGIERS, Algeria
Instituto Cervantes
9, rue Khelifa Boukhalfa
16000 ALGERS
Tel: 213 - 2 - 92 28 20 / 63 76 15
Fax: 213 - 2 - 63 76 25

ATHENS, Greece
Instituto Cervantes,
Skoufá 31,
10673 ATHENS
Tel: 30 - 1 - 363 41 17
Fax: 30 - 1 - 364 72 33
ice-atenas@ath.forthnet.gr

BEIRUT, Lebanon
Imm.Youssef Assaf, 1 Ëtage,
rue Baalbeck-Commodore
B.P. 113-5344,
BEIRUT
Tel: 961 - 1 - 34 77 55
Fax: 961 - 1 - 35 24 48
icbeirut@inco.com.ib

BREMEN, Germany
Instituto Cervantes,
Schwachauser Ring, 124,
28209 BREMEN
Tel: 49 - 421 / 34 40 90
Fax: 49 - 421 / 34 99 964
cervante@uni-bremen.de

BRUSSELS, Belgium
Instituto Cervantes,
64, Avn. Tervuren,
1040 BRUSSELS
Tel: 32 - 2 - 737 01 90
Fax: 32 - 2 - 735 44 04
cenbru@cervantes.es

BUCHAREST, Romania
Instituto Cervantes,
Strada París, 34,
71249 BUCHAREST
Tel: 40 - 1 - 230 13 54
Fax: 40 - 1 - 230 15 67
cervantes@instfrbuc.ro

BORDEAUX, France
Instituto Cervantes,
27, Cours Xavier Arnozan,
33000 BORDEAUX
Tel: 33 - 556 52 79 37
Fax: 33 - 556 81 40 71
ic-burd@worldnet.fr

CASABLANCA, Morrocco
Instituto Cervantes,
31, rue d'Alger,
21000 CASABLANCA
Tel: 212 - 2 - 26 73 37
Fax: 212 - 2 - 26 86 34
cervante@open.net.ma

CHICAGO, USA
Instituto Cervantes,
John Hancock Center,
875, North Michigan Avenue,Suite 2940
CHICAGO, Illinois 60611
Tel: 1 - 312 - 335 19 96
Fax: 1 - 312 - 587 19 92
chicago@cervantes1.org

DAMASCUS, Syria
Instituto Cervantes,
Nazem Pasha, 400,
Muhajerine P.O. Box 224,
DAMASCUS
Tel: 963 - 11 - 3737 061
Fax: 963 - 11 - 3737 062

DUBLIN, Ireland
Instituto Cervantes,
58, Northumberland Road,
Ballsbridge,
DUBLIN 4
Tel: 353 - 1 - 668 20 24
Fax: 353 - 1 - 668 84 16
cervante@indigo.ie

CAIRO, Egypt
Instituto Cervantes,
20, Boulos Hanna St. Dokki,
CAIRO
Tel: 20 - 2 - 360 17 46
Fax: 20 - 2 - 360 17 43
spcc@idsc.gov.eg

FEZ, Morocco
Instituto Cervantes,
7, rue Abdelkrim el-Khattabi
B.P. 2253 FEZ
Tel: 212 - 5 - 62 22 54
Fax: 212 - 5 - 65 32 40
i.cervantes@fesnet.net.ma

LEEDS, UK
Instituto Cervantes,
169, Woodhouse Lane,
LEEDS LS2 3AR
Tel: 44 - 113 - 246 17 41
Fax: 44 - 113 - 246 10 23
ic-admin@leeds.ac.uk

LISBON, Portugal
Instituto Cervantes,
rua Santa Marta, 43 F r/c
1150 LISBON
Tel: 351 - 1 - 352 31 21
Fax: 351 - 1 - 315 22 99
cervanteslisboa@mail.telepac.pt

LONDON, UK
Instituto Cervantes,
102 Eaton Square,
LONDON SW1W 9AN
Tel: 44 - 171 - 235 03 53
Fax: 44 - 171 - 235 03 29
iclondre@globalnet.co.uk

MANCHESTER, UK
326/330 (Unit 8) Deansgate,
Campfield Avenue Arcade,
MANCHESTER M3 4FN
Tel: 44 - 161 - 661 42 00
Fax: 44 - 161 - 661 42 03
cenman@cervantes.es

MANILA, Philippines
Instituto Cervantes,
2515 Leon Guinto Corner Estrada,
1004 Malate Metro-MANILA
Tel: 63 - 2 - 526 14 82-85
Fax: 63 - 2 - 526 14 49
icmanila@skyinet.net

MILAN, Italy
Instituto Cervantes,
Via Dante, 12,
20121 MILAN
Tel: 39 - 02 - 720 23 450
Fax: 39 - 02 - 720 23 829
instcerv@tin.it

MUNICH, Germany
Instituto Cervantes,
Marstallplatz, 7,
80539 M/NICH
Tel: 49 - 89 - 22 52 11
Fax: 49 - 89 - 29 32 17
cervantes.munich@t-online.de

NAPLES, Italy
Instituto Cervantes,
Via S. Giacomo, 40,
80133 NAPLES
Tel: 39 -0 81 - 552 04 68
Fax: 39 -0 81 - 552 04 69
cernap@na.flashnet.it

NEW YORK, USA
Instituto Cervantes,
122 East 42nd, Street,
Suite 807,
NEW YORK NY 10168
Tel: 1 - 212 - 689 42 32
Fax: 1 - 212 - 545 88 37
ny@cervantes.org

PARIS, France
Instituto Cervantes,
7, rue Quentin Bauchart,
75008 PARIS
Tel: 33 - 1 40 70 92 92
Fax: 33 - 1 47 20 27 49
106135.3434@compuserve.com

RABAT, Morocco
Instituto Cervantes,
5, Zankat al-Madnine,
10000 RABAT
Tel: 212 - 7 - 70 87 38
Fax: 212 - 7 - 70 02 79
dirrab@cervantes.es

ROME, Italy
Instituto Cervantes,
Via di Villa Albani, 16,
00198 ROME
Tel: 39 -06 - 855 19 49
Fax: 39 - 06 - 854 62 32
cervantes.roma@agora.stm.it

SAO PAULO, Brazil
Instituto Cervantes,
Av. Jorge Joao Saad, 905,
CEP 5718-001 MORUMBI, SAO
PAULO
Tel: 55 11 846 51 67
Fax: 55 11 842 36 04 (Provisional)
dirsao@cervantes.es

TANGIER, Morocco
Instituto Cervantes,
99, Av. Sidi Mohamed Ben Abdellah,
90000 TANGIER
Tel: 212 - 9 - 93 20 01
Fax: 212 - 9 - 94 76 30
dirtan@cervantes.es

TETUAN, Morocco
Instituto Cervantes,
3, Mohamed Torres,
B.P. 877 TETOUAN
Tel: 212 - 9 - 96 12 39
Fax: 212 - 9 - 96 61 23
ictetuan@cybermania.net.ma

TEL AVIV, Israel
Instituto Cervantes,
7, Shulammid Street,
TEL AVIV
Tel: 972 -3- 609 50 68
Tel: 972 -3- 529 06 32
cervante@netvision.net.il

TOULOUSE, France
Instituto Cervantes
31, rue des Chalets
31000 TOULOUSE
Tel: 33 - 5 - 61 62 80 72
Fax: 33 - 5 - 61 62 70 06
centou@cervantes.es

TUNIS, Tunisia
Instituto Cervantes,
120, Avn. de la Liberté,
1002 TUNIS - BELVEDERE
Tel: 216 - 1 - 78 88 47
Fax: 216 - 1 - 79 38 25
ictunez@cervantes.intl.tn

UTRECHT, Holland
Instituto Cervantes,
Domplein 3,
3512 JC UTRECHT
Tel: 31 - 30 - 233 42 61
Fax: 31 - 30 - 233 29 70
cervante@globalxs.nl

WARSAW, Poland
Instituto Cervantes,
Ul. Mysliwiecka, 4,
00-459 WARSAW
Tel: 48 - 22 - 6 22 54 22
Fax: 48 - 22 - 6 22 54 13
cervars@ikp.atm.com.pl

VIENNA, Austria
Instituto Cervantes,
Goldeggasse, 2,
A 1040 VIENNA
Tel: 43 - 1 - 505 25 35
Fax: 43 - 1 - 505 25 35 18
ic.viena@magnet.at

COURSES FOR TEACHERS OF SPANISH AS A FOREIGN LANGUAGE

Refresher courses for teachers of Spanish as a foreign language are generally only available for a couple of weeks in the summer months. Only one or two schools (such as schools in the don Quijote group) offer such courses all year round (one to one only).

MASTERS COURSES IN SPANISH LANGUAGE AND TEACHING SPANISH AS A FOREIGN LANGUAGE

Universidad Complutense de Madrid: *Magister En Formación de Especialistas en la Enseñanza del Español comeo Lengua Extranjera* (one year, 395,000ptas), involves the analysis of errors in Spanish as a second language through the influence of English, German, French, Italian, Korean, Japanese, Arabic and Chinese.

Universidad de Alcalà de Henares: *Curso de Lengua y Cultura Española para Extranjeros* (one year, 235,000ptas). This course aims to provide an overview with regard to language (grammar, writing, conversation, etc.) and culture (history of art, history of Spain, Spanish literature, etc.)

Universidad de Barcelona: *Master en Formación del Profesorado del Español como Lengua Extanjera* (one year, 220,500ptas). For teachers of Spanish as a foreign language.

Universidad del País Vasco: *Master Universitario en Formación de Profesorado de Español como Lengua Extranjera* (one year). A course aimed at imparting different methods for teaching Spanish as a foreign language. *Master Universitario en Traducción:*

Especialidad Euskera (two years), for those intending to use their translating skills on a professional basis, specialising in Euskera.

Centro de Lenguas Modernas de la Universidad de Granada, Viejo, s/n (Realejo), 18071 Granada, tel +34 958 220 790, fax +34 958 220 844: *Curso de Estudio Hipsánicos* (eight months, 181,000ptas), a programme for degree holders and professionals who wish to broaden their knowledge of Spanish culture. Subjects include translation, politics, literature and islamic culture in Spain.

CLUNY-ISEIT Instituto Superior de Interpretación y Traducción, C/Infanta Mercedes, 93, 28020 Madrid, tel +34 91 571 0430, fax +34 91 571 0458: *Master en Traducción (Interpretación/Terminología)* (18 months, 927,000ptas). With specialities in simultaneous translation and lectures in the fields of economics and the law, this is suitable for both degree holders and overseas students with equivalent qualifications.

Estudio Internacional Sampere, Castelló, 50, 28001 Madrid, tel +34 91 575 9790, fax +34 91 576 3910. *Curso de Interprete Jurado (versión presencial o distancia)* (nine months, 262,500ptas (learning in situ) or 208,000ptas (distance learning)); *Curso de Traducción General (versión presencial o a distancia)* (nine months, 199,500ptas (learning in situ) or 208,000ptas (distance learning) and *Curso de Traducción Jurídica (versión presecial o a distancia)* (nine months, 141,000ptas (learning in situ) or 208,000ptas (distance learning). These courses are suitable for those whose mother tongue is not Spanish, but who speak it to a very high level (level five of the Escuela

Oficial de Idiomas *(see p102)*. The material used is based on a selection of texts (general, legal and economic).

ENROLMENT/PAYMENT

When booking a course, you will be asked to fill in an application form and send off a deposit (prior to your arrival) in the region of between 10,000ptas and 20,000ptas (sometimes more). This amount will either be deductible from the total cost of the course or additional to it; the individual prospectuses should make this clear. Many schools in Spain do not accept cheques, so you may have to organise to pay by bank draft or by postal order.

PLEASE NOTE: the list of language schools in this chapter is by no means exhaustive. If you have heard of, or been to, a school that we have failed to mention here we would be most grateful if you would write to us (snail mail or email) or ring us to tell us more about it. We are always on the lookout for schools, particularly those which offer interesting courses that combine language learning with something else (such as cookery or dancing). We look forward to hearing from you.

LANGUAGE SCHOOLS

ALICANTE

Altea Cursos (Babel Idiomas)
La Mar, 109, 03590 Altea, ALICANTE
Tel: +34 96 584 5851
Fax: +34 96 584 5851
Established: 1990
Level: None

Further information

To obtain a booklet containing information about language schools accredited by the Spanish Ministry of Education and Culture, contact any one of the addresses below. Alternatively, you can consult the list of language schools officially recognised by the Spanish Ministry of Education and Culture at the end of this chapter.

Sección de Información, Iniciativas y Reclamaciones
Alcalá, 36, 28014 Madrid, Spain
Tel +34 91 521 5511 Email: informa@mec.es Website: www.mec.es

Ministerio de Educación y Cultura, Secretaría General Técnica, Subdirección General de Cooperación Internacional, Paseo del Prado, 28, 28071 Madrid, Spain; Tel +34 91 506 5600

Language school information is also available on the World Wide Web. Useful sites include: **www.studyabroad.com/simplehtml/Spain.html** which lists (mainly American) institutions offering study abroad programs in Spain. A service called Spanish Abroad, Inc. (**www.spanishabroad. com/excalibur.htm**) provides "quality immersion programs" in language schools in Spain and Latin America. The cost for registering with this service is $65, however, when you sign up at a language school and you are registered with Spanish Abroad Inc., you will be exempt from paying the normal registration fee of between 10,000ptas and 20,000ptas.

Nearest Station: Alicante
Contact: Jose Quirante
Santacruz

This is a small school in Altea, a tiny seaside village of a few thousand inhabitants, situated on the Costa Blanca between the towns of Alicante and Valencia. This is possibly the only language school in the entire town, so it is probably a good place to avoid meeting too many other foreign students. The intention here is to provide Spanish classes to people aged 18 and over in a relaxed and tranquil environment away from the chaos and traffic of big cities. This is probably the ideal place to get away from it all and is considered by many to be one the most beautiful parts of Spain.

There are three categories of courses: 'Intensive', 'Regular' and 'Individual'. The 'Intensive' courses comprise 40 hours of classes over two weeks, with four hours of tuition per day. They begin on the first and third Monday of each month during the summer months and cost 25,000ptas. These classes are directed by Don Luis Quirante, a professor of Literature at the University of Valencia, and are suitable for people who are in Spain with the specific purpose of learning the language. The Regular courses are aimed at people who live in Altea and the surrounding areas. They consist of four hours of classes a week and cost 10,000ptas per month. The one-to-one classes cost 3,000ptas per hour. The cost of the course includes the accommodation, learning materials, transport to and from the airport or railway station, use of the town library and sports club, an optional touring programme and information about things to do.

There are three levels of ability – elementary, intermediate and advanced.

Classes are focused on building up the student's self-confidence when speaking Spanish and there is a maximum of eight students in each group. At any one time there are between 50 and 100 students at the school. Classes take place in the mornings, between 9am and 1.30pm. The school does not arrange excursions as such, but they can offer some suggestions as to where you can go in and around the town. They can also recommend places to sample the specialities of the region (*paella*, *gazpacho* and other delicacies).

There are three different accommodation possibilities: staying with a family (selected by the school), in hostel or in a hotel. You need to send an enrolment deposit of 10,000ptas and the outstanding amount will be payable on your arrival. For enrolment details and an application form, contact the school.

Taller Lingüístico – Instituto Berlin

San Fernando, 49-2, E-03001
Alicante
Tel: +34 96 520 9442
Fax: +34 96 520 9442
Established: 1996
Level: None
Nearest Station: Alicante
Contact: Angels Oliver I Carrió

Alicante is a well-known seaside town in Spain, most popular among Spanish holiday makers. Many people from other parts of Spain have holiday homes here, so it is probably a very good place to come to learn Spanish in the summer as you will be surrounded by people actually speaking the language! (Rather than tourists speaking anything but, which is usually the case in Spain at that time of the year.) The official prospectus for this school is written in German, which is a fairly good indication that the majority of students will be from that country. That might be a good reason to come here as the absence of a shared common language (as long as you are not German) will encourage you to speak Spanish with your fellow students. The school is situated in an old renovated building in the centre of the city on the Esplanada – Alicante's emblematic walkway, which separates the city from the beach.

Spanish and German are the languages taught at this school, so you will be studying alongside Spanish students whom you will probably be able to impress with your new-found language skills. The ethos of the Instituto Berlín is to integrate your understanding of the language with an introduction to Spanish culture. They want you to appreciate that learning a language is not a purely linguistic exercise. The objective of classes is to equip students with the skills needed to communicate with native speakers in every day situations. To this end, students are given exercises, assigned tasks and provided with texts that emphasise the linguistic differences between each language. The programmes are tailored according to the needs of each student within this framework.

The basic characteristics of the Spanish courses are straightforward and are as follows. Group sizes are between three and six people and courses last from two weeks. The student can extend their course for as long as they deem necessary. New courses begin every two weeks and the school is open from 9.30am to 12.30pm and from 5pm to 8pm. The cost of courses is 42,000ptas for two weeks and 69,000ptas for four weeks. One-to-one classes cost 2,000ptas per hour. Full-board accommodation costs from 2,800ptas per day. There are classes for beginners without any prior knowledge of Spanish, beginners with some previous knowledge of Spanish, intermediate, advanced and superior.

Students can participate in a variety of extra-curricular activities. They are particularly encouraged to take part in the local and regional fiestas and celebrations, a large number of which take place during the summer months. There are excursions to areas of interest in the province of Alicante. Sailing expeditions on the school's boat are organised to places such as the famous coves of the Costa Blanca and to the Island of Tabarka. Students can also take part in numerous water-sports.

According to the director's description of the Instituto Berlin, there are six classrooms, an office, a staff room, two bathrooms, air conditioning. Above all, the school gets a lot of light (this may sound unremarkable, but Spanish buildings can often be quite dark). For enrolment details, contact the school.

Universidad de Alicante

Oficina de Relaciones Interna-cionales, Campus San Vicente, Edificio Aeroclub, 03690 Alicante
Tel: +34 96 590 3793
Fax: +34 96 590 3794
Email: sri@ua.es
Website: www.ua.es
Established: 1979
Level: None
Nearest Station: Alicante
Contact: Pilar Barra, Assistant Director
Alicante is a popular holiday destination on the east coast of Spain and the university, situated a few miles from the town of Alicante, was founded in 1979. It offers a wide range of facilities on a self-contained campus and has about 30,000 students, 800 of whom come from overseas.

There are two types of Spanish language and culture courses on offer at Alicante: summer courses and semester courses. The months of July to September are for the summer courses, which last four weeks. There are four levels of Spanish: beginners, intermediate, advanced and perfection, for which there are three compulsory hours of Spanish language classes daily, between 9am and 12pm. Thereafter, between 12pm and 2pm, there are optional modules which include 'Conversation Courses,' 'Spanish Culture and Civilization,' 'Business Spanish' and 'Spanish Literature and Art.' The prices range from 63,000ptas to 98,000ptas depending on how many hours you choose to do (three is the minimum, five the maximum.) As well as these, you can sign up for activities such as Spanish dancing, sailing, windsurfing and diving or for one day excursions around the region. All of these will cost extra. Longer trips further afield (to Madrid, Barcelona, etc.) can also be arranged. There are three accommodation possibilities: staying with a family, in a student residence or alternative accommodation. Family half-board for a single room costs 62,100ptas, for a shared room the cost is 56,700ptas; full-board for a single room is 73,000ptas and for a shared room it costs 67,500ptas. The fee per day for half-board in en-suite single rooms is in the region of 2,150ptas.

The semester courses take place from mid-October to mid-February and mid-February to mid-June. You can choose to do either semester, or both. There are two options for each semester course A and course B. On course A, students attend two sessions of two hours of Spanish a week, while on course B, they attend three hours of Spanish daily from Monday to Friday.

The fees for these are 37,000ptas for one semester of course A, and 67,000 for two semesters of course A; 97,000 for one semester of course B and 175,000 for two semesters of course B. Optional modules, as listed above for the summer courses, are also available. You can also take part in other activities, as listed above for the summer courses. Monthly accommodation charges inlcude a room in a family (83,700 ptas for a single room, 77,500ptas for a shared room), University residences (85,600 ptas for a single room, 74,900ptas for a shared room) and 20,000ptas for a shared flat.

Class sizes are usually no larger than twelve people. For enrolment details, contact the university.

ASTURIAS

Hispalingua – Secretariado Internacional

General Yagüe, 3-entlo, 33004 Oviedo
Tel: +34 98 524 3186/596 5100
Fax: +34 98 524 3186
Email: hispalingua@ cyberastur.es
Website: www.cyberastur.es /hispalingua
Established: 1958
Level: None
Nearest Station: Oviedo station
Contact: Francisco Norman Alonso

Oviedo is a university town and capital of Asturias, a province in the north of Spain. As the name suggests, this is a secretarial college as well as an English school and a centre for teaching Spanish to foreigners. As a centre which calls itself *internacional*, this school aims at creating cosmopolitan students and professionals who wish to create ties with people of other nationalities. A bit of a tall order perhaps, if all you want is to learn the language in a part of Spain that is more off the well-beaten tourist track than most, but there it is.

Hispalingua has about 200 students, the majority of whom come from France, the USA and Holland and classes have, on average, about eight students. There are nine well-equipped classrooms and a multimedia room with 12 stations.

Three Spanish language courses are offered here. One-to-one costs 65,000ptas for one week of three hours daily tuition and includes accommodation with a family (full board). For those who already have an organised group who know what they want, the centre can offer Grupos a la Carta, which means that you can choose a course tailor-made to your requirements. The summer courses are suitable for three different levels of competence – beginners, intermediate and advanced – and run from the beginning of July to the end of August. Contact the school for more information.

For those whose Spanish is good enough, there is the 'Curso de Secretariado Internacional', which is a two year programme involving a bit of everything: office administration, computer skills, business law, marketing and multimedia techniques. This is not for foreign students, but it may be of interest to those who are thinking of a future in Spain. Both years involve 20 weekly hours and 600 hours of tuition in total; the fee is 125,000ptas per year.

Help in finding accommodation is available. Contact the school for enrolment details.

ÁVILA

Instituto Español "Murallas de Ávila" – IEMA

"El Patio Chico", Martín Carramolino, 6, E-05001 Ávila
Tel: +34 920 222 773
Fax: +34 920 252 955
Established: 1989
Level: None
Nearest Station: Ávila
Contact: Dr Rainer Rutkowski

Located half way between Madrid and Salamanca, Ávila is famous for being one of the only fortified cities in the world whose walls remain intact to this day (hence the name of the school – 'Murallas de Ávila' – means 'The Walls of Ávila'). Perched on the brow of a hill that emerges from the fairly barren landscape of Castilla y León, at first sight it seems to have been caught in a time warp at some point in the Middle Ages.

Students at IEMA come from all over the world, mainly from Germany, the USA and the Philippines. Ages and backgrounds vary, and students have included people who are already in retirement. Courses are geared towards perfecting language skills and acquiring a certain in-depth knowledge about Spanish culture. The school strives to knock down student's pre or misconceptions about the Spanish. The ethos is that in order to learn the language properly, and in order to be able to use it correctly, you must be able to understand the mentality of the people.

There are more than five language classes a day, from Monday to Friday and there are three levels: beginner, intermediate and advanced. You can begin at any level on almost any Monday of your choice. (Although you are advised to start on the first Monday of the month.) Once you have sat a level test, you will be placed in the appropriate class. December and January are reserved for private courses and special groups.

Classes take place in Mini-groups, and fees for each person start at 40,000ptas for one week and go up to 85,000ptas for four weeks. Thereafter, fees range from 100,000ptas for five weeks to 200,-000ptas for 12 weeks. (The entire amount must be paid on the first day of the course. A special discount is available for courses from one-five weeks from November to February. Contact the school for further information.) The school can also prepare you for the official DELE exams. Cultural courses include Spanish Cooking and Spanish dancing' (free of charge), Spanish History, History of Spanish Art and History of Spanish Literature (10,000ptas for 16 classes), Spanish for Business, Spanish Current Affairs, and Spanish Conversation (15,000ptas for 24 classes). There is also a week-long course in the summer for teachers of Spanish who wish to brush up on their knowledge (appropriately, it's called *Recíclate!* – Refresh yourself!), this course costs 20,000ptas. The maximum number of students in the school at any one time is 50.

There is a varied programme of extra-curricular activities available and these include excursions to places of interest around Ávila (such as Salamanca,

Instituto Español "Murallas de Ávila" – IEMA

Segovia and El Escorial), film evenings and meals out. The school (a medieval hotel which had also been a mosque!) houses a cafeteria, satellite TV, library, garden and courtyard.

There are various accommodation possibilities including two to four star hotels and living with Spanish people (the cost for this varies according to whether you are staying full board, half board or with breakfast only). IEMA also operates a special service whereby you can give someone a course at the school as a present. The school can provide you with a glowing list of comments (all in different languages) from past students. For an enrolment form and leaflet, contact the school.

Letras Castellanas

Batalla de Brunete, 5,
E-05003
Ávila
Tel: +34 920 257 444
Fax: +34 920 257 444
Email: letrascast@nexo.es

Established: 1997 (under construction)
Level: None
Nearest Station: Ávila
Contact: Sonsoles Pardo Santamaria

Ávila, a beautiful medieval walled city, may look like a town untouched by the twenty first century but once you enter it this illusion vanishes and you find yourself in a university town like any other, with bars, pubs and discos. In fact, it is one of the oldest (though less well-known) university towns in Spain and a very good reason to study here is that this part of the country is, supposedly, where the purest Spanish is spoken. Also, although it may not be as well-known as nearby Salamanca, it is probably a lot less packed with foreign students and therefore you will have a better chance of meeting native Spanish speakers.

There is no fixed learning method at this school, which claims to take the best from lots of different Spanish teaching techniques, while bearing in mind the specific needs of each student. The principal course offered by the school' is the four-week 'Intensive Spanish' course which involves a fully structured daily routine of grammar (9am to 10.30am), practical communication skills (11am to 12.30pm), conversation (1 to 2pm). Lectures, discussions, film shows, documentaries, complementary activities or the optional cultural courses take place in the afternoon. There are half hour breaks between classes when coffee is prepared and students can converse with one another or with their teachers. There are no more than eight students in each class and there are three levels - elementary, intermediate and advanced. You can start the course on any Monday of the year unless you are a beginner, when it is obligatory to start on the first Monday of the month. You will be given a level test on your first day in order to place you in the right class. Work materials are included in the price of the course. The cost ranges from 40,000ptas for two weeks to 190,000ptas for three months.

Intensive group courses are available for a minimum of nine people. There are also Individual courses for up to three people at a time(2,800ptas per hour for one person; 2,250ptas per hour each for three people) and a Catch Up course for teachers who need to refresh their knowledge. The culture courses on offer cover Spanish History (eight hours, 7,000ptas), Spanish Art (eight hours, 7,000ptas), a writing workshop (six hours, 7,500ptas), Spanish Civilization (eight hours, 7,600ptas), the Dance Workshop(three hours, 3,000ptas), Conversation course (eight hours, 6,400ptas), Business Spanish' (eight hours, 10,000ptas), Gastronomy/Cookery (six hours, 6,600ptas), Phonetic Workshop (pronunciation and intonation) (six hours, 8,100ptas), Singing Workshop (four hours, 4,000ptas), Literature (eight hours, 7,000ptas).

The school is on three floors. There is a video/lecture room, a library, a music room and terrace and a patio. The maximum number of students in the school at any one time is about 65. The cities of Salamanca, Valladolid, Segovia, Madrid, El Escorial and Toledo are only an hour away from Ávila and excursions to all of them are organised by the school. Accommodation with a family can be arranged. This will cost 1,700 per day for full board and 1,400ptas per day for half board. You can also rent a bicycle from the school itself for 15,000ptas per month. You must pay a deposit of 15,000ptas on enrolment. For enrolment details, contact the school.

Universidad de Barcelona/Universidad de las Islas Baleares, Cátedra Ramon Llull

Secretaría de los Cursos de Verano, Estudio General Luliano, San Roque, 4, 07001 Palma de Mallorca
Tel: +34 971 711 988
Fax: +34 971 719 105
Level: None
Contact: Secretaría de los Cursos de Verano (Secretary for the Summer courses)

The principal reason why the summer courses at this university faculty may be of interest is that they take place in Mallorca, as part of a collaboration between the universities of Barcelona and Mallorca. Mallorca is an island to the east of the Iberian peninsula, immortalised in the famous lines of the rhyme from the film My Fair Lady: "The waughta in Majorca don't taste quite wot it oughta." and now a popular tourist destination.

The summer course in Spanish for foreigners runs for two weeks at the end of July only and lessons are given at four levels: 'Preparatorio' (first level), 'Elemental' (second level), 'Medio' (third level) and 'Superior' (fourth level). At the start of the course, all students sit a level test so that they should be placed in the appropriate level. The course involves four hours of tuition, from 9.30am to 1.30pm. In the first two levels, lessons are concentrated purely on language learning, while in the last two levels, the final hour of classes is taken up with a module from the monothematic course in Spanish Culture. Modules for this are History of Art, History of Spain and Spanish Literature, and all lectures are given in Spanish by professors from the Universidad de las Islas Baleares (University of the Balearic Islands). The enrolment fee is 53,000ptas. Winter (October to January) and Spring (February to May) programmes are also available. The enrolment fee for these is 35,000ptas.

There is a programme of cultural activities that takes place on week day afternoons and Saturday mornings and involves guided tours to places of interest. There is a library and a bar at students' disposal on class days. Students will be awarded a certificate of attendance (Certificado de Asistencia) and those who successfully complete the exams will be presented with a Spanish Language Certificate (Certificado de Lengua Española), (students in the higher level classes receive a Spanish Language and Culture Certificate (Certificado, de Lengua y Cultura Españoles).

For students who already have a competent grasp of the language, a cycle of courses in Spanish *filología* (Literature and Culture) take place simultaneously. There are three courses, each lasting five days and in 1998, the themes were: The text and its frame: genre and context; Literary Madness and Literature, Cinema and the City. Each course lasts ten hours and is the equivalent of one academic credit. Where the timetable permits, they can be combined with the courses in Catalan literature and culture that are also available. The enrolment fee for each course is 5,000ptas plus 1,000ptas for taxes. Grants are available.

Accommodation for a limited number of students is available at the centrally located, Hotel Cannes. Prices range from 4,500ptas for a single room to

2,800ptas per person for a triple room. Alternatively, rooms are available at Residencia Alberg, a student residence situated twelve kilometres from Estudio General Luliano in a beach area. Half board costs 2,000ptas daily.

For more information and enrolment details, contact the faculty.

BARCELONA

AC Idiomas

Plaza Francesc Macia, 2 entlo 3, Barcelona .08021
Tel: +34 93 200 0263
Fax: +34 93 200 39 59
Established: 1980
Level: None
Nearest Station: Barcelona Sants
Contact: Marta Caballe (Director of the school) or her secretary

A small school, with no more than 50 students at any one time, this is well situated in a residential part of Barcelona's business area. Tuition here is very personalised and lessons are tailored to the individual needs of each student. The methods used are AC Idiomas's own and they can prepare you for official exams (DELE). Students come here from all over the world and include Europeans and East Asians.

The 'Executive' course lasts 12 days and involves 80 hours of classes (90,000ptas); the 'Intensive' year round course costs 67,100ptas for three weeks and 90,000ptas for four weeks. The school also provides special semi-intensive Erasmus/Socrates courses which last 40 hours (about two weeks). AC offers preparation all year round for the ICC (International Conference Certificate) European Language Exam (valid throughout Europe) as well as summer courses including sports, other activities and excursions. Special courses for au pairs include living with a family in Barcelona. The school also caters for individuals who wish to take one-to-one classes in specific areas such as business Spanish. There are discounts available on certain courses such as Erasmus/Socrates and Au Pair.

All classes begin on the first Monday of each month and the school is open the whole year round except for during fiestas and official holidays, as well as during Semana Santa (Easter) and at Christmas time. The timetable is from 9am to 1pm and there is a maximum of ten students in each class.

The cost for courses is 22,370ptas for one week (20 hours), 67,100ptas for three weeks (60 hours) and 90,900ptas for four weeks (80 hours). Prices can also include course and lodging and fees range from 132,600ptas for three weeks in a family with bed and breakfast to 171,300ptas for three weeks in a family staying full-board. The cost of staying with a family (not including course) is 22,900ptas for one week, extending to 91,500ptas for four weeks.

Contact the school for enrolment details.

Barna House – Centro de Estudio de Español

Roger de Lluria, 123, .08037 Barcelona
Tel: +34 93 488 0080
Fax: +34 93 488 0169
Website: www.bhouse.es
Established: 1979
Level: None
Nearest Station: Barcelona Sants
Contact: Cristina Giménez

This is one of several CEE centres in Spain – the others being in Málaga, Madrid and Salamanca – and it is centrally located within Barcelona, a short metro journey away from the Old Port and Las Ramblas. An unusual feature of this group of schools is that you can spend a minimum of two weeks in each one instead of spending all your time in one centre. This will give you a bit of variety and a chance to visit four very diverse parts of Spain. You cannot spend any less than two weeks in each school.

This school may appeal to younger students who are spending the third year of their university course abroad as its language courses can include a period of time spent working in a Spanish company. Barna House, the language school of which CEE forms a part, offers training with work experience and a careers advisory centre for students who have been studying for more than three weeks at the school. In the short course prior to work experience, students will learn how to create their own CV and will have the use of all the school's facilities: library, laboratory, modems, fax, language learning computer programmes and so on. There is also the possibility of student exchanges between countries.

There are five levels of courses: beginners, intermediate One and Two, advanced and superior. These cost from 40,900ptas for two weeks to 189,400ptas for 12 weeks and start on the first Monday of every month. Also available are special courses in Literature, Business Spanish and Translation. Business Spanish programmes take place at set weeks during the year in February, April, May and October; 51,600ptas is the fee for three weeks. This course is geared towards people

with an intermediate to high standard of Spanish. The course in Writing and Conversation Skills takes place twice a year in March and June and is suitable for people who already have a good command of the language and use Spanish in their profession (eg journalists or teachers). The cost is 51,600ptas for three weeks and 66,900ptas for four weeks. There is also a course in Practical Spanish that includes a stage (period of unpaid work experience) in a Spanish company. This takes place according to demand and costs the same as the basic language courses (see above) with an additional 38,000ptas. Courses last a minimum of two weeks and a maximum of six months. Four weeks is the period of study recommended CEE. The enrolment fee is 12,000ptas and if you wish to stay on for an additional week, the cost is 17,500ptas.

CEE will, on request, find appropriate accommodation for you – with Spanish families, in university residences (summer only) and in hotel or apartments. Prices are: 20,100ptas for a week's half board with a Spanish family; 17,200ptas for a week's bed and breakfast with a Spanish family. Hotels range from 3,800 to 6,000ptas a day. Excursions and sporting activities are organised by the school.

Contact the school for enrolment details.

Centro Humboldt
Via Augusta, 18,08006
Barcelona
Tel: +34 93 237 5111/217 5675
Fax: +34 93 218 4739
Email: humboldt@arrakis.es
Website: www.arrakis.es
/~humboldt
Established: 1986
Level: None

Contact: Sra Victoria Vega/Sra Ana Sánchez Suárez

Located in the centre of Barcelona, behind the grand boulevard that is the Passeig de Gracia, this school is attended by seven hundred students, the majority of whom are Spanish. The school is run by Sr Schumacher from Germany hence the fact that this is a school popular among German students. The centre's motto is *'Comunicación Intercultural'* (Intercultural Communication), which is basically another way of saying that this is a language school that emphasises the conversational/communicational element of language learning.

Four different types of course are on offer. The 'Intensive' course (available at four different levels) lasts for a minimum of two weeks, with five hours of fifty-minute classes a day, from 8.45am to 1.45pm. Eight is the maximum number of students in each class. It is designed for those who need to learn the language quickly, with some emphasis on reading and writing skills and costs from 55,000ptas for two weeks to 99,900ptas for four weeks; should you decide to stay on, an additional week will cost 22,500ptas. You can supplement these classes with one-to-one lessons in the afternoons. Combined courses are, as the name suggests, a mixture of group courses and one-to-one lessons. Course 30 offers 25 hours per week of group classes with five hours of personal tuition. Course 35 offers the same, with ten hours of one-to-one tuition instead of five. The price of Course 30 ranges from 99,000ptas for two weeks to 186,000ptas for four weeks; each additional week costs 44,000ptas. The price for Course 35 ranges from 142,000ptas

for two weeks to 268,000ptas for four weeks; each additional week costs 63,000ptas. These fees include the cost of materials, the use of the Mediathéque (the multimedia centre) and participation in the free time programme. One-to-one courses, which can take place at any time of the year, can be arranged to last a variety of lengths of time. A four-day course, with six hours of tuition a day would cost 124,800ptas; for eight hours, the cost of tuition would be 163,200ptas. A nine-day course, with four hours of tuition a day would cost 296,000ptas; the cost of eight hours of tuition a day would be 389,000ptas. Lunch with your teacher will cost an extra 7,000ptas (both lunches included). The Flexible One-to-one course allows you to book a block of tuition hours which you can attend as when suits you during the week. Fees range from 102,000ptas for 20 hours to 396,000ptas for eighty hours.

Family homestays can be organised, at a cost of 2,500ptas a day for single room and breakfast or 3,500ptas for single room and half board. An administration fee of 8,000ptas will be charged on top of this. The school can also provide students with lists of alternative accommodation. Culture and leisure activities form a part of the courses and include the 'Barcelona Discovery' city tour, practical exercises outside of the classroom and showings of Spanish films.

Contact the school for enrolment details.

Esade Escuela de Idiomas
Avda d'Esplugues, 92-96,
08034 Barcelona
Tel: +34 93 495 2095
Fax: +34 93 495 2075

Email: Idiomas@esade.es
Website: www.esade.es
Established: 1965
Level: None
**Nearest Station: Barcelona
Sants**
Contact: Carita Benejam

ESADE (Escuela Superior de Administración y Dirección de Empresas) is a private foundation encompassing a business school, a law faculty and this, the language school. It was founded in 1958 by a group of business people from Catalonia and its ethos lies in the fact that its courses are open to anyone, whatever their race, colour, sex or creed. It is situated in a residential area of Barcelona and its law and business courses are attended by more than 7,000 people.

The language school caters for students over the age of 18 and offers a range of courses for people with different needs. The provision offered is very well organised and would probably suit the person who likes everything arranged and scheduled for them. The variety of courses shows that the school recognises the fact that people often have very different requirements when it comes to learning a language (will you need colloquial or business Spanish?, for example) as well as different time scales (a month, a term, a year?).

The prospectus gives a clear and comprehensive outline of each course, including details of course content and the aim of each course (ie an idea of the skills that it is meant to provide you with). General courses are the 'Semintensive' and 'Intensive'. 'Semintensive' costs 76,000ptas for three months (ie a term); the 'Intensive' costs 125,000ptas for 80 hours (about four weeks) and 75,300ptas for 40 hours (about two weeks). The Business courses cost: 76,000ptas, for the 'Semintensive' (three months) and 76,000ptas for the 'Intensive' (40 hours in two weeks). The 'Executive' courses cost: 280,000ptas for the 'Super Intensive' (90 hours in two weeks) and 135,000ptas for the Intensive (40 hours in two weeks). These last two courses are designed with an emphasis on functional business areas, political, economic and social issues. Individual tuition costs from 112,000ptas for 10 hours a week to 784,000ptas for 70 hours a week. These take place any week of the year whereas there are set start times during the year for the other courses. There are also two teacher-training courses: Workshop in Methodology for Spanish Teachers and Business Spanish. Each of these takes place only once during the year.

Various complementary programmes include working lunches, where you get to practice your conversational Spanish as well as learn how to cook typical Spanish dishes. There are also social, cultural and excursion programmes, each of which costs extra. The cultural programme costs 19,500ptas and 26,500ptas depending on whether you sign up for three or four weeks. The social programme costs 4,250ptas for an outing every Wednesday night for a month and excursions cost 9,500ptas for two Saturday excursions per month. Students can also make use of ESADE's Resource Centre by having a lesson with a tutor there three times a week for two weeks, the cost for this is 12,000ptas.

To help you with accommodation, ESADE has links with various companies that deal with finding suitable lodgings in hotels, halls or residence, with host families or in shared apartments. Contact the school for enrolment details.

Escola Oficial d'Idiomes Barcelona – Drassanes

Av de les Drassanes s/n, 08011 Barcelona
Tel: +34 93 329 3412
Fax: +34 93 442 0820
Established: 1972
Level: None
Nearest Station: (Metro) Drassanes or Parallel
Contact: Fuensanta Puig or Isabel Soler (Summer courses)

For those searching for a no-frills and straightforward selection of language courses this, the Official School of Languages for the Generalitat (province or 'Comunidad') of Catalunya, is ideal. Situated in the centre of the city, it is attended by about 250 students out of season and about 400 in the summer, the majority of these from the UK, Germany and Japan (there are fewer British students on the summer courses). Class sizes are larger than average, with a maximum of 20 in each (30 in the summer). Students must be 16 years of age or over (14 for the summer courses). The school is based in its own building on seven floors, and each classroom is well equipped with a television, video recorder and cassettes and transparency projector. Students of all standards – from beginners to the most advanced levels – are accepted onto the language programmes.

Courses are divided into two types: summer courses and the academic year Spanish course. The academic year programme offers semi-intensive language tuition (two hours of lessons daily) and comprises two courses, the 'Ciclo Elemental' and the 'Ciclo Superior', spread over two semesters. The Elementary Cycle (October to January) is composed of three 125-hour modules while the Superior Cycle (February to June) is made up of two 125-hour modules. If you wish to join any one of the five modules, you can only do so on the given date when that particular course begins. Therefore, if you wish to study at the highest level, your course will begin in the last part of the academic year, ending in June. The price is approximately 30,000ptas for each course.

The summer courses – 'Cursos Intensivos de Español' – which offer intensive tuition at five different levels (absolute beginners to 'perfeccionamiento'), all begin either at the end of June or the beginning of July and finish at the end of that month, (the school is closed during the month of August). The fee is 37,400ptas for eighty hours of classes (four hours daily, from 9.30am to 1.30pm), whatever your level and does not include the cost of books. The courses in Catalan offer a similar structure and the cost is 33,900ptas (books not provided).

There is a supplementary programme of cultural activities, details of which will be provided for students on the first day of their course. The school can only supply accommodation lists to those students who require help in finding a place to stay for the duration of their course. Please note, the school does not accept payment by cheque. To enrol you will need one passport-sized photograph, 10,000ptas and a photocopy of your passport. Contact the school for further details.

Instituto Mangold

Rambla de Catalunya, 16, 08007 Barcelona
Tel: +34 93 301 2539
Fax: +34 93 412 1879
Email: mangold@mhp.es
Established: 1960
Level: None
Nearest Station: Plaza de

**Catalunya or Passeig de Gracia
Contact: Francisco
Martínell/Anna Ayesta**

Located right in the centre of city, this branch of Instituto Mangold is a short walk down Las Ramblas from Barcelona's famous old port. It forms part of the Mangold group, which also has a school in Madrid and several franchises in Valencia. This is also an affiliated school of Eurocentres (a Swiss organisation) which guarantees the standard of teaching in all its centres. The school is also approved by the Instituto Cervantes, for whom it is an official DELE examination centre. With 1,500 students per year and a maximum of 14 students in each class (though 12 is usually the norm), this is a large school. It has 12 classrooms, a library, a language laboratory, a computer room and an open-air terrace. For those with an interest in studying Barcelona's other official language – Catalan – the school also offers courses in that subject. The cost per term is 31,050ptas.

The school runs three different kinds of Spanish courses: Eurocentres Language Plus Courses, Mangold Intensive Courses (20 hours language tuition per week) and Mangold Extensive Courses (four hours language courses per week). Students are mainly European and about thirty percent are executives or professionals who have been sent on a course by their firms.

The 'Eurocentres Language Plus' course includes 20 hours of tuition per week as well as optional modules that include conversation classes, Spain and Latin America Today and Art and Literature in Spain and Latin America Today. These modules cost extra and take place four times a week. If you choose to pay for one or two modules at the same time as the basic course, there will be 10% reduction on the cost of the modules. The scale of costs for the modules is from 8,000ptas for one module for two weeks to 50,400ptas for two modules for seven weeks. There is also a complementary programme, which involves two or three weekly activities. These include museum visits, film outings and excursions in and around Barcelona.

Prices for this course are divided into two categories: the tuition fees on their own (A) or the tuition fees, plus the price of a single room in a house, with half board (B). Prices for the courses vary as to the number of weeks of study (the cost per week is less, the greater the length of the course) and it is possible to do certain numbers of weeks only at certain times of the year. A two-week course costs 49,860ptas and can be taken at particular dates in March, April, June and July. This works out at an average of 24,930ptas a week. The seven week course, available only from mid February to early April costs 146,160ptas, which works out at an average of about 20,880ptas a week. These fees are for tuition only and their equivalent in the B category is 97,320ptas for two weeks (48,620ptas per week) and 299,120ptas for the seven week course (considerably cheaper, working out at 42,732ptas per week).

Instituto Mangold is also an English language teaching centre. Contact the school for enrolment details.

International House Barcelona

**Trafalgar 14, entlo. 08010, Barcelona, Spain
Tel: +34 93 268 45 11
Fax: +34 93 268 0239**

Email: spanish@bcn.ihes.com
Website: www.ihes.com/bcn
Established: 1972
Level: None
Nearest Station: Plaza Urquinaona
Contact: Elisenda Durany, Head of Spanish

Barcelona, a city to rival Madrid, is in fact considered by many to be a far superior alternative to the official capital of Spain. It is elegant and fascinating, with long, boutique-lined boulevards that lead down to the old port via the city's main thoroughfare and tourist attraction, Las Ramblas. Although Barcelona has two official languages, Catalan and Castellano (the name given to the Spanish spoken by most people in Spain), there is no reason why you shouldn't study Castellano here, and International House is one of the most well-established language schools in the city. Its main building is located at the very centre of Barcelona, five minutes away from the Plaza de Catalunya, the main square of the city which also leads on to Las Ramblas. Apart from teaching Spanish to students from all over the world, IH in Barcelona also teaches other languages to people from the city, which means that students of Spanish can meet native Spanish speakers at the school. IH also trains teachers of English and Spanish and sends students from Spain to study abroad.

IH aims to improve students' communication skills and offers intensive group courses (four hours of lessons per day, Monday to Friday), which can be supplemented with optional courses in 'Spanish Culture' (Spanish social customs, media, politics, literature, etc). IH can also prepare students for the DELE examinations, which are held twice a year in May and November.

The course lasts eight weeks, starting in March and September and there are four hours of lessons per day. A fee in addition to the course fee is charged for the exam, which takes place at the University of Barcelona. Individual tuition is available and can be combined with the intensive group course. Other Spanish language courses include the executive plus course, custom-designed courses for younger learners and special groups, extensive group courses and combined intensive group courses. Fees (not including accommodation) range from 50,000ptas for two weeks intensive group course to 250,000ptas for the executive plus course.

A range of accommodation options are available, these include host family (bed and breakfast or half board; there is also a executive host family option), student residence (bed and breakfast or half board; there is a supplement for a single room), a room in an apartment with other students, a one, two or three bedroom furnished apartment. Prices range from 19,500ptas per week for a room with a host family (bed and breakfast only) or a room in an apartment with other students to 32,000ptas per week for executive host family accommodation (with half board). A one-bedroom furnished apartment costs 130,000ptas for four weeks.

A social programme of parties, visits and excursions is organised for students at IH, most of whom come from western Europe and north America. Accommodation can be arranged with host families and executive host families, in furnished apartments, university residences (July, August and September only) or hotels. The school's "electronic classroom" can provide Internet access to individual students for up to two hours a day.

To book a place on one of the courses you can either complete an IH application form, write to them, telephone them, fax or email them. All invoices must be paid in full before the starting date of the course, in pesetas, by cheque or bank transfer.

Kingsbrook

**Trav de Gracia, 60-1-3a, 08006
Barcelona
Tel: +34 93 202 3763
Fax: +34 93 202 1598
Email: kingsb@teleline.es
Established: 1986
Level: None
Nearest Station: (Metro) Plaza
de Catalunya
Contact: Albert Goedhart**
Located in the heart of the city, in a bustling area filled with restaurants, shops and cafes, this school offers Spanish courses to groups of up to 10 students. The school has six classrooms, a cafe area and a video room. As well as courses, Kingsbrook provides help in finding accommodation, transfers from the airport and tourist information. Staff at the school speak English, French, German and Dutch and students are predominantly European.

The school offers four types of courses: the academic year course, (from September to June), intensive summer courses, business courses and one-to-one tuition. Prices are calculated according to the number of tuition hours that you choose per week. For three hours a week, the enrolment fee is 5,000ptas, with the option of paying tuition fees per term (31,000ptas) or per month (11,000ptas). For six hours a week, the enrolment fee is 5,000ptas and you can choose between the full academic year course (October to June, 97,000ptas), October to February (64,000ptas) or March to June (51,000ptas); you also have the option of paying per term (41,500ptas) or per month (16,000ptas). Students on these courses will have to pay an additional fee of 4,500ptas for materials. For

Kingsbrook

twelve hours per week (three hours daily), the price ranges from 44,000ptas for one month to 225,000ptas for ten months (the full Academic year course) and includes the enrolment fee and learning materials. You can start on any Monday. One-to-one lessons must last for a minimum of 28 hours, for which the cost is 68,000ptas. As well as language courses, Kingsbrook provides three other courses: Literature, Geography and Spanish History. The price for these is 84,000ptas, for 28 hours of lessons (the minimum).

Kingsbrook can arrange accommodation with Spanish families whose homes are within walking distance of the school. The cost for this is either 35,000ptas per month for a single room, meals not included, or 75,000ptas per month for single room plus breakfast and dinner. The other option is to stay in an aparthotel, in either a single or a shared room. The price for this is about 70,000ptas per month for a single room and 35,000ptas for each person in a shared room.

Linguarama Iberica, SA

Gran Vía Carlos III, 98, 08028 Barcelona
Tel: +34 93 330 1687
Fax: +34 93 330 8013
Email: 106536@ compuserve.com
Website: www.linguarama.com
Established: 1971
Level: None
Nearest Station: Barcelona Sants
Contact: Yvonne Feltham

Another well-placed language school in the centre of Barcelona, this school has a capacity for about 1000 students and concentrates on teaching foreign language to adults. The majority of its students are actually Spanish, as the other languages taught at the school include English, French, German and Dutch. Linguarama is an international organisation (part of the BPP training group) and it has 35 centres in 12 countries, with four centres in Spain alone (in Madrid, Pamplona and Seville as well as Barcelona). What is interesting about this school is that you can start taking classes at one of the Linguarama centres in the UK. Once you have attained a certain level of Spanish you can then sign up for one of the courses in Spain in order to perfect your knowledge and to give yourself the opportunity of learning to language in the only place where you'll really learn it properly.

Despite the number of students at this school, class sizes are kept small - the average is about four in each class. Four different types of courses are offered. For one week (40 hours) of 'Total Impact' the cost is 235,000ptas and includes lunch with your teacher. Teaching on this course is one-to-one and the programme is developed according to the student's particular needs. The 'Crash Course' is suitable for students who do not have the time to devote an entire day to studying, but who require an intensive course. As with the 'Total Impact' course, teaching is one-to-one and tailored to the needs of the individual. For thirty hours of teaching a week, the cost is 162,000ptas. The 'Intensive' courses have been developed for those people to whom language learning does not come easily. This course is more suitable for those who can spare some time away from work commitments and who can therefore devote themselves entirely to learning the language. Once again, these courses are one-to-one and cost 121,500ptas for 22.5 classes a week. The 'Semi-Intensive' programme (15 hours of teaching a week), costs 81,000ptas. From 1998 onwards, the school is offering Spanish in Open Groups. For two days a week (each lesson lasting one and a half hours) the cost is approximately 15,000ptas per month.

As will be apparent from the course descriptions, the programmes provided by Linguarama are suitable for, and aimed at, executives with limited learning time. The school has traditionally offered courses to executives and in keeping with that, the centres throughout Spain are located in the business districts of the cities that they are in. In order to give students a taste of the Spanish way of life, outings are organised to nearby galleries and museums, as well as restaurants and bars.

Courses can begin any day of the year and the school remains open in August. Each student's level of Spanish is assessed prior to the course so that the teacher can provide them with the teaching most suitable for them. The school can offer help in finding accommodation.

Contact the school for enrolment details.

The Lewis School of Languages

Gran Vía Carlos III, 97K, .08028 Barcelona
Tel: +34 93 339 2608
Fax: +34 93 411 1333
Email: lewischool@mail.seric.es
Established: 1985
Level: None
Nearest Station: (Metro) Maria Cristina
Contact: Caroline Lewis
This is a small school (about 200 students), located in a residential area of Barcelona. The school claims to "pride [itself] in giving a high degree of attention to each student". Students have the opportunity to prepare for the Spanish examinations of the Universidad de Salamanca which cover three categories: Diploma Inicial de Español como Lengua Extranjera (Basic Level), Diploma Básico de Español como Lengua Extranjera'(Intermediate Level) and Diploma Superior de Español como Lengua Extranjera (Advanced Level). Class sizes are small, with an average of about six students in each.

The school operates on six levels of ability: beginner (básico 1), pre-intermediate (básico 2), intermediate (medio 1), upper-intermediate (medio 2), Lower advanced (superior 1) and advanced

"I'm a student from France and I wanted to learn Spanish because eventually I want to work in Barcelona. The teachers at the school are very good and they seem to show a genuine concern for each student. I would definitely recommend Tandem because I have learnt a lot and I they have helped me a great deal."

Axel Leuvret, France

Student Story

Tandem Barcelona

(superior 2). Lessons focus on oral communication. Some lessons are devoted to Spanish culture, civilisation and current affairs. Students are expected to complete homework assignments.

The school's Activities Coordinator plans trips each week to famous sites in Barcelona itself, such as the Picasso Museum, the Miró Foundation, the Gothic Quarter, and to places and interest outside the city (Tarragona, Montserrat). Accommodation options are either living with a family or student residence. Included in the cost of the course are accommodation, course books and study material, a level test, a full social programme, excursions and an attendance and progress report (for courses lasting more than four weeks). The registration fee is 11,000ptas, with an additional 5,000ptas payable for late registration. An optional airport transfer service costs 6,000ptas.

The cost of a two-week intensive course (20 classes per week) varies. If you will be staying in a single room in student residence (half board), which is the most expensive option, the costs will be 106,600ptas. Staying with a host family for the same amount of time works out at 88,900ptas, the cheapest possibility. Other options are: sharing a double room in a student residence and paying either for half board or for bed and breakfast only or a single room, bed and breakfast only, in a student residence. Courses last up to 12 weeks, with additional weeks thereafter costing extra (37,450ptas if you are staying with a host family, 46,850ptas for a single room in the university residence, half board). A single room in a student residence (half board) for 12 weeks costs 560,600ptas, while staying with a host family for the same amount of time costs 449,400ptas. The minimum age for students is 16.

To enrol, you must fill in and sign a copy of the school's registration form and send it together with a copy of your bank transfer document, showing payment of 50,000ptas (11,000ptas for registration plus 39,000ptas, to be deducted from your total course fees). If you are applying less than four weeks before the start of the course, you must send the full fee. Contact the school for more information.

Tandem Barcelona

**Rda Sant Antoni, 100, 08001
Barcelona
Tel: +34 93 301 4634
Fax: +34 93 301 4634
Established: 1986 (Under construction)
Level: None
Nearest Station: (Metro)
Universidad
Contact: Nicolás Ruiz**

Another of the many language schools situated in the very centre of Barcelona, Tandem Barcelona is attended by about 300 students annually, most of whom fall between the ages of 23 to 27. Part of the Tandem group of language schools, the school has five well-equipped classrooms and a team of young, recently qualified teachers, all of whom have experience of teaching Spanish to foreigners.

An interesting feature of the school is the fact that its accommodation scheme allows you to share with Spaniards. These flatshares, comprise a single room with access to cooking facilities (11,000ptas per week). This is an excellent way of getting some concrete language practice and it is worth bearing in mind that this particular opportunity is rarely offered by most language schools. Generally, these can only organise family homestays; however, the arrangement at Tandem allows you to live with people who are likely to be of a similar age and with whom you will probably have more in common. Alternative arrangements, in hotels or hostels, can also be organised.

The school offers one type of course: the 'cursos intensivos de Español'. This runs throughout the year and can be attended for a minimum of two weeks by students of Spanish at all levels, from beginners to advanced. Once there, your stay can be extended for as long as you wish. Those with previous knowledge of the language can start at any time of the year; those learning Spanish for the first time will have to start classes on given dates every month (details will be supplied by the school). The course fees range from 39,000ptas for two weeks to 102,000ptas for six weeks. If you wish to prolong the length of your course, the cost per week will be 19,750ptas. Students participating in two consecutive courses will receive a 10 per cent discount on the second course. The course comprises four hours of lessons a day, which are divided into two hours of grammar and two hours of communication/conversation exercises. All teaching material is included in the price of the course.

"I wanted to come to Barcelona to learn Spanish and a friend of mine recommended this school. I'm enjoying my course and the atmosphere here is friendly. The grammar classes are practical and the communication exercises are very relevant to everyday situations. The cultural programme has been interesting, particularly because everything is explained for us. The school helped me find an apartment in the city."

Sven Stöcker, Germany

For more advanced students, there are complementary classes in conversation, business correspondence, contemporary Spanish literature and Spanish history and art. These cost an additional 15,000ptas for an hour a day for two weeks (ten hours). There is also an optional Cultural Programme, available to all students. This involves excursions in and around the city, film showings and discussions. The costs of museum entrance and transport are extra.

The school is closed for a week at the end of January and on various fiestas throughout the year. If a fiesta happens to fall during your course, you will not be able to recover the lessons that should have taken place that day. Students requiring them will receive revision classes free of charge. Before the start of their course, all students must sit a level test in order to be placed in the appropriate class.

Contact the school for enrolment details.

CANARY ISLANDS

Gran Canaria School of Languages

Grau Bassas, 27, E-35007 Las Palmas de Gran Canaria
Tel: +34 928 267 971
Fax: +34 928 278 980
Email: gcschool@intercom.es
Website: www.step.es/gcourses
Established: 1964
Level: None
Nearest Airport: Gran Canaria
Contact: Oliver Belz
A group of volcanic islands situated off the south coast of the Iberian Peninsula, the Canary Islands are probably best known for being the preferred destination of most German holiday-makers. They have a reputation for being over-crowded with tourists and the Spanish from the mainland tend to shun them as a result. However, it would be a shame to dismiss them on this basis as many of the less well known ones are said to be areas of great natural beauty. Gran Canaria – or at least, the south of the island – is one of the most popular islands in the archipelago and is the second largest in size. Las Palmas, its capital, is in the north of the island. The island is renowned for its variety of climates: Mediterranean beaches in the south and tree-covered mountains at its centre.

This school is in Las Palmas, a university city famous for welcoming Columbus on leave from his trips across the Atlantic. It is enticingly located about 50m from the beach in a traditional house on two floors. It has 10 classrooms and two large atriums. At night the school is used as a party venue.

There are four courses on offer at the school: 'Intensive Spanish' course, 'Private Spanish' course, the 'Semiprivate (Semiprivado)' Spanish course and a 'German Language' course. The intensive course is suitable for beginner, intermediate and advanced level students (beginners have to start on the first Monday of every month, other levels can start on any Monday). There are between si and 13 students in each group, classes are from 9am to 1pm and the price is 15,000ptas per week. For the Private Spanish course (suitable for students at any level) the number of class hours are chosen by the individual student. The course can begin on any day and costs 3,650ptas per hour. The Semiprivate course is for two students who wish to study together and costs 2,500ptas per hour. The students can choose their hours and it is suitable for students at any level. All courses last a minimum of one week.

The school owns its own residences – Plus Residence (built in 1992) and Best Residence (built in 1997). The latter also has facilities that enable handicapped students to move around the building unimpared. Accommodation costs 34,000ptas for a single room, 25,000ptas for one bed in a double room and 43,000ptas for a couple sharing a double room. The price includes the laundering (not ironing) of your clothing, breakfast and lunch on class days and a cold dinner instead of lunch on Saturdays, Sundays and holidays. There is also a babysitting service for accompanying children.

Excursions with a teacher can be arranged on request (as long as there are four or more students participating) and the school can provide information about things to do in your spare time. Contact the school for enrolment details.

GRANADA

Carmen de las Cuevas

Cuesta de los Chinos 15 – Albaicin, 18010 Granada
Tel: +34 958 221 062
Fax: +34 958 220 476
Email: info@carmencuevas.com
Website: www.carmencuevas.com
Established: 1984
Level: None
Nearest Station: Granada
Contact: Carmen Linares Gil

Walking through the Albaicin, Granada's old Arabic quarter, is at best a fairly perilous undertaking: narrow cobbled streets slope sharply up or down and map reading becomes impossible as you negotiate its labyrinthine structure. However, the approach to Carmen de las Cuevas (so called due to the two cave-like dance studios on the ground floor of the school) is probably more precarious than most as the higher you climb, the steeper the path becomes, until finally you arrive at the school. Even if you choose not to study

Gran Canaria School of Languages

here, a visit is worthwhile as the school's location is wonderful and the building itself (a multi-leveled structure that seems to spiral upwards) is very unusual. The spectacular views of the city, the mountains and the Alhambra, for which the Albaicin is so famous, are probably best witnessed from the terrace of this school.

This started as a language school and flamenco classes were introduced little by little until they eventually became an important part of the school's provision. This school is perhaps the only one of its kind, in that you can study Spanish, flamenco dancing or flamenco guitar, separately or combined. The only option that you can't take are intensive courses in language and dancing/guitar simultaneously. As well as the language classes, cultural courses are offered in History and Art and Literature (both at an additional cost of 7,800ptas a week.) Emailing facilities are available.

The school has about 350 students every year, with a maximum of 70 students at any one time. Nationalities vary, with more Germans attending the language courses while the flamenco side seems to attract British, American and Swedish students. Flamenco classes are suitable for anyone, from beginners to professionals and classes depend on which teachers are available in a given week. Summer courses lasting four weeks, with 15 hours of tuition a week, cost 72,000ptas (129,600ptas for eight weeks of dancing). During the rest of the year, intensive courses lasting one week with 15 hours of tuition a week cost 21,000ptas. Introductory classes to dancing and *compás* (flamenco rhythm) cost 6,500ptas and 5,500ptas respectively for five hours of tuition a week. There are occasional courses with

famous teachers as well as more regular classes with teachers who reside in Granada. Some evening classes are attended by people who live in Granada and the odd coach party has been known to drop in for an introductory flamenco lesson en route to their next destination.

There are five levels of language classes, all of which are outlined in the school's multilingual prospectus/newsletter. The Intensive language course (15 hours a week) lasts for a minimum of two weeks and a maximum of five weeks and costs from 40,000ptas (36,000pts in low season) for two weeks to 89,500ptas (81,300ptas in low season) for five weeks. The extra-intensive course (20/30 hours a week) lasts for a minimum of two weeks and a maximum of five weeks and costs from 63,300ptas for two weeks to 148,800ptas for five weeks. The Long-term language and culture (15 hours a week) lasts from six weeks to 20 weeks, with a fee of 15,600ptas per week. The special course for Spanish teachers (15 hours a week) takes place for two weeks once a year and costs 40,000ptas. The Intensive DELE Preparation course (15 hours a week) lasts for four weeks and costs 67,000ptas. Start dates for all of these courses vary. Private tuition costs from 3,000ptas per hour for general language courses to 5,000ptas per hour for thesis preparation. The school can also organise group programmes.

Several types of accommodation are available: from double room in a flat shared with other students (from 10,000ptas a week) to family homestay (from 26,100ptas a week) to hotel accommodation. Accommodation is available in the Albaicin. Contact the school for enrolment details.

Castila – Centro de Estudios Hispanicos

Carmen de los Gatos, Aljibe del Gato, 1, Albaicin, 18010 Granada
Tel: +34 958 205 863
Fax: +34 958 277 240
Email: castila@redestb.es
Website: www.castila.es
Level: None
Nearest Station: Granada
Contact: Antonio Perales Castro

Another school situated in the picturesque Albaicin of Granada, you will know when you get to Castila as the gates to the school are adorned with the figures of two black cats. Behind these is a pretty front garden, with steps leading to the main building of the school. On your left as you enter is the school's annex – a smaller building housing a kitchen (where paella demonstrations take place), a couple of classrooms and a video room. Castila is pretty and tranquil – it is essentially a fairly run of the mill language school made special due to its location: proximity to the centre of the city (which is only five minutes walk away) combined with the peacefulness of the countryside.

There are six courses on offer. The 'Cursos Intensivos de Lengua General A': from 42,000ptas for two weeks to

Student story

"I'm still at high school and am getting credits for doing this course. I've applied to different universities in the states to do different things – I'm still very undecided about what I see myself doing in the future. I found out about Carmen de las Cuevas through the Internet and chose it because I like the idea of combining language learning, flamenco guitar and cultural lessons with living with a Spanish family. I get on well with the family I'm staying with and it really is excellent practice for my Spanish. They live in the Albaicin and I have a room of my own. I think that they had quite a stereotypical image of what an American would be like and I sense that they're quite surprised as I don't think that I fit into that image. If I had one misconception about the school, it's that I didn't realise quite how intensive the language courses would be and I had hoped to spend more time focusing on the music. However, the teaching is really good. The classes are hard and fast moving, but they're very small as there are only four or five of us in a class and everything is explained very well. I also think that the class is fairly evenly matched. Granada is absolutely wonderful.

If I have any advice to offer people thinking of doing a course in Spain, it's that you should go for a small school such as this one because its not so easy to find people of the same nationality as you. Therefore Spanish becomes the language you share with your fellow students."

Robert Sayre, USA.

265,000ptas for sixteen weeks for 20 fifty-minute classes per week (four classes a day, maximum of six people per group). The lessons are divided between two daily classes of theory and exercises and two daily classes of conversation. The 'Cursos Intensivos de Lengua General B': from 57,000ptas for two weeks to 399,000ptas for 16 weeks for 30 fifty-minute classes a week, with a maximum of six people per group. This course is based on the same principal as the General A, with two extra hours of classes a day. Students on this, and on any other course, may choose to present themselves for the DELE exams. The 'Curso de Literatura y Comentario de Textos (Literature and Textual Analysis)' offers an introduction to Spanish literature. The 'Curso de Literatura y Comentario de Texto Complementario (A)' focuses more on individual works by a variety of Spain's most well-known authors. The 'Curso de Cultura y Sociedad (Culture and Society)' offers an insight into modern Spain. All of these involve 10 50-minute classes per week (two classes a day), with a maximum of five students per group and cost from 41,000ptas for two weeks to 135,000ptas for eight weeks. Courses in business Spanish (from 98,000ptas for four weeks to 280,000ptas for 12 weeks) involve 40 hours of classes spread over two, three, four or more weeks, with a maximum of five students per group. It is possible to sit the exam for the 'Certificado de Español Empresarial' (Certificate of Business Spanish). DELE preparation courses (from 80,000ptas for four weeks to 271,000ptas for 14 weeks) involve 25 classes per week. The Complementary DELE course (five hours a week) costs 7,500ptas per week. Private (one-to-one) classes cost 2,950 ptas and semi-private classes (two people) cost 4,200ptas. The school offers a very comprehensive range of daily afternoon activities, including films, visits to the Alhambra and a day out skiing in the mountains. The maj-ority of students at

Castila – Centro de Estudios Hispanicos

this school are between the ages of 20 and 30 and about 85 per cent are from Europe.

Accommodation is available in shared flats or with Spanish families. Prices in a shared apartment range from 17,500ptas per person for two weeks in a double bedroom to 140,000ptas for 16 weeks in a single room. Prices of family homestay range from 43,000ptas per person for two weeks in a shared double room to 339,000ptas for 16 weeks for one person in a single room.

The school also has a branch in Mojácar, on Spain's "Tropical" South Coast. Courses offered here take place in the summer only, in a hotel on the beach. Classes are held on the hotel's terrace and are probably suitable for those who have the time to learn in a relaxed environment at a more leisurely pace. The options are General A (from 42,000ptas for two weeks to 135,000ptas for eight weeks) and General B (from 52,500ptas for two weeks to 203,000ptas for eight weeks). Private classes are 3,000ptas and semi-private classes are 4,200ptas. You can stay in an apartment (from 20,000ptas a week for a double room)or with a Spanish family (from 48,000ptas a week for a double room).

Contact the school for enrolment details.

Escuela Montalbán – TANDEM Granada:

C/Conde Cifuentes, 11, 18005 Granada
Tel: +34 958 25 68 75
Fax: +34 958 25 68 75
Established: 1986
Level: None
Nearest Station: Granada
Contact: Margaret Fortmann

Granada, one of Spain's most historic cities, is home to the famous Alhambra, the wonderful and imposing Moorish castle that dominates the city against the dramatic backdrop of the mountains of the Sierra Nevada. Granada is a university town, inhabited by both Spanish and overseas exchange students. In the winter it becomes a popular skiing resort and in the summer, tourists brave the intense, dry heat of Andalucia to visit the Alhambra. The small school is located in a quiet residential street close to the centre of Granada and is run by a German lady, Margaret Fortmann and, as a result, students tend to come from German-speaking countries (Germany, Austria, Switzerland).

Classes at Escuela Montalban take place throughout the year and numbers are small: from two-six students in each level, with numbers raised to a maximum of eight, if necessary, in the high season. Students or those who are unemployed receive a 10% discount on course fees. The school is part of a network of schools called TANDEM, which enables students to get to know Spanish students and emphasises the importance of language learning both in and outside of the classroom. The school itself offers 'Standard' and Intensive courses, 'Standard plus' (includes two private classes a day), individual courses, and training courses for teachers of Spanish. The examination courses offered are 'Preparation for DELE,' 'Examination courses for DELE,' 'Preparation courses for business Spanish' and 'Examination courses for business Spanish'. The course duration for these is from 1 to 16 weeks, with four-six hours of lessons a day, and fees range from 25,000ptas for one week of the Standard course to 216,000ptas for the

DELE Preparation course. The school has about 400 students a year, most of whom come from western Europe. All teachers at Escuela Montalban are fully qualified.

All students are tested on their first day to ensure that they are placed in the appropriate class for their level. In the spring and autumn, the school offers an unusual combination of Spanish and rock-climbing courses. Classes take place in the morning while rock-climbing, in the nearby Sierra Nevada, is reserved for the afternoon (when the rest of Spain is having its siesta!). A cultural programme is also organised and includes lectures, film sessions, guided tours around Granada and a taste of Andalucian cooking (for those who always wanted to know how to make that delicious Andalucian speciality, *gazpacho*).

Help with accommodation can be provided by the school and is selected by them. It includes shared housing with young Spanish people, living with a Spanish family, self-catering apartments or hotels. For enrolment details, contact the school.

Universidad de Granada – Centro de Lenguas Modernas (CLM)

Placeta del Hospicio Viejo, s/n (Realejo), 18071 Granada
Tel: +34 958 220 790
Fax: +34 958 220 844
Email: infoclm@esperanto.ugr.es
Website: www.ugr.es/~clm
Established: 1992
Level: None
Nearest Station: Granada
Contact: Minerva Alganza Roldán or Juan Antonio Díaz López

The second oldest University city in Spain, there are faculty buildings scattered throughout Granada and it is alive with students, both from Spain and overseas. This, the official Language Centre of the University of Granada, is located on the slopes beneath the Alhambra, in a large, magnificent building typical of the area. The patio (atrium) at its centre serves as the main meeting place for students during their breaks. The building preserves its traditional essence and yet within, it contains the latest in modern technology (including emailing facilities) and an impressively equipped library. The school is the result of a merger of the university's language centre and its centre for teaching Spanish to Foreigners (founded in the 1970s) and is therefore, with about 2,000 students, probably the largest language school in the city.

Apart from Spanish, the other languages offered at CLM are English, French, Italian, German, Portuguese, Arabic (modern), Greek (modern), Russian, Swedish, Dutch and Japanese and students on the more extensive cultural Spanish courses can study one of these as a second language. On the Spanish courses, most students come from the USA, the UK and Sweden. CLM has links with a number of universities, including the University of Leeds, which sends many third year Spanish students here. These students usually take the Hispanic Studies course whose modules include lectures given by tutors from the university itself, who adapt the lectures they would usually give to Spanish students to their needs (linguisitic and otherwise).

The core provision offered at CLM is made up of the Intensive Spanish Language courses, the Hispanic

Studies course and the course in Specific Studies in Spanish Language and Culture. The intensive courses are for language only and are intended for those who can only spend a short time in Spain. The Hispanic Studies course is geared towards university students and professionals who already have prior knowledge of Spanish. The course is divided into two semesters and subjects are separated into five sub-divisions: Language, Literature, Geography, History, Art History, Sociology-Politics and Culture. The Specific Studies course is also aimed at university students and professionals with prior knowledge of the language but who, in this case, wish to concentrate on a particular topic. There are eight different areas of study, each of which is grouped under the following headings: Language, Literature, History, Art History or Culture.

Apart from these, there are courses in 'Methodology for the Teaching of Spanish as a Modern Language' and in 1999 a new course – Spanish for Professionals – will be introduced. The centre already has a link with France Telecom, for whose employees it provides special programmes. CLM can provide tailor made courses (for large companies, universities, official institutions and so on) and will give a quote on request. In addition, they can also offer courses for DELE (Diploma in Spanish as a Foreign Languag) preparation (for which it is an examining centre) and for the 'Certificate of Attainment in Modern Languages' (CEIM), a diploma based on the four communication skills (reading, writing, listening and speaking).

Every student will sit a level test at the university a couple of days before the start of their course. Fees range from 40,000ptas for a semester studying an individual subject on the Hispanic Studies or Specific Studies courses to 196,000ptas for the full Hispanic

"I'm waiting to find out if I have a place at university and in the meantime decided to do a Spanish course. I found out about this school when I found its prospectus in a batch given to me by my sister. I chose this one simply because I liked the look of its leaflet. I'm here for two months and have four more weeks to go. I was only meant to be here for four weeks but I wanted to stay on. I think it's very important to be able to speak Spanish as it is now one of the most important languages in the world. I like the Spanish – they're open-minded and much more relaxed than the Germans. I'm living in one of the teacher's flats, which is working out very well. I really like the school but preferred it earlier on in the year when there were fewer people and classes were more intimate, so you could get to know the teachers. It's a bit disruptive when you've been here for a while and new people join mid-course."

Irina, Germany

Studies course. Pure language courses range from 44,000ptas for 40 hours to 109,000ptas for 160 hours. Accommodation details are available from the University of Granada's accommodation service (+34 958 243 137). There is a programme of excursions and cultural activities. Contact the centre for enrolment details.

CEGRI – Centro Granadí de Español

Sacrisitía de San Matías, 12, E-18009 Granada
Tel: +34 958 228 602
Fax: +34 958 228 657
Email: cegri@cece.es
Website: www.cece.es/cegri /index.htm
Established: 1986
Level: None
Nearest Station: Granada
Contact: Sandra Willems

Founded in 1986, this began as a language school based on Gran Vía, the city's principal main street. At that time, Spanish courses only formed a fraction of its provision. However, this section of the school expanded until in 1994 it overtook every other language to become the only language taught there. The school is now located behind a church in a lovely 17th-century building that used to be a palace. It has been revamped to preserve details of its former splendour while providing up to date equipment and modern classrooms.

CEGRI has about 100 students, mainly from Germany, the US and Japan and the average age is around 28. The school is very flexible and can offer courses tailor made to individual requirements providing students inform the school beforehand of their needs. There are Spanish courses at all levels and a range of options for individual tuition in combination courses. These include current affairs, literature, sociopolitical topics, art, business, the environment, tourism and public relations, translation and Spanish for medical purposes as well as preparation for examinations, including the DELE. Courses in the 'Methodology of Teaching Spanish as a Foreign Language' are also provided.

There are about 12 to 18 teachers at the school (fewer out of season) all of whom have degrees and have taken part in teaching courses. Excursions are used as a basis for classes and these take place twice a week for two hours, both in and out of Granada. Students have the rare opportunity of taking classes in flamenco, sevillanas and Spanish guitar at the school itself as there is a dance studio actually on the premises. Social outings and trips to the cinema outings are also organised.

There are six courses on offer. The Main Course (20 lessons a week, six 10 students per class) costs from 34,000ptas for two weeks to 250,000ptas for 16 weeks. The Intensive Course (25 lessons a week, six-ten students per class) costs from 42,000ptas for two weeks to 160,000ptas for eight weeks. The Combination Course (20 Main Course lessons plus five private tuition hours a week) costs from 69,000ptas for two weeks to 135,000ptas for four weeks. The Super-Intensive Combination Course runs for two weeks only and costs 105,000ptas for 20 Main Course lessons with an additional ten private tuition hours a week. The Spanish Language Diploma (DELE) Preparation Course (20 lessons per week, six-ten students per class, beginning on fixed dates) costs from 34,000ptas for two weeks to 130,000ptas for eight weeks. The examination fees are extra and cost from 9,000ptas for the Diploma

Inicial to 13,000ptas for the Diploma Superior. Private tuition costs from 4,000ptas per lesson for one-to-one to 7,000ptas per lesson for three-to-one.

There are five accommodation categories. Shared apartment with other CEGRI students or a flat shared with Spanish students/people (from 18,000ptas for two weeks to 98,000ptas for 16 weeks for one person in a shared room). Staying with a Spanish family will cost from 30,000ptas for two weeks to 210,000pta for 16 weeks. Charges for hotel or hostel accommodation vary according to their category. An airport pick-up service is operated for students staying with host families (there is a charge for this). The school has a library and a multimedia room is about to be installed, offering students access to email and the Internet. The school is closed from mid-December to mid-January. For enrolment details, contact the school.

Instituto Español de Granada – Centre de Estudios y Vacaciones Almuñecar

Santa Isabel la Real, 11, Granada
Tel: +34 958 275 424
Email: ceva@valnet.es
Established: 1981
Level: None
Nearest Station: Granada
Contact: Fina Barragán

Finding this school is a bit tricky as the road on which it stands looks like a main road on the map. This being the Albaicin however, (the Albaicin is the ancient Arabic quarter of Granada, famous for its labyrinthine streets), it is easy to lose your bearings, but don't be shy about asking someone the way: the residents of this unusual *barrio* (district) are used to giving directions to confused foreigners. The school,

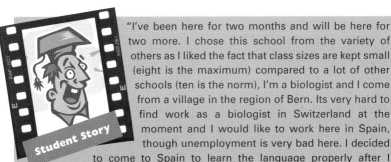

"I've been here for two months and will be here for two more. I chose this school from the variety of others as I liked the fact that class sizes are kept small (eight is the maximum) compared to a lot of other schools (ten is the norm), I'm a biologist and I come from a village in the region of Bern. Its very hard to find work as a biologist in Switzerland at the moment and I would like to work here in Spain, though unemployment is very bad here. I decided to come to Spain to learn the language properly after I worked here for a month last year. Spain is a lot more fun than Switzerland as you can actually talk to people here! I live with a Spanish bloke and we only speak to one another in Spanish, though I do find his Andalucían accent a bit hard to understand sometimes. We get on well, though there are inevitably things that I don't really like, primarily the fact that he's a smoker and I'm not. My flatmate is more of a nightbird, whereas I'm better during the day, but whenever his friends come round they always invite me to cook with them."

Hans, Switzerland

which recently moved here from a location in the city (watch out, the prospectus still bears the school's old address) is in a charming building, typical of the area. Its focal point is a patio (atrium) with plants in the middle of it and benches all around. It is on three floors and has rooms for accommodation as well as for classes and a kitchen at the student's disposition, all of which makes it feel a bit like a boarding school. This centre is actually one of three owned by the school and seems to attract students (mainly female) who have just left school and are preparing to go to university. There is also a school on the coast at Almuñecar – a beach resort and therefore suitable for those who wish to work and play, and another one in the Albaicin is in the process of being given a complete overhaul, ready for classes in the summer.

The school is open all year and can offer courses from one week to nine months. It offers preparation for DELE and encourages suitable candidates to sit it even if they have not planned to do so. All levels are accepted, from beginners to advanced and the school is keen to fit students into the right class for their level. Depending on your level your course will have a greater or lesser content of cultural topics such as History of Spanish Art (beginners, obviously, will concentrate purely on the language). The school has a list of Spanish students who wish to do conversational exchanges with English students. If you are interested, the school will make the preliminary call for you and will organise a first meeting at the school.

Prices for the schools in Granada and that in Almuñecar are different. At Almuñecar the programme – 'International courses in Hispanic Literature and Culture' – costs from 36,000ptas for two weeks to 216,000ptas for 12 weeks. At the Instituto Español de Granada there are ten types of courses, from the academic course to one-to-one courses. On the academic (once and for all) course, you will be prepared for the DELE exams. It lasts a full academic year and costs 299,250ptas. The DELE preparation course costs 217,125ptas for five months tuition, 188,250ptas for four months tuition and 153,600ptas for three months tuition. Hispanic studies courses cost 190,575ptas for five months, 161,700ptas for four months and 127,050ptas for three months. There are monothematic summer courses ('Spanish and Latin American history or Business Spanish') costing 60,000ptas per course. Long term Spanish courses vary from one month to nine months and cost varies according to the amount of daily hours you sign up to do. The minimum, three hours a day for a month, will cost 38,115ptas whereas the maximum, six hours a day for nine months will cost 686,070ptas. There are refresher courses for teachers (35,000ptas), super intensive course short term courses (up to four weeks only) costing from 15,885ptas for five lessons a day for a week to 76,248ptas for six lessons a day for four weeks. Special two-week Easter and Christmas courses cost 42,000ptas and one-to-one courses cost 100,000ptas for 20 lessons (five hours a day).

Accommodation at the school in Granada varies according to whether you are staying for a few months or a few weeks, from 12,500ptas per week for a single room to 80,000ptas per month to stay with a Spanish family. At Almuñecar there are six different accommodation options. A double room in an apartment with other foreign students (the apartments are usually owned by the school who then rents them out to its students) costs from 8,000ptas per month. It costs 88,000ptas per month to stay as a paying guest (in your own room) with a Spanish family. There are notices (mainly hand written) on the school's information board advertising dance classes (salsa, merengue), excursions, cookery classes and so on.

García Lorca courses at Instituto Español de Granada

To celebrate the centenary of Granada's most cherished son, there will be a special cycle of García Lorca for the 1998/99 academic year (which, depending on its success, may be provided on a regular basis thereafter). This will take place at both centres at certain times of the year (usually out of season when there aren't so many language students). The courses will involve total immersion in all subjects related to García Lorca. The basis of the programmes is that you will take Spanish lessons at the same time as reading and studying Lorca's works and those of the poets and writers of his era. These classes will take place for four hours a day, and you will then spend time taking flamenco lessons, visiting places related to the poet,

learning about the theatre, the gitanos (gipsies) and the guardia civil (the police) – all of them important Lorca topics. Cookery classes are also available. The idea is for you to learn as much about Granada – in particular, Lorca's Granada – as possible.

There are five different courses, which take place at different times of the year: Sierra Nevada courses (Jan-Feb), Carnaval courses (Feb), Mar y Sierra courses (Jan-Feb, April-May and May-June), San Juan courses (June and July) and Otoño courses (Nov-Dec). They will take place in either Granada or Almuñecar or both (depending on the course). Prices are quoted for the course on its own or including accommodation (double or single room). Prices range from 20,000ptas for two weeks in June to 200,000ptas for 24 weeks (Jan-June), course only. With accommodation (single room) the prices range from 38,000ptas for two weeks in June to 392,000ptas for 24 weeks (Jan-Junc).

Sierra y Mar

Ferreirola,
E-18416
Granada
Tel: +34 958 766 171
Fax: +34 958 857 367
Established: 1985

LANGUAGE SCHOOLS

123

Level: None
Nearest Station: Granada-Málaga
Contact: Giuseppe Heiss

Situated in the valleys of the Alpujarras, to the south of Granada, Ferreirola is a small village very much off the well-beaten tourist track. What Sierra y Mar offers is an interesting combination of language courses with walking tours around the area, and accommodation in the school/hotel for the duration of your stay. This school/small hotel is a converted traditional Alpujarran house (built with thick, rough walls to allow respite from the summer heat and protection from the harsh winter) and is run by two northern Europeans who will provide breakfast. There is room for 18 people in either double or single rooms and there is a guest kitchen where you can cook all your meals. Alternatively, you can visit the bars and restaurants in the town.

The school has about 100 students annually and class sizes are small, at around three or four in each level. There is a minimum age of 16 and courses are suitable for all levels. Lessons take place outdoors and are centred on everyday spoken Spanish. There are four lessons every day and these are mainly scheduled for the morning. Emphasis is on conversation with insights into the music, history and culture of Spain. The courses run from March to September and last from two to five weeks. The costs are 70,000ptas for two weeks, 93,000ptas for three weeks and 112,000ptas for four weeks. One week (available to advanced students only) costs 40,000ptas. These prices all include accommodation at the school. For participation on the course only, the cost is 25,000ptas per week. Private lessons cost 5,000ptas per hour and the extra charge for a single room per week is 7,500ptas. (Please note: these are 1997 prices.)

The leisure activities are really the main attraction of these courses, as they will allow you to discover a magnificent and little known part of Spain. (This could not be further from the beaches of the Costa del Sol). The activities include walks along old mule tracks, mountain hiking in the Sierra Nevada, visits to nearby villages and swimming in the nearby Río Trevélez. In addition to this there is trout fishing and horseback riding. There are also visits to the traditional fiestas that take place in the neighbouring villages at this time of year. Activities such as the guided walking tours cost about 12,000ptas for a full day and 6,000ptas for a half-day.

As people come here purely for the walking holidays as well as for the language school, Sierra y Mar's guests are a combination of students and trekkers. As a result, this is the type of place that will appeal to those who want something less rigid than a traditional language school. It is probably ideal for people who want a more mentally stimulating holiday, but nothing too taxing nonetheless.

LÉON

Universidad de Leon – Cursos de Español Lengua Extranjera

Pabellon de Rectorado, Avda
Facultad 25, 24071 – Leon
Tel: +34 987 291 650/646
Fax: +34 987 291 693
Email: germmc@isidoro
.unileon.es
Website: www.unileon.es/veuri
/cele/cursos
Established: 1956

Level: None
Nearest Station: León
Contact: Bonifacio Rodriguez Diez or Jose Luis Blanco

Capital of the province of Castilla y León, which is located at the most north-westerly tip of Spain, León boasts a rich history, beginning with its foundation as a Roman military camp. Today, its major landmark is the Cathedral, an impressive Gothic structure with beautiful stained glass windows. Since the establishment of its university in 1979, it has also become a lively student town. Despite the university's considerable youth, one of the longest stablished academic activities in this town have been its Spanish courses for foreigners, which started over 40 years ago as an extension of the courses of the Sorbonne in Paris.

There are three types of courses on offer, available at three levels: 'Inicial' (beginners), 'Intermedio' (Intermediate) and 'Superior' (Advanced). Where appropriate, students can be moved up a level. The 'Spanish Language' and 'Culture for Foreigners' course can be attended either for a full academic year or for one of two sessions (October to January or February to June). Fees are 95,000ptas per session and 180,000ptas for the full academic year, with an enrolment fee of 25,000ptas. Lessons take place in the afternoons from 4.30pm to 8pm, allowing students on different programmes to pursue their individual studies in the mornings. The programme involves cultural activities (lectures, films, excursions, Spanish dancing lessons and so on), some of which are included in the fees and some of which are not. A maximum of 150 students are allowed on each course. Students on international programmes such as Erasmus/Socrates will receive a 25% discount. Students are free to make use of the university facilities and there are no more than 15 students in every class.

The summer courses comprise two sessions: one in July and the other in August, and students can sign up for both (an option which is confusingly called "The Full Academic Year"). The fee for a month is 65,000ptas with an enrolment fee of 15,000ptas. For both months the fee is 85,000ptas, with an enrolment fee of 20,000ptas. These courses take place in the mornings, from 9am to 12.30pm, with an additional hour dedicated to lectures, Spanish films or monothematic cultural courses. Also included are outings, sporting activities and fiestas.

Three types of accommodation are available: self-catering, living with a host family and Halls of Residence. Self-catering is available to those students who are at the university for a minimum of four months and involves sharing a flat with other students of any nationality. It will cost about 25,000ptas a month (excluding utilities). Living with a host family will cost from 2,400ptas a day for one person in a double room to 75,000ptas a month in a single room (full academic year students only).

Prices for Halls of Residence vary according to the number of people in each room (up to three) and the type of room; the range is from 540,000ptas to 760,000ptas for the full academic year. An Attendance certificate is issued to students who have attended classes regularly. Students who successfully complete the Final Exam (taken in the last week of the course) will also receive a certificate.

The University of León is an examining centre for the DELE examinations, which students are encouraged to take. Specific Courses in Spanish Language and Culture can be arranged for universities, educational institutions, etc. For more information and enrolment details, contact the university.

LA CORUÑA

Liceo Internacional Agarimo

Valdoncel 20, 1I, 15300
Betanzos, A Coruña
Tel: +34 981 774 667
Fax: +34 981 774 667
Established: 1994
Level: None
Nearest Station: Betanzos de los Caballeros
Contact: Carmen L Villasol

Betanzos is a Galician town dating back to 1219 which, in 1970, was declared Patrimonio Histórico (the Spanish equivalent of National Heritage). The town's full title – Betanzos de los Caballeros – was given to it during the fifteenth and sixteenth centuries when Galicia's highest-ranking families owned houses here. Situated on a bend of the River Mandeo, Betanzos is less than an hour's drive from A Coruña and Santiago de Compostela (European Capital of Culture for the year 2000). The beaches of the Rías Altas Gallegas are 10 minutes away.

Liceo Internacional Agarimo is the only private school in Spain whose courses in Gallego (Galician) have the official seal of approval of the Instituto Cervantes. The school also offers courses in Spanish (Castellano). Courses are grouped under three categories: 'Cursos Intensivos', 'Cursos de Preparación para el DELE' and 'Cursos Específicos'. The 'Intensive' courses (Castellano only) include 20 hours of tuition a week (18,000ptas).

They focus on the communication aspect of language learning, and involve a minimum of two extra-curricular activities such as wine and food tasting, cultural visits, concerts and so on. Students of all levels, from 'Elemental' (beginners) to 'Perfeccionamiento' (Fine-tuning advanced language skills), can join these courses. DELE preparation courses begin two months before the date of the exams and cost 45,000ptas a month for three hours of tuition a day.

Within Cursos Específicos there are four options: courses in 'Galician Culture' (suitable for Spanish speakers only, as lessons are in Spanish), 'Galician for Overseas Students' (which includes preparation for the official exam in Galician), one-to-one classes (3,500ptas per hour) and 'Spanish for Relatives of Emigrants' (i.e. children/relatives of Spanish people who have been brought up in non-Spanish speaking countries). Contact the school for prices.

There is a 5,000ptas registration fee for all courses. This includes a guided tour around the city on your first day, all written materials, use of the library and resource centre, a diploma (which students will receive at the end of their course), at least two extra curricular activities per week, museum entrance fees and transport from the airport to Betanzos. Students with an ISIC card will receive a 50 per cent discount on the enrolment fee.

Family homestays can be arranged via the school. The cost of these range from 18,000ptas a week for one person sharing a double room (half board) to 24,000ptas a week for a single room (full board). The school can provide information about other options such as staying in a country house, apartments and camping.

The minimum age for students is 18. The duration of most courses is from two to three weeks. Contact the school for enrolment details.

MADRID

ACE Consultores de Idiomas

Capitan Haya, 21, 1, 28020 Madrid
Tel: +34 1 555 0800
Fax: +34 1 597 3262
Email: ace.consultor@mad .servicom.es
Established: 1987
Level: None
Nearest Station: (Metro) Cuzco
Contact: Robin Gravina

Located close to Madrid's main business district, Azca, in the north of the capital, the school is situated in a building set back from the main road between two large office blocks. To access it, go through the main entrance of building 21 (on the side of building 22) and take the stairs up to the first floor. This is a school for people who need to learn Spanish for the specific purpose of using it in a business context and it is usually the client company, not the students them-selves, who pays for the lessons. The school calls itself a consultancy and to this end is geared entirely towards busy executives who do not possess the luxury of time and who need to learn specifically business oriented Spanish. Hours are therefore very flexible and based around the client's timetable, rather than the other way around. A measure of the school's success is the fact that many client companies send employees to ACE on a regular basis. A more official seal of approval is that of the European Training Quality System, which is awarded only to institutions whose clients are 80 per cent (or more) satisfied with them. The academy is based on one floor, classrooms are small and there are rarely more than about ten students in the school itself at one time as teachers frequently give lessons in company headquarters or outside of the classroom context.

The school is supplied with students from multinational and domestic companies who send employees who are either about to be transferred to work in Spain or who are already based there. Clients include Marks and Spencer, Citibank, Phillip Morris and Barclays UK. Lessons are tailored around the specific professional needs of each student, whose ages range between mid-20s to late 40s. Students are mainly from

Liceo Internacional Agarimo

the UK, Germany, Sweden and Switzerland and have included the director of the Swedish furnishing company, IKEA. Essentially, students come here with the fundamental objective of learning enough Spanish in order to do their present job in Spain. This means that they require the basic communication skills of listening, reading and speaking in order to make themselves understood by their new Spanish colleagues who, frequently, have a very limited knowledge of English. This is because until recently, the second language in Spain was French.

Students can spend a weekend or up to several months at ACE, depending on whether they are already working in Spain or whether they are on a crash course to prepare them for when they do go out to work there. Students do not receive any diploma as such, as according to Robin Gravina, the real test is when they go out there and actually have to get on with their job, in Spanish. Although the school is officially open from 8am to 8pm, teachers can see busy executives after hours or at the weekend, in such diverse locations as bars, restaurants or a flamenco show, and conduct lessons then. For those who are too busy even for that, classes via telephone are also available. Telephone/fax or email support for students who, having completed a programme have the odd query once they are back at work, is also included in the price of the course.

ACE tend to employ university graduates to whom they give basic teacher training and they seek out people who have been formally trained by the Instituto Cervantes or International House. There are classes in presentation and phone techniques and making the most of limited Spanish and

facilities include video cameras, which are used to film students while they give mock presentations and which are then played back to them. Students can also use the school's telephone system for information gathering exercises, which are recorded for them to listen to afterwards. When ACE was founded 10 years ago, there was a dearth of teaching material for business Spanish, which meant that it created a lot of its own material which is still used in the classes today. All the teachers at the school are urged to constantly create new material for their classes.

Accommodation can be booked via the academy in apart-hotels or with host families. Once you have applied to ACE, they will contact you by phone and fax in order to confirm your booking as well as to give you a level test. Rates are negotiable, depending on the volume of business (i.e., how big the group is or how long you will be studying for). Other languages taught at the school include French, German and Portuguese. A social programme is available and usually involves drinks, tapas or movies with the teachers. Contact the school for enrolment details.

Academia Eureka

Arenal, 6-4d, 28013 Madrid
Tel: +34 91 521 8275
Fax: +34 91 531 4948
Email: eureka@adv.es
Website: www.adv.es/eureka
Established: 1988
Level: None
Nearest Station: (Metro) Sol
Contact: Sr Angel Luis Piñuela Perez
If you aren't put off being in the tourist magnet of Madrid, the one place in Spain where you are almost guaranteed to hear the least Spanish spoken, then

Eureka is ideal. It really is situated in the heart of Madrid, or at least a few metres away from its geographical mid-point – the Puerta del Sol – in an old and completely restored building. The school has about 300 students every year, about half of whom are from Germany, with Europeans making up another 40 per cent and the remainder being Americans and Japanese. Class groups are small, with an average of four and a maximum of six.

Of particular interest to prospective students is the complementary cultural programme available to participants on the 'Intensive' course. Many language schools offer such "extras", but few are as fully comprehensive or as interesting as this. This extensive programme includes trips to all of the most famous sites in Madrid (the Prado et al) as well as to many less well known places of equal historical/cultural significance (the

Student Story

"We have a large number of customers in Spain and language has always been a bit of a barrier because although I speak French and Dutch (my mother tongue), I've never learnt Spanish. I'm at ACE doing the intensive one-to-one course, which involves eight hours of lessons a day (including my lunch hour!) for two weeks. I've only been here for three days, but I feel that there's already been progress and they're definitely giving me as much teaching as I can take. However, I'm really beginning to miss speaking English and would love to find some English speakers to have a bit of normal conversation with. I found out about the school by going to the Spanish embassy, accessing their database of language schools in Spain and coming up with a shortlist of about 20 names. I faxed them all and chose ACE because they had the most professional approach: they called immediately to determine my level of Spanish. I'm staying with a family – a mother and her daughter – in order to immerse myself completely in the language. I would prefer to be in an hotel as it's a bit heavy going. The family speak to me in Spanish only, as does the other student there (from Switzerland). Still, it's what I came here for. I chose to be in Madrid as the Spanish spoken here is probably the most universal and the accent is fairly neutral. I've been to Spain before: to Madrid on business and to the Costas for pleasure. I liked Bilbao and Barcelona but I have no real opinion of Madrid. I do like the food though - makes a change from beans on toast! I've found the people here to be helpful, direct and honest; sometimes extremely blunt in fact. I think the Spaniards view the British as a nation who are inordinately proud of their country and as a people who are diplomatic and polite."

Stephane Rosseneu, Belgium

Academia Eureka

Encarnación Monastery, the Planetarium). Worthy of note, because they are rarely offered, are the visit to the El País to visit the production facilities of Spain's national newspaper; the excursion to the Rastro (Madrid's flea market) and the trip to the Spanish Parliament. Excursions outside of Madrid are also offered.

The school is open all year round, with courses beginning on the first and the fifteenth of every month for those who have no previous knowledge of the language. Others can begin on any Monday and have to take a written and oral level test to be placed in the correct class. At the end of each course the student must take another test, on successful completion of which they will receive a certificate.

There are three types of classes: Intensive (twenty or thirty hours a week), Afternoon classes and One-to-one classes. Intensive classes take place in the mornings and afternoons and prices range from 55,000ptas for two weeks of tuition only (twenty hours a week) to 390,000ptas for 12 weeks of tuition only (thirty hours a week). Additional costs include complementary activities (from 7,500ptas for two weeks to 30,000ptas for 12 weeks), accommodation (from 20,000 for two weeks to 120,000ptas for 12 weeks) and meals (from 15,000ptas for two weeks to 80,000ptas for 12 weeks). The whole package therefore ranges from 97,500ptas for two weeks (20 hours a week) to 620,000ptas for 12 weeks (30 hours a week). Afternoon classes are suitable for those who have less time to spare and who already have a place to stay in Madrid as these students do not benefit from the accommodation or activities programmes. There are three options: five days a week (Monday to Friday), three days a week (Monday and Wednesday) and two days a week (Tuesday and Thursday). The fees for these range from 9,000ptas for two days a week for 2 weeks to 110,000ptas for five days a week for 3 months.

DELE preparation is also available and fees are based on these. One-to-one classes cost from 37,000ptas per week for two hours per day to 145,000ptas for 8 hours a day. These fees include tuition, enrolment and transport from the airport to the academy. Activities, excursions, meals and accommodation are all extra.

Accommodation is available with Spanish families, in studio flats, in apartments, in shared apartments, in hotels, hostels or student residences. Breakfast and lunch are offered at the school from Monday to Friday. Contact the school for enrolment details.

ALBA Language Consulting SL

Avda Pio XII, 3, 28016 Madrid
Tel: +34 91 359 6016
Fax: +34 91 359 4981
Email: 101764.2473@ compuserve.com
Established: 1965
Level: None
Nearest Station: (Metro) Pio XII
Contact: Francisca de Andres

An enthusiastic (though not entirely grammatically correct) approach to marketing characterises the leaflets supplied by this school whose founder, Francisca de Andres, is undoubtedly the driving force behind her empire. There are two Alba centres: in Madrid (head office) and Marbella, and courses are evidently geared towards professionals, employees of large corporations and couples (particularly from the American market, as prices are quoted in dollars as well as pesetas). The school has about 500 students annually, and there are no more than 12 students in each class (summer courses usually), though the average is nearer three to six. The school in Madrid is based in an apartment with seven classrooms in the

north of the capital (a residential area called Chamartín), while the branch in Marbella is a house complete with garden, swimming pool and two large terraces.

Spanish courses come under various categories and are given at four levels: 'Principiantes' (beginners), 'Intermedio' (intermediate), Avanzado (advanced) and 'Superior'. An unusual programme is the 'Teacher at Home' course (Madrid only) which does involve, literally, living and being taught in your teacher's own home, with 15/20 hours of classes a week. The cost per day (half board) is 4,000ptas for Juniors (from 15 to 18 years old) and 6,300ptas for Seniors (from 18 upwards). One-to-one courses (Madrid and Marbella) involve from two to ten hours of individual tuition a day, with options tailor made to each individual's requirements (business Spanish, DELE preparation, etc.) and the possibility of basing the occasional lesson on an activity such as a museum visit. The rate per hour is 4,000ptas, with an additional 5,000ptas for learning material. Accommodation can be arranged with a Spanish family or in a hotel. Preparation for DELE preparation is an option available as part of the Intensive Spanish course (two weeks minimum). The course takes place in Madrid only, beginning on the first Monday of every month, with four hours of lessons a day. Prices range from 90,000ptas for juniors to 210,000ptas for seniors and include homestay with a Spanish family (half board) and learning material.

Summer programmes take place in Madrid and Marbella, with two weeks in each, beginning on the first Monday of either June, July or August. The course involves three hours of lessons daily and the price (215,000ptas) includes homestay with a Spanish family (full-board), the price of the bus trip from Madrid to Marbella, excursions to sites such as Toledo and Ronda and all course material. 'The Triple Winner Programme' (131,250ptas, Madrid only) includes three weeks in Madrid, three hours of tuition a day, three meals a day (full board with a Spanish family), three excursions, three trips to the swimming pool (!) and three cultural and recreational activities in Madrid. Also included in the price are all course materials.

Other courses are the au pair service (ALBA organises the family and the price starts at 16,500ptas for four hours of classes a week per month) and tailor-made programmes, where you provide the structure of your course. ALBA can organise courses for groups of executives as well as groups of friends. Also available are APT (Association for Professional Training) courses, Spanish for Business Professionals and weekend Spanish courses in Chinchón and

Miraflores (from 40,000ptas for one person to 20,000ptas each for a group of three.) There is a course for teachers of Spanish as a foreign language (Didactical course for Spanish teachers – Madrid only), which lasts a week (end of July or August only) and costs 100,000ptas. The fee includes board with a Spanish family.

Contact the school for enrolment details.

Aliseda – Escuelas Internacionales de Español

Goya, 115-3º, 28009 Madrid
Tel: +34 91 309 1176
Fax: +34 91 401 0673
Email: aliseda@correo.com
Website: www.chester.es
/aliseda
Established: 1986
Level: None
Nearest Station: (Metros) Goya
or O'Donnell
Contact: Felipe Martín
With a prospectus including a helpful chart designed to help you decide the

ALBA Language Consulting S.L.

level of Spanish that you realistically wish to achieve (and how long it will take you), Aliseda offers a no-nonsense, professional approach to language learning. It is located in Madrid's exclusive Barrio de Salamanca and claims that its teaching staff are all university graduates with plenty of experience in teaching Spanish as a foreign language. The aim of the school is to get you communicating in Spanish as fluently as possible.

Courses are grouped under five categories and the school caters for eight levels of Spanish competence, from beginners up to higher. Students can be prepared for the DELE exams (Initial, Basic and Higher) or *selectividad (see p240)* (the university entrance exam), the cost for which courses is 45,000ptas. The Intensive Mini-groups (three to eight people, 45,000ptas) involve 50 hours of lessons (two and a half hours a day for a month, Monday to Friday). The personalised intensive Course (97,500ptas per week) is tailored to the timetable of each student. It begins every Monday for a minimum of one week, with four and a half hours of tuition a day and however many hours of assisted study in the school's Resource Centre that the student requires. The tailor-made intensive course is really a variation of the personalised intensive Course, only with greater flexibility: lessons at the weekend, more class hours, lessons in a closed group and so on (price according to course content). One-to-one classes (4,600ptas per hour) can take place from one hour a week and you even have the option of having lessons in your own home. There is a 6,000ptas enrolment fee for all courses in addition to the course fee.

Aliseda has a Student Welfare Department offering students help in finding accommodation, whether in hotels, with host families or in apartments, all as close to the school as possible. A programme of free and reduced-price complementary activities are also on offer. The mix of students at the school is international.

Contact the school for enrolment details.

Carpe Diem Escuela de Español

Fuencarral, 13-1, 28004 Madrid
Tel: +34 91 522 3122
Fax: +34 91 532 8509
Email: car-diem@encomix.es
Website: www.encomix.
es/car-diem
Established: 1997
Level: None
Nearest Station: Gran Vía
Beatriz González García or
Contact: Ester Parra Fuente
This small, friendly school is situated above a shop on a street running off Gran Vía, one of Madrid's most central avenues. It is ideally situated, as Sol (the geographical heart of the city) is only a couple of minutes walk away. Carpe Diem is run by five women, four of whom originally worked at another well-known language school in Madrid; they decided to set up on their own once their contracts there ended. Three of them have degrees in Filología Español (Spanish literature) while the fourth has a degree in Linguistics. The décor of the school is very simple and clean: white tiled floors and white washed walls with the occasional blue stripe painted along the top and the odd poster. The school is all on one floor, there are four classrooms and a hall area where students can stand around and chat during breaks. There is also a drinks vending machine.

The 'Semi-intensive' course includes 20 lessons per week (ten grammar, ten conversation) and starts at 20,000ptas per week. The 'Intensive' course comprises 30 weekly lessons and starts at 30,000ptas. One-to-one lessons cost from 35,000ptas per week and lessons are from two to eight hours per day. The content and cost of the 'Immersion' course depends on the individual needs of the student. The price of courses is reduced the longer a student stays on. The above prices are applicable for the first two weeks of each course.

The school attracts people in the age bracket of about 20 to 30 years of age. There are students of every nationality and in particular, the school seems to attract a large number of Korean and German students. Students are taught with material developed by the founders of Carpe Diem themselves (a grammar book and conversation book). This material is included in the fee. Class sizes are no larger that six and the maximum number of students in the school at any one time is 24.

The school organises excursions outside of the capital to nearby cities such as Toledo, Segovia, El Escorial, Aranjuez and others. They also take advantage of the numerous cultural opportunities available in the city itself and trips to museums and galleries in Madrid also take place. Students can receive emails, mail and faxes at the school and there is a small library at their disposal. Once a week, students can take advantage of free flamenco classes.

Accommodation close to the school can be arranged. The cost of living with a Spanish family is 20,000ptas per week including half board. Courses begin every Monday and daily sessions are from 9.30am to 1pm and from three to 6.30pm. For enrolment details contact the school. Fees include the enrolment fee and materials, lessons, a certificate of attendance and a diploma.

Centre for Cultural Interchange
(Head Office): Hermanos Bécquer, 6-4 izda, 28006

Carpe Diem Escuela de Español

Madrid
Tel: +34 91 564 0162
Fax: +34 91 561 5116
Email: ccisp@genio.infor.es
Website: www.
cci-exchange.com
Established: 1985
Level: None
Nearest Station: Not applicable
Contact: Paloma Ortega

As the name of this organisation suggests, it provides programmes for Spanish people who wish to learn English in either the US or the UK and programmes for English speakers (mainly Americans) who wish to learn Spanish in Spain. It is a non-profit organisation and its aims are, according to its prospectus, to "promote cultural understanding, academic development and world peace through cultural interchange." The majority of its programmes are suitable for Spanish speakers wishing to learn English and these are suitable mainly for younger students spending a school year abroad. There are several programmes for English speakers in Spain: the 'High School Programme in Spain', 'Programs for Spanish Teachers' and 'School Groups and the Independent Homestay Programme in Spain'.

Of these three programmes, only the 'Independent Homestay' programme is suitable for students over 18 years of age.

ENFOREX – Centro de Estudios Internacionales

Alberto Aguilera, 26, 28015
Madrid
Tel: +34 91 594 3776
Fax: +34 91 594 5159
Email: international@enforex.es
Website: www.enforex.es
Established: 1989
Level: None
Nearest Station: (Metro)
Argüelles
Contact: Secretary

ENFOREX is an institution that specialises in designing and organising language courses and providing links and collaborating with language courses in specialist schools around the world. It also helps those who wish to complete a Mini masters or participate in a particular course at various universities outside of Spain. Although it is dedicated mainly to the teaching of languages other than Spanish (predominantly, French, German and English), ENFOREX has a centre for teaching Spanish to overseas students in the heart of the university district of Madrid, with courses available throughout the academic year and the summer months. Courses are aimed at a younger market (university students).

The centre has 28 classrooms and a minimum of six students and a maximum of ten in each group. Hours are very flexible, as the school is open from 8am to 9pm from Monday to Friday and from 8am to 2pm on Saturdays. The summer courses (July, August and September) involve 12 hours of tuition a week at a cost of 31,500ptas (including course material and enrolment fee). The academic year programme runs from October to June and it is possible to join it at any moment of the year. It involves either, three hours of tuition per week at a cost of 6,900ptas per month or 9,900ptas per term or, twelve hours of tuition a week at a cost of 19,900ptas per month or 26,900per term. In addition to these, students may participate, free of charge, in the Friday afternoon conversation classes.

The school will prepare you for the DELE examinations, for which it claims to have a ninety five percent success rate. You can also take one-to-one lessons which can be paid for in lots of ten (3,400ptas per hour), 25 (2,900ptas per hour) or one hundred (2,400ptas per hour).

If you are unable to finance the full course in one payment, ENFOREX can offer a special payment programme. Contact the school for more information and for enrolment details.

Escuela Oficial de Idiomas de Madrid

Jesús Maestro (Avda Islas Filipinas), 28003 Madrid
Tel: +34 91 554 4492
Fax: +34 91 533 5331
Email: eoi-idiomas@med
.servicom.es (CHECK)
Established: 1911
Level: None
Nearest Station: Guzmán el Bueno
Contact: D Francisco Meno

Based in a modern building, on seven floors and with 60 classrooms, this is one of the larger language schools that you are likely to come across. The school's Department of Spanish alone is attended by 1,300 students annually and its provision includes a variety of European languages, Chinese, Japanese, Iraqi and Moroccan. Class sizes are considerably larger than average, with a norm of 20 students and a maximum of fifty. This is probably as basic as Spanish courses get – there's no pampering here, no excursions or "fun"activities. These are language classes, plain and simple, and are probably as good a way as any to acquire the language, whatever your purpose for learning it may be.

The course offered by the Department of Spanish for Foreigners, in line with every other language course provided by the school, is composed of two cycles, the 'Ciclo Elemental' (Elementary Cycle) and the 'Ciclo Superior' (Superior Cycle). The first takes place from October to February and is composed of three modules and the second takes place from February to June and is composed of two modules. In 1996/97, the fee for each module was 9,100ptas.

The courses are entirely language based, with an element of Spanish culture in the higher levels. At the end of each cycle, students will be tested on aural comprehension (15 minutes, 10 points), reading comprehension (30 minutes, 10 points), writing skills (60 minutes, 25 points), grammar (60 minutes, 15 points), vocabulary (20 minutes, 10 points) and oral expression (15 minutes, 30 points). In order to pass the exam, students must achieve a minimum of 60 points, having achieved a minimum of 50 per cent of the pass mark in each module. The content of each course is outlined in the information sent out by the EOIM.

Prior to the course, those students with previous knowledge of Spanish will sit a level test to place them in a class suitable to their level. The school cannot offer help with accommodation and is closed during the month of August. Students who wish to attend the courses must show proof that they have achieved the minimum school qualification (the equivalent of GCSEs).

Contact the school for enrolment details.

Eurocentres Madrid

Paseo de la Castellana, 194, 28046 Madrid
Tel: +34 91 345 3512
Fax: +34 91 345 3513

Email: mad-info@
eurocentres.com
Website: www.eurocentre.com
Established: 1960
Level: None
Nearest Station: (Metro) Plaza
de Castilla
Contact: Javier Lopez de
Ceballos

Stretching from the heart of Madrid up to its northern edge, to the point where the city meets the suburbs, the Paseo de la Castellana is one of the Madrid's longest and most prestigious avenues. This school is located at the top of the Castellana, near the impressive Plaza de Castilla, with its modern fountain and the Torres de Castilla – a pair of buildings (office blocks) that lean towards one other. The school is based in a two-storey building, surrounded by shops and it has nine classrooms equipped with video and audio facilities and a resource centre. Of particular interest is the fact that the school has a policy of not accepting more than 15% of students of the same nationality at any one time. For those who cannot resist the temptation (or feel idiotic not doing so!) of speaking to their fellow countrymen in their common/own language, rather than the language that they are learning, this school may be ideal.

Eurocentres is a non-profit making organisation based in Switzerland, dedicated to the teaching of languages. There are three programmes offered at the school in Madrid: the Curso Intensivo de Español (the Intensive Course); the course for teachers of Spanish and Módulo "Plus", a package deal whereby students on the Intensive course can choose up to two extra modules from a selection of five. The five modules are: 'DELE preparation', 'Art and Museums in Madrid', 'Food and Customs in Spain', 'Business Spanish and Communicating with the Spanish'. It costs from 8,000ptas to do one module for two weeks to 93,600ptas to do two modules for thirteen weeks. If you choose to do two modules, you will receive a 10 per cent discount on both. Each course involves four hours of lessons per week.

Prices for the Intensive course are divided into two categories: the tuition fees on their own (A) or the tuition fees, plus the price of a single room in a house, with half board (B). Prices for the courses vary as to the number of weeks of study (the cost per week is less the greater the length of the course) and it is possible to do certain numbers of weeks only at certain times of the year. A two week course costs 48,600ptas (24,300ptas per week), a 12 week course costs 249,000ptas (20,750ptas per week) and a 34 week course costs 549,200ptas (16,153ptas per week). These fees are for tuition only and their equivalent in the B category is 97,120ptas for two weeks (48,560ptas per week) and 506,920ptas for 12 weeks (42,244ptas per week). The course involves 20 lessons per week and can include preparation for the DELE exams for those who require it. DELE preparation takes place only at certain times of the year, prior to the exams themselves. The course for teachers of Spanish lasts for three weeks in the summer (from July to August) and the cost for 25 weekly lessons is 74,160ptas for tuition fees alone and 142,420ptas for tuition fees and accommodation.

On enrolment, all students automatically become members of the Express Club, the benefits of which include a phone card, a student card and information about trips. Membership to the club also entitles you to take part in

LANGUAGE SCHOOLS

activities such as fiestas (parties), excursions to museums and places of interest in Madrid and outside the city, cultural events and lectures.

Contact the school for enrolment details.

Experimen/Intercambio 66
Fernández de los Ríos, 80, 28015 Madrid
Tel: +34 91 549 3368
Fax: +34 91 544 7962
Email: experiment-inter66@mad.servicom.es
Established: 1932 (Experiment) and 1966 (Intercambio 66)
Level: None
Contact: Pilar Mascaraque

Experiment and Intercambio 66 are two separate organisations. Experiment is the Spanish member of the Experiment in International Living (EIL), a non-governmental organisation. Intercambio 66 is a cultural organisation which, since 1966, has promoted and arranged cultural programmes to and from Europe, the USA and Australia. It offers six different programmes in Spain in various parts of the country and in collaboration with different institutions such as the Universidad Pontificia Salamanca.

Homestays – that is, staying with a Spanish family – are open to participants over the age of 16 (couples will be placed with the same host family). This option does not include language classes of any type, you will simply experience life in a Spanish family and the opportunity to practice and hone your language skills 24 hours a day. You may not necessarily be placed in the city of your choice, but preferences will be taken into account. The prices range from 43,000ptas for one person

for one week to 184,000ptas for a couple for 4 weeks. Each additional day will cost 3,000ptas for individuals and 5,000ptas for couples. It is possible to stay for longer periods, from two months (150,000ptas) to six months (415,000 ptas).

The organisation can arrange for participants to be placed on a language course at one of six different centres throughout Spain. At the Universidad Pontificia of Salamanca, courses cost from 113,000ptas for two weeks to 189,000ptas for four weeks. At Individual Language Study in Seville programme fees, including half board accommodation costing from 96,000ptas for two weeks to 169,000ptas for four weeks. At Instituto de Español Hidalgo 2000 in Valladolid, programme fees range from 93,000ptas for two weeks (20 lessons) to 227,000ptas for five weeks (30 lessons). At Enforex Madrid, prices range from 103,000ptas for two weeks to 183,000ptas for four weeks and include accommodation. At Language Plus in Málaga, prices include accommodation and range from 106,000ptas for two weeks with a family to 480,000ptas for 12 weeks with a family; lodgings in apartments are also available. At the International Summer School in Marbella prices range from 151,000ptas for two weeks to 305,000ptas for six weeks and include accommodation with full board, course materials, activities and health insurance.

Homestay groups provide groups of twenty people or more with the opportunity of living with Spanish families, with additional options of a cultural tour and a Spanish course. This is available in various Spanish cities and any preference will be noted but cannot be guaranteed. Fees for 21+2 days are 120,000ptas and 140,000ptas for 28+2 days.

'Au Pair in Spain' involves 30 hours per week of childcare and light housekeeping and two or three evenings of babysitting. Full board, and 7,000ptas pocket money a week, will be provided by the host family. Applicants must be at least 17 and no older than 30 years of age.

A high school programme and tailormade programmes are also available. For more information and enrolment details, contact Experiment-Intercambio 66.

Hispania Estudio – 2

Santiago, 3-1 dcha, 28013 Madrid
Tel: +34 91 559 3261
Fax: +34 91 559 3261
Email: hispa.estudio.2@ mad.servicom.es
Established: 1991
Level: None
Nearest Station: (Metro) Sol or Opera
Contact: Maria Belén Prieto García

A small school located in the centre of historical Madrid, near the Puerta del Sol, the Plaza Mayor and the Royal Palace, the majority of its students come from Japan, Germany and the UK. Teaching is based on three principals: Listening, Writing and Speaking, with the aim of helping you to use the language in the most grammatically correct way possible.

The school offers five types of courses: One-to-one, 'Standard', 'Intensive', 'Summer' and 'DELE preparation'. All are open all year round, apart from the Summer courses, which are available from July to September. The minimum course length for the 'Standard' and 'DELE preparation' courses is four weeks, for the 'Intensive' course it is one week and for the Summer course it is two weeks. There are no time restrictions on one-to-one courses. The maximum number of students per class is eight (for the Intensive courses) and fees per week range from 7,500ptas for five Standard lessons a week to 25,000ptas per week for the Intensive course (20 lessons per week). Up to four 'One-to-One' lessons cost 3,500ptas per hour; thereafter there is a discount according to the number of classes you sign up for. There is a registration fee of 5,000ptas on all courses. Language courses, including modules such as Spanish History, Spanish Literature and preparation for the entrance exam for Spanish universities (Selectividad), can be arranged on request. Ask the school for details.

Lodging in Spanish families can be arranged. There are three types of accommodation: Bed and Breakfast, Half board and Full board. The price for a single room ranges from 15,960ptas for Bed and Breakfast to 26,880ptas for Full board. For one person sharing a double room the price ranges from 14,280ptas for Bed and Breakfast to 23,100ptas for Full board.

The school provides a programme of complementary activities such as lectures and visits to museums. Excursions can also be organised, at extra cost.

Contact the school for enrolment details.

Instituto de Formación Empresarial de la Cámara Oficial de Comercio e Industria de Madrid – IFE

Pedro Salinas, 11, 28043 Madrid
Tel: +34 91 538 3838
Fax: +34 91 538 3803
Email: ife1@camaramadrid.es
Website: www. camaramadrid.es
Established: 1992
Level: Intermediate level
Nearest Station: (Metro) Chamartín
Contact: Juliana Moreno (+34 1 538 3866)

Claiming to be one of the most prestigious centres for vocational training in the world of business and commerce, IFE has eight centres, of which the language school is one. The courses offered here are oriented solely towards those who wish to learn Spanish for the purpose of using it in a business context and they allow you to sit one of three different exams in Spanish for business purposes. These are: 'Certificado Básico de Español de los Negocios para Extranjeros', 'Certificado Superior de Español de los Negocios para Extranjeros' and 'Diploma de Español de Negocios para Extranjeros'. If you don't understand what any of that means, then these courses aren't for you, as they are suitable only for those with intermediate level Spanish.

The courses offered are 'Español de los Negocios', 'Nivel Certificado' (for students with a basic understanding of the language); 'Español de los Negocios', 'Diploma' (for students with a good command of the language); and 'Titulación de Profesor de Español de los Negocios' – (TEPEN; for teachers of Spanish who wish to specialise in the field of business Spanish. There are two seminars: Seminario para la Preparación de los Exámenes de Español de los Negocios and 'Seminario para Profesores de Español de los Negocios'. All of these take place at various points throughout the year according to the dates of the relevant exam. About five hundred people sit the exams annually, of these sixty have attended these courses. Classes have an average of 25 students and the majority of students come from Germany, the USA and France. All students sit a level test prior to the start of their course. The building in which courses take place has computer laboratories, a library, parking facilities and a canteen. All Business Spanish certificates and diplomas are issued by the Madrid Chamber of Industry and Commerce and the University of Alcalá.

Contact the IFE for more information and enrolment details.

Instituto Hernán Cortés

Diego de León, 16-5, 28006 Madrid
Tel: +34 91 563 4601
Fax: +34 91 563 4526
Email: hernancortes@nauta.es
Website: www.nauta.es/ hernancortes
Established: 1995
Level: None
Nearest Station: (Metros) Nuñez de Balboa or Diego de León
Contact: Laura H Arnal

Hernán Cortés, a near contemporary of Christopher Columbus, was one of the great travellers/adventurers of the fifteenth century. In any case, despite calling itself an institute, this is a language school like many others and it is a member of the ASELE (Asociación para la Enseñanza del Español como Lengua Extranjera). You will find it to the west of the centre of Madrid, in a bustling residential and shopping area that is well connected to the rest of the city by bus and metro.

The centre offers an impressive variety of courses and of particular note are the unusual specialised courses in Spanish for: Tourism, Health Services, Business, Legal purposes, History, Art and Literature and Secretaries. The prices of these courses are the same as for Intensive courses *(see below)*. The prospectus includes a detailed timetable of the topics covered in each course. In Health services, for example, the course covers ten themes, such as contagious diseases, AIDS, internal medicine and surgery. Each of these topics is related to a different grammatical, oral and written activity, as well as a role play situation, such as "Getting to know the patient". These courses are only suitable for students who already have previous knowledge of the language.

The other courses offered are 'Curso General' (General Course), 'Curso Intensivo' (Intensive Course), 'Curso Junior' (Junior Course, suitable for 14 to 17 year olds), 'Curso DELE' (DELE preparation course), Private lessons, Living with a teacher and Courses for professionals. The General Course (20 hours a week) covers the four language skills (speaking, reading, writing and listening) and costs from 46,000ptas for two weeks up to 205,000ptas for 12 weeks (17,500ptas for an extra week). The Intensive Course (30 hours a week) costs from 70,000ptas for two weeks to 302,000ptas for twelve weeks (23,000ptas for an extra week). DELE preparation (20 hours a week) prepares students for the beginners and intermediate exams in May and for the interme-

diate and advanced exams in November. The fees range from 66,000ptas for three weeks to 205,000ptas for twelve weeks (17,500ptas for an extra week). The Teacher Host option (i.e. living with your teacher) allows for total immersion in the language, with the benefit of a teacher to correct your mistakes 24 hours a day, and a programme of one-hour lessons. The fee for this course ranges from 130,000ptas for 20 hours of tuition per week to 180,000ptas for 30 hours of tuition a week. Private tuition costs 3,900ptas per hour. Contact the school for information about tailor-made programmes. In 1997, the school had about 270 students, the majority of them from Italy, Germany and the USA. On average, classes have a maximum of eight students.

Accommodation is available with host families (full or half board) and in student apartments. One week with a family, full board, will cost 25,000ptas (3,900ptas for an additional night) and a student apartment will cost 55,000ptas for the month. An airport transfer service is available at a cost of 6,000ptas. The course price includes all learning materials, a welcome kit, a diploma once you have completed the course, registration fees and a social programme (visits, guided tours, excursions, films, etc)

Contact the school for enrolment details.

Instituto Mangold
Gran Vía, 32-2, Madrid 28013
Tel: +34 91 522 8300
Fax: +34 91 521 5803
Established: 1943
(Mangold)/1960 (Eurocentres)
Level: None
Nearest Station: Gran Vía,
Callao, Sol

Contact: Victor Martinez or Siân Hicks

A member of the Mangold group, which has been going since the 1950's, this school is located right in the heart of Madrid, on one its busiest streets. It is on the second floor of a building that extends the length of the whole block. You get to the school via the entrance next to the Zara shop (a clothes shop). With 500 students annually, and a maximum of ten students per class, this is not as big a school as its counterpart in Barcelona. The school has twenty classrooms, a library, video and video cassettes, a computer room and a language laboratory. The school also gives classes to Spanish students in English, French, Italian, German and Japanese. This branch has just started offering preparation for the DELE examinations.

The school is very flexible as concerns its provision for students of Spanish and will organise private classes if requested. The school offers one to three hours of classes a day or two hours a day on alternate days (Monday, Wednesday and Friday). You can pay for your course per month or per term. Monthly costs range from 16,500ptas for one hour a day to 42,500ptas for three hours a day. Fees per term range from 43,350ptas for one hour a day to 111,600ptas for three hours a day. There is no enrolment fee for students on the Spanish courses.

Accommodation is available in families (half board, which includes breakfast and evening meal). For those who want a bit more freedom, it is possible to simply rent a room with a family. Except for beginners, there are no starting dates and you can begin whenever you wish to, staying for as many weeks as you want. There is a range of age groups, from university students to professionals and there is a cosmopolitan mix of nationalities. The centre itself doesn't organise extra-curricular activities, but it provides flyers for Forocio, an organisation that coordinates get-togethers for foreigners (such as a St Patrick's Day party), as well as weekends away and trips to different parts of Spain.

There is a Mangold school in Barcelona and several Mangold franchises in Valencia.

Instituto Vox

Gran Vía, 59, 28013 Madrid
Tel: +34 91 547 1759
Fax: +34 91 547 2753
Established: 1950
Level: None
Nearest Station: Metros Callao, Santo Domingo and Plaza de España
Contact: Eva Maria Alcalde Diaz

Gran Vía, a main road located behind the Puerta del Sol, is perhaps not one of Madrid's most charming areas, but its location in the centre of the capital is ideal. It was perhaps quite grand once upon a time, but today it is lined with enormous cinemas. In the summer, it is crowded with vacant-looking tourists who have wandered up from the Puerta del Sol. Instituto Vox has been here for almost half a century. Having started out as a Language School, it has gone on to acquire a range of specialist teaching areas such as marketing and advertising, tourism and secretarial skills (all attended by Spanish students).

Three courses are offered here: the Intensive Spanish course for Foreigners (starting every month), Spanish for

Business (starting every month) and the Special Summer course (July, August and September). The first two courses begin on the first of the month and end on the last day of the month. Worthy of note is the fact that the school does not even close at Christmas or during Easter week (the two occasions in the year when the rest of Spain shuts down completely). Courses cater for 4 levels of competence. The Intensive course costs 45,000ptas per month with a fee of 3,000ptas for enrolment at levels one, two and three (9am to 1.15pm Monday to Friday). At level four (5pm to 7pm, Monday to Friday) the course costs 27,000ptas per month, with a fee of 1,500ptas for enrolment. The Business course costs 30,000ptas per month with an enrolment fee of 2,000ptas and the cost of the Special summer course is calculated according to your timetable. There is a maximum of 12 pupils per class.

A programme of cultural and social activities is also available. This includes museum visits, excursions, lectures and film shows. All activities are included in the cost of the course. A certificate is available at a cost of 300ptas; a diploma will set you back 2,000ptas.

Three categories of accommodation are available: family homestays, in student residences (summer only) and in a hostel or one star hotel. Prices range from 1,850ptas per day for bed and breakfast with a family to 3,000ptas per day for full board in a student residence.

Contact the school for enrolment details.

Language Studies International (LSI)

Luchana, 31-1, 28010 Madrid
Tel: +34 91 446 0999
Fax: +34 91 593 3685
Established: 1965
Level: None
Nearest Station: (Metro) Bilbao
Contact: Eugenia Saez Sánchez

Language Studies International is an organisation with language schools in ten countries that has been running for over thirty years. The majority of their schools are based in the UK and this is their only centre in Spain. The school is attended by more than 250 students a year, the majority of them from Germany, Italy and Japan, and the number of students per class is, on average, eight.

There are eight courses on offer at the school in Madrid. The 'Standard 20' (20 hours of lessons per week), 'Intensive 30' (30 hours of lessons per week) and 'Plus' (either one of the above, with five or ten additional private lessons) courses last from two to forty-eight weeks. Students with prior knowledge of Spanish can start on any Monday; there are specific start dates for beginners, which are outlined in the prospectus. The Standard 20 costs 50,000ptas for the first two weeks and 20,000ptas for each week thereafter, up to sixteen weeks. The course is further reduced to 17,000ptas per week from weeks seventeen to forty eight. The 'Intensive 30' costs 70,000ptas for the first two weeks and 23,000ptas for each week thereafter, up to sixteen weeks. The course is further reduced to 19,500ptas per week from weeks 17 to 48. The 'Plus five' costs 40,000ptas for the first two weeks and 20,000ptas for each week thereafter, up to 48 weeks. The 'Plus 10' costs 80,000ptas for the first two weeks and 40,000ptas for each week thereafter, up to 48 weeks.

LANGUAGE SCHOOLS

The DELE preparation course begins in March or September, in order to groom students for exams in either May or November (depending on your level). The cost for this is 293,000ptas for the eleven-week course, and it includes the examination fee. One-to-one courses range from 80,000ptas for 20 lessons per week for one week to 200,000ptas for 50 lessons a week for up to sixteen weeks. The nine-day course involves 82 or 92 one-to-one lessons over nine days, beginning every Saturday, and costs 328,000ptas for 82 lessons and 368,000ptas for 92 lessons. The academic year course costs 466,000ptas for 24 weeks and 636,000ptas for 34 weeks. Students are given thirty hours of lessons per week and have the opportunity to sit the DELE exams (Basic and/or Superior Diplomas).

Three categories of accommodation are available: with a family (15,500ptas a week for bed and breakfast, 23,000ptas a week for half board), in a university residence (full board, summer only, 28,000ptas per week) or in a hotel. Transfer to or from the airport will cost you 5,500ptas. LSI Madrid's programme of activities includes museum visits, flamenco and salsa lessons, excursions to surrounding areas of interest (Toledo, Segovia, etc.) and trips to bars.

Contact the school for enrolment details.

Madrid Plus S.L.
Arenal, 21-6 dcha, 28013 Madrid
Tel: +34 91 548 1116
Fax: +34 91 559 2904
Email: madrid.plus@jet.es
Established: 1990
Level: None
Nearest Station: Metro Opera
Contact: Eugenia Caballero

Part of the Idiomas Plus groups, which also has schools on the Costa Brava and in Málaga, Madrid Plus is attended by about 800 students a year. However, the school's size is not reflected in class numbers, which are kept to an average of about seven, with a maximum of ten. It is situated just off the Puerta del Sol, the tourist centre of the capital, but being on the sixth floor, is far enough removed from the distractions offered below.

There are four courses on offer here: the 'Plus' course (one and a half hours per day), the 'Standard' course (three hours per day), the Intensive course (four and a half hours per day) and Courses in the Evening (three hours per week). 'Plus' courses start at 12,000ptas for one week and last up to 12 weeks (82,000ptas). Standard courses start at 20,000ptas for one week and last up to 12 weeks (144,000ptas). Intensive courses start at 25,000ptas for one week and last up to 12 weeks (204,000ptas). Courses in the evening range from 10,000ptas for four weeks to 26,000ptas for 12 weeks. An enrolment fee of 3,000ptas must be paid for each course. This is deducted when the total amount for eight and 12-week courses is paid in one go. Individual tuition is also available, as is preparation for the DELE exams.

Accommodation is available in apartments, with families (single rooms only) and in hotels. The cost of staying in an apartment ranges from 32,000ptas for one person in a double room for two weeks to 252,000ptas for 12 weeks in a single room. Family homestays range from 51,000ptas bed and breakfast for two weeks to 396,000ptas for 12 weeks at half board. A room in a hotel will range from 86,000ptas for one person in a double room for two weeks to 240,000ptas for four weeks in a single room. There will be weekly surcharges of 4,000ptas in high season and 6,000ptas in low season.

The school's programme of activities includes dinners, parties, discos, visits to the cinema and excursions to areas of interest outside of Madrid such as El Escorial. At the end of the course, each student receives a certificate.

Contact the school for enrolment details.

Paraninfo

Princesa, 70, 28008 Madrid
Tel: +34 91 543 3139
Fax: +34 91 544 9787
paraninfo@mundivia.es
Website: www.empresas.
mundivia.es/paraninfo
Established: 1975
Level: None
Nearest Station: (Metro)
Argüelles
Contact: Dominique Rousset

Paraninfo is situated on the corner of a long and busy shopping street in the west of the capital, a two minute walk away from one of the larger branches of Spain's most famous department store, El Corte Inglés. At 9am in the morning it is packed with traffic and people on their way to work and throughout the day is crawling with people. Located on one floor of the building, the school is composed of language classrooms, two computer rooms and a typing room. The school possesses 23 computers, testament to the fact that computer courses have now begun to take over from the language classes which were once all that were taught here. Indeed the teaching of Spanish to foreigners now only represents a small part of the school's business.

Paraninfo is run by a French woman, Dominique Rousset, one of the founders of the school, who moved to Spain over 20 years ago and who teaches French at the school. Students of Spanish at the school are usually au pairs, aged between 18 and 23, who are in Spain for the year. Other students are Japanese and German professionals in their mid-30s who have been posted to Spain and who attend the school for a couple of years, bringing their wives along with them.

The school prepares students for the DELE ('Diploma de Español como Lengua Extranjera') exams. Since 1991 it has also been a member of and examining centre for the ERASMUS/SOCRATES scheme run by the University of Granada. For this, students take an oral exam (10mins) that is assessed directly by the teachers at Paraninfo, and a written exam (1 hour 30mins) which is sent off to the University of Granada to be marked. Students can also receive the school's own diploma at the end of their course.

Accommodation can be arranged in the homes of Spanish families (the most popular option amongst students) and the school has contact with certain families to whom it sends students on a regular basis. It also has links with a special accommodation service called Room Madrid (see p.31), which helps foreign students to find Spanish flatmates with whom they will have something in common. To this end, they conduct a personality test and match your details up with similar Spanish people.

As the school also gives lessons in languages and computer skills to Spanish people, overseas students will have the chance to study alongside native speakers themselves negotiating a new language. There are plenty of opportunities to meet Spanish speakers and students with a fairly good level of Spanish can participate in the computer courses. At intermediate level, overseas students can also take lessons in writing business letters and the language of business and finance. The school caters both for those who wish to have private lessons and larger groups, though class sizes are never larger than eight people. A number of Japanese companies send there employees here and these groups are usually no larger than four people. Of the 320 students at the school, about 20 per cent are there to learn Spanish.

Paraninfo organises day excursions to surrounding areas, such as Toledo, and longer weekend visits to Granada and Seville. It is open from 9am to 9pm every weekday and the usual hours for those learning Spanish are 11am to 12pm and 4pm to 7pm. There is a 10 per cent discount for groups of 15 people or more. These are then divided into smaller groups for teaching purposes.

There is a 3,000ptas registration fee. For further enrolment details, contact the school.

Sampere Estudio Internacional

Lagasca, 16, E-28001 Madrid
Tel: +34 91 431 4366
Fax: +34 91 575 9509
Email: estudiointer.sampere
@mad.sevicom.es
Website: www.worldwide.edu
/spain/eis/index.html
Established: 1956
Level: None
Contact: Paloma Rodero

There are four Sampere centres, three in Spain (Madrid, Salamanca and El Puerto de Santa Maria – near Cádiz), and one in Ecuador. The majority of students come from the USA, Germany and Sweden and class size averages are between six and eight, with a maximum of nine students. The minimum age is 17 and Spanish is taught at seven levels, from beginners to advanced. The Sampere brochure is slick, glossy and aimed at a twenty-something market, with a helpful checklist of the reasons why you should choose each city as a place to work and play. The great advantage of studying with this group of schools is that on some courses you have the option of centre-hopping: that is, studying in each centre for the same price as staying in one.

Sampere offers an impressive provision of ten different courses, plus a DELE preparation course. The Intensive involves twenty lessons per week in small groups and various social activities. It costs from 49,000ptas for two weeks to 210,000ptas for twelve weeks. 'Español para Siempre' (Spanish Forever) is a three month or Semester (sixteen week) course which involves preparation for the DELE examinations and includes the possibility of staying in all three Sampere centres in Spain. The courses cost 192,000ptas for three months and 240,000ptas for the Semester. 'Español Aqui y Alli' is a combined course based on the same concept as the Intensive course, but allowing students to study in more than one Sampere centre. The price is the same as the Intensive course (transfer between each centre is not included) and you pay for as many weeks as you are enroled for, regardless of where you are studying. The Grupo 5 programme is suitable for anyone who needs to learn Spanish in a short space of time (professionals, university students and so on) and is available at Madrid centre only. The course involves twenty or thirty lessons per week with a maximum of five students in each group (hence the name) and are suitable for all students up to Advanced I level. The cost ranges from 60,000ptas for 20 lessons a week for two weeks to 144,000ptas for 30 lessons a week four weeks. The 'Commercial and Business Spanish course' (Madrid only) involves 30 lessons a week, with 20 classes devoted to learning business and commercial formalities, and 10 language lessons. This course lasts for two weeks only and costs 80,000ptas.

The 'Super Intensive' course is a hybrid of the Intensive course combined with ten lessons per week in mini groups. It is not available at any of the centres in July and August or in Salamanca in June. The price for this is 80,000ptas for two weeks (35,000ptas for an additional week). 'Total Immersion ('One-to-one') (Madrid only) is aimed at gaining the basic language skills in as short a time as possible and each student can tailor the length and intensity of the course to meet their own requirements. Fees range from 87,000ptas for twenty lessons in one week to 700,000ptas for forty lessons a week for four weeks. Courses for DELE preparation take place at all three centres in Spain (not in Ecuador). A course in Teaching Spanish as a Foreign Language is available at El Puerto; contact the school for more information. A more deluxe language course, involving golf lessons, four lessons a day and accommodation in a 4 star hotel, is also available at El Puerto from October to March. The cost for one week is 295,000ptas, with an additional 10,000ptas or 15,000ptas for transport from Jerez or Sevilla airports respectively. Junior courses (14 to 16 year olds) take place in Salamanca in June and July.

A variety of accommodation options are available and prices differ according to location. As an illustration, a student room costs 45,000ptas for four weeks in Madrid, 30,000ptas for four weeks in Salamanca and 15,000ptas a week in low season and 22,000ptas a week in high season at El Puerto. Airport transfers are available, at extra cost.

For more information about the centre in Ecuador and for enrolment details, please contact the school.

Universidad de Alcalá de Henares

Universidad de Alcalá, Cursos de Lengua y Cultura Españolas para Extranjeros, Plaza de San Diego, s/n, 28801 Alcalá de Henares (Madrid)
Tel: +34 91 885 4089
Fax: +34 91 885 4089/4126
Email: cursos.extranjeros@ cele.alcala.es
Established: 1988
Level: None
Nearest Station: Alcalá de Henares
Contact: Fernando Fernández Lanza/Juan Carlos Izquierdo Villaverde

One of Spain's oldest universities, the university of Alcalá de Henares was founded in 1293. The town of Alcalá de Henares is most famous for being the birthplace of the country's best known novelist, Cervantes. It is situated just outside Madrid, and is only half an hour away from the centre of the capital by train (trains run every 10 to 15 minutes). Since then, the university has attracted a great many of Spain's well known literary figures, such as Lope de Vega and Quevedo. One thousand or so students who come to learn Spanish at the university every year. Students of all nationalities attend – Swedish, Taiwanese, German, Brasilian, American, Japanese, English, etc.

The courses offered by the university cover a comprehensive range of options. In July and August only, there are the 'Intensive Courses in Spanish Language and Culture' which cost 90,000ptas per course for five hours of tuition a day. The Intensive Course in Spanish Language runs in the months of May, June and September and costs 70,000ptas. The termly courses in Spanish Language and Culture run from January to March, April to June and October to December. The cost for these is 110,000ptas. The year-long course in 'Spanish Language and Literature' runs from October to June and costs 260,000ptas. The above courses cover all levels from elementary to superior and run for four hours a day (except for the Intensive Course in Language and Literature). There is a 30,000ptas booking fee for all courses.

Special courses in Spanish Language, Hispanic Studies, Business Spanish and other areas are available and can be tailored to your specific requirements or those of your group. They are suitable for all levels of Spanish. The person-alised one-to-one programme costs 6,000ptas per hour and can also be tailor made to the requirements of the individual. The personalised programme for preparation for certificates and diplomas in business Spanish also cost 6,000ptas per hour and cover the Basic Certificate, the Superior Certificate and the Diploma. All these courses run throughout the year.

The course for teachers of Spanish who wish to learn the latest methods runs during the month of August and costs 70,000ptas for four hours a day, with a maximum of 20 teachers in one class. The booking fee is 30,000ptas. The courses to prepare you for the DELE examinations take place three weeks before the examination dates in May and November and last two weeks. The price is 35,000ptas for four hours a day, plus a booking fee of 30,000ptas. The course is suitable for students at Basic and Superior levels.

No prior knowledge of Spanish is necessary to attend the courses, but you must be over 16 years of age. Classes are never have more than 15 students at any one time. As a student of the university's courses for overseas students, you will have the opportunity to sign up for health insurance costing 2,500ptas per month.

Contact the university for enrolment details.

Universidad Antonio de Nebrija – Centro de Estudios Hispánicos

Pirineos, 55, 28040 Madrid
Tel: +34 91 311 6602
Fax: +34 91 311 6613
Email: cehi@dii.unnet.es
Website: www.unnet.es
Established: 1985
Level: None
Nearest Station: Metro Metro-politano
Contact: Christine Jensen/Marina Español

A private Spanish university, the Universitas Nebrissensis (UNNE) spe-cialises in the fields of law, business studies, computer studies, journalism, PR and advertising and English. It also participates in a range of international exchange programmes with other European and American universities. The university has two campuses. The Dehesa de al Villa campus is in the north of the capital, on the edge of Moncloa – the "studenty" area of Madrid. The La Berzosa campus is located in the mountains, 28 kilometres northwest of the city. The Nebrissensis has been offering Spanish language courses at its Centro de Estudios Hispánicos since its foundation in 1985 and has links with several British universities, such as the University of Northumbria, which send Spanish students there during their third year. Antonio de Nebrija was responsible for publishing the first grammar book for a romance language, Gramática de la Lengua Española, in 1492.

There are two types of courses on offer – International University Programmes and Spanish Language and Culture Programmes. The former are suitable for university students only, but it isn't necessary to belong to one of the participating universities in order to take part in them. There are four different courses available with this option: the Spanish Studies Programme, the Spanish and International Relations Programme, the Spanish and Business Programme and the Spanish in Spain, summer term programme. The first three are available for one or two semesters and the last only takes place in June and July. As well as language classes, they all include modules in a variety of topics such as Translation Techniques, Business and Legal Spanish, The Golden Age in Spanish Literature, The Contemporary Spanish Novel, Current Spanish Politics, A Survey of Spanish History, Spain and the European Union and so on. (Consult the prospectus for the complete list.) These cost 325,000ptas per semester with an additional 45,000ptas for the Optional Intensive Course.

The 'Spanish Language and Culture Programmes' offers four possibilities: the intensive course, the general course, the annual course and the summer course. These cost from 84,000ptas for the intensive course (80 hours of lessons over four weeks) to 398,200ptas for the Annual course running from the beginning of September to the end of May. Summer courses cost 86,000ptas for one month (June or July) and 165,000ptas for the two combined. The courses cover both Spanish language and culture, with classes offered at four levels: beginners, intermediate, advanced and superior.

Complementary activities included in the cost of the course included lectures, film shows and guided tours around Madrid. Activities for which the student must pay extra are excursions outside of the capital (Toledo, Segovia, etc.) and sports. Accommodation is available in Spanish families (from 50,000ptas per month, room only), university residences (100,000ptas per month, full board) and in apartments and hotels.

Contact the university for enrolment details.

Universidad Complutense de Madrid – Cursos para Extranjeros
Facultad de Filosofía y Letras (Edificio A), Universidad Complutense, Ciudad Universitaria, 28040 Madrid
Tel: +34 91 394 5325
Fax: +34 91 394 5336
Established: 1960s
Level: None
Nearest Station: Ciudad Universitaria
Contact: Marifrán Cuerpo

My personal experience of the courses at

this, Madrid's most revered university, was rapidly cut short due to the fact that they do not accept Eurocheques. This was, perhaps, a blessing in disguise as I realised (too late) that it was the wrong place to be in the summertime. On reflection, why else would such a lovely city be abandoned by its inhabitants during July and August? Madrid was like a furnace and for some reason, all the university outdoor pools had been drained and the minute rooms in the university residences were not air conditioned. I was left to find my own way around the university campus and in general, received very little direction from the course organisers. While I was there, the Madrid equivalent of the London Underground Circle line - which links the university to the rest of the city – had not yet been completed, which meant that the city was difficult to access from the campus and vice versa. The situation today – at least transport wise – is much improved. The Circular has now been completed, so that you can reach the campus from the centre of the city within 15 minutes.

Summer courses are not the only provision offered by the Complutense and there can be no doubt that Madrid is one of the most interesting and exciting cities in which to study throughout the rest of the year. There are nine courses in total, of which four – 'Intensivo I and II' and 'General and Advanced Courses in Spanish Language and Culture' -take place in July. The remainder are: 'Otoño' (Autumn, Oct to Dec), 'Invierno' (Winter, Jan to Mar), 'Primavera' (Spring, April to June), 'Intensivo de Primavera' (Spring Intensive, April to May, four weeks) and the 'Curso de Estudios Hispánicos' (Spanish Studies Course lasting a full academic year). The 'Otoño' (Autumn), Invierno (Winter), 'Primavera' (Spring) courses all involve compulsory language classes that take place from 3pm to 6pm from Monday to Friday. An optional 'Cycle of Hispanic Culture' that takes place every afternoon after these lessons. The 'Intensive Spring' course involves Spanish language classes only, with 'Practical Spanish', 'Spanish Texts', 'Conversation' and 'Language Laboratory' classes taught by Philology graduates training for their Masters in Teaching Spanish as a Foreign Language. A good command of Spanish is required for students attending the Hispanic Studies course, which involves lectures in seven areas (Language, Literature, History, Art History, Spanish Texts, Geography and History of Spanish Thought) in Spanish, given by professors from the Complutense's Faculty of Arts.

Before the start of certain courses, students will have to sit a level test. Activities and excursions are organised and have to be paid for in addition to the course fee. Fees range from 50,000ptas for the 'Intensive Spring' course to 140,000ptas for the 'Hispanic Studies' course. Certificates are awarded on successful completion of the end-of-course exams. Help in finding accommodation is offered to students on the summer courses.

Contact the university for enrolment details.

Universidad Internacional Menéndez Pelayo

Isaac Peral, 23, 28040 Madrid (until June 20th) and Avda de los Castros s/n, 36005 Santander (June 20th to Sept 20th)
Tel: +34 91 544 8374/592 0600 (Madrid); +34 42 360 055 (Santander)
Fax: +34 91 543 0897 (Madrid); +34 42 280 816 (Santander)

Email: se@extra.uimp.es
Website: www.uimp.es/uimp
Established: 1932
Level: None
Nearest Station: Santander
Contact: Yolanda B Temprano

Santander, an elegant town on the north coast of Spain, comes alive in the summer when it plays host to an International Music, theatre and dance festival and the town's own piano competition. This is a particularly beautiful part of the peninsula, noted for the contrast between its beaches and the Picos de Europa (a mountain range). The Universidad Internacional is based on three sites. One, the Palacio de la Magdalena, was built at the end of the last century and has been completely restored outside, with modern facilities within and is dramatically situated on a cliff overlooking the sea. The Residencia de la Playa, not far from the Palacio, is where Spanish students and overseas students live during the academic year. The third campus – Las Llamas – is where the courses for overseas students take place during the summer. Until recently, Spanish courses for foreigners only took place in the summer however, the university has just instigated an academic year programme, that runs from January to June. The university is known not only for its Spanish summer courses, but also for summer courses for Spanish students. Every summer about five thousand students attend courses in either category, with one thousand students for the Spanish courses alone.

The course in Spanish as a foreign language is organised according to level (elementary, intermediate, advanced and higher) and there is a maximum of eighteen students in each class. At Elementary level the course includes Spanish language, phonetics and language laboratory, written comprehension and expression and aural/oral practice. At Intermediate level students move on to conversation, literature, contemporary history of Spain and politics, economics and society in Spain today. The core content is similar for students at advanced and higher levels, with the introduction of a module in translation. There are 25 hours of lessons per week. Students can sit an optional exam to receive a Certificate in Spanish. Students at advanced level who pass this as well as the examination in literature, history and art are awarded the Diploma on Hispanic Studies.

Courses take place in two week modules at a fee of 27,500ptas each; for four weeks the cost is 55,000ptas and the optional examination costs 3,000ptas. Special conditions are available for group registration and courses can be attended for up to five months. Students can opt for cultural activities folk dancing and trips to the Picos de Europa, Burgos, Madrid and the south of France.

There are four accommodation options. To stay in the halls of residence at the university's Las Llamas Campus will cost 90,000ptas a month (full board). Family accommodation costs from 30,000ptas a month for bed and breakfast (65,000ptas full board). A single room in an apartment will cost 35,000ptas a month and (30,000ptas for one person sharing a double room). Bed and breakfast at Hotel-Residencia Aragón will cost 65,000ptas a month for one person sharing a double room.

Contact the university for enrolment details.

LANGUAGE SCHOOLS

MÁLAGA

Al-Andalus, S.C.

Herrera, 12, 29017 Málaga
Tel: +34 95 229 1741
Fax: +34 95 220 3785
Email: Under construction
Website: Under construction
Established: 1980
Level: None
Nearest Station: Málaga
Nearest Airport 'Picasso'
Contact: Josefa Almoguera
Sánchez/Ilse Vink

The birthplace of arguably Spain's greatest artist, Picasso, Málaga is situated on the South coast of the Iberian Peninsula. This school is located in Pedregalejo, an old fishing village that has been engulfed by the city but which still retains its charm. It is small, with a maximum of fifty students in high season and 15 to 20 out of season, the majority of whom come from Switzerland and Central Europe. The teachers all have university degrees and experience of teaching Spanish to foreigners. Each group has no more than eight students.

The provision here is fairly standard, with five courses ('Standard', 'Intensive', 'Super Intensive', 'Summer and Courses for Teachers') and a limited programme of complementary courses (cookery, sevillanas, art, literature, history and business Spanish). The fees for the 'Standard' course (four hours a day) range from 40,000ptas for two weeks to 295,000ptas for 24 weeks. The 'Intensive' course (five hours a day) cost an additional 7,000ptas per week and the 'Super Intensive' course (six hours a day) cost an additional 13,000ptas per week. The Summer course (three hours a day) cost from 32,000ptas for two weeks to 118,000ptas for twelve weeks.

Preparation for DELE is categorised as a complementary course (i.e. it is taken in addition to one of the above) and costs 3,500ptas for 3 hours of tuition per week. The other complementary courses range from 17,000ptas to 20,000ptas (Cookery) per week. Private tuition is available at 3,000ptas per hour and the course for teachers of Spanish (four hours a day) costs 50,000ptas for two weeks. Tailormade courses can be arranged on request.

Accommodation can be arranged by Al-Andalus and will be no more than 15 minutes walk away from the school. You can choose between family homestays and shared apartments. The cost of living with a family ranges from 25,000ptas for one person sharing a double room for two weeks to 72,000ptas for a single room for four weeks. One person sharing a room in an apartment will have to pay 20,000ptas for two weeks and a single room in a shared apartment for four weeks will cost 36,500ptas. These will cost 15 per cent more in June, July and August

A variety of activities are organised, including beach volleyball with fellow students and Spaniards, bar hopping, fiestas at the school, films and excursions. Contact the school for enrolment details. Al-Andalus is a member of AEEA (Asociación de Escuelas de Español de Andalucía) and of ASELE (Asociación para la Enseñanza de Español como Lengua Extranjera).

Centro de Estudios de Castellano

Avda Juan Sebastian Elcano, 120, Málaga 29017
Tel: +34 95 229 0551
Fax: +34 95 229 0551
Email: ryoga@arrakis.es
Website: www.arrakis.es

/~ryoga
Established: 1960
Level: None
Nearest Airport: 'Picasso'
Contact: F Marin Fernández

Situated 70 metres away from the beach in the residential area of Pedregalejos. The school building is a typical Spanish "chalet" (a villa, rather than the cosy wooden edifice that British people associate with skiing holidays) surrounded by gardens. CEC is attended by about twenty to thirty students at any one time. The majority of students come from Germany, Switzerland, the USA and the UK and the minimum age is 16.

Since 1960 the school has been entirely dedicated to teaching Spanish to foreigners. It offers a simple course at several levels, without any gimmicks or fancy names – four hours of tuition a day for any number of weeks. There are four levels of competence: preparatory, elementary, intermediate and advanced and the school can prepare you for the DELE examinations. There are never more than six students in each class and lessons take place between 9am and 1pm from Monday to Friday. The areas studied are grammar, vocabulary, conversation, translation, reading, business Spanish and Spanish topics. At the end of the course, students will either receive a Diploma (if they have successfully passed the end of course exam) or a certificate of attendance. Course fees range from 30,000ptas for two weeks to 185,000ptas for 16 weeks and prices include course materials. Private lessons are available and cost 2,500ptas per hour.

The course is available throughout the year and begins at the beginning of each month. Accommodation is available with families (half and full board), apartments and in shared flats, all within walking distance of the beach and the school. Full board with a Spanish family costs 65,000ptas per (single) and 60,000ptas per person in a double room for a month. Flatshares with other students from CEC costs 30,000ptas for a single room and 25,000ptas for a

Student Story

"This is the third summer in a row that I've taken part in the courses at Al-Andalus. I keep coming back because I like to combine studying and meeting people of other nationalities while having a holiday. The lessons are interesting and varied – we read newspaper articles, watch videos and listen to tapes, all of which lead to general discussions about current affairs in Spain and Spanish culture. I have stayed with the same family every time I've been here in order to understand Spanish customs properly. The mother cooks me different dishes every day and at fiesta time she cooks food that is like manna from heaven it's so good! Afterwards, she's only too happy to give me the recipes so that I can take them home with me. It has been wonderful to visit the nearby villages (pueblos blancos) and to get a real taste of Hispano-Arabic culture."

Lise Mosbek Gade, Al-Andalus

Centro de Estudios de Castellano

double room per month. Your own, self-contained and furnished apartment will cost 50,000ptas for a month. A deposit of 20,000ptas is required if the school is arranging accommodation for you.

Colegio Maravillas

Avda la Paloma, 1, 29630 Benalmadena
Tel: +34 95 244 7000
Fax: +34 95 244 7377
Email: maravillas@raronet.es
Website: www.eel.es/ maravillas/
Established: 1978
Level: None
Nearest Airport: 'Picasso'
Contact: Paola Vecchi

Benalmadena, once a fishing village, is now a small town situated at the foot of the Mijas mountain range. It has evidently become something of a modern resort and among its attractions are a newly built marina and a number of eighteen-hole golf courses. This language school is part of a private school for Spanish students that was founded in 1976, and courses are mainly geared towards adults, though it also runs a programme for school groups (Mini Stay) and one for teenagers. There are seven classrooms, all of which possess air-conditioning and audio-visual equipment. As with all other schools in this part of Spain, Colegio Maravillas' proximity to the beach means that these courses are ideal for those who wish to combine a holiday with language learning. The school is attended by approximately 600 students annually and these come mainly from France, Scandinavia and Austria. All classes have an average of about seven students.

There are 10 programmes on offer, the longest being the Academic year course (one to three terms), which takes place at the Spanish secondary school and is suitable for 15- to 18-year olds. There is also a one to two week course for teachers (summer only, 15 hours per week, 48,000ptas for two weeks). The school's 'general' course lasts from one to 48 weeks at a cost of 12,000ptas for one week to 44,000ptas for four weeks (10 hours a week). The Intensive course (twenty hours per week) costs from 22,000ptas for one week to 66,500ptas for four weeks. The 'Executive' course (30 hours a week) includes 10 one-to-one lessons a week and costs from 52,000ptas for one week to 180,000ptas for four weeks. The Business course/Group Company programme is designed for groups of up to four employees from the same company and cost from 50,000ptas for two students at 10 hours per week up to 252,000ptas for four students at 40 hours per week. All of the above begin every Monday and last up to 48 weeks. Private lessons cost 3,300ptas per hour.

The Examination preparation course for DELE lasts for six weeks, with 25 hours of tuition a week at a cost of 125,000ptas. The DELE preparation course involves twenty hours of group lessons and five extra lessons per week focused on work for the exam. The cost for these five additional hours is 35,000ptas for six weeks. The cost for long-term intensive courses ranges from 95,000ptas for six weeks to 224,000ptas for 16 weeks.

Accommodation is available in four different options – host family, aparthotel (two- or three-star) and hotels. There are two price categories – high and low season. These range from 21,500ptas a week in a host family (bed and breakfast) to 42,000ptas for half board in a hotel, at high season. Out of season, the cost ranges from 21,500ptas for one week with a host family (bed and breakfast) to 28,800ptas for half board in a three-star hotel. There is also the possibility of flatsharing with other students; for one person sharing a twin bedroom the cost is 17,500ptas out of season, rising to 24,500ptas at high season.

An organised activity programme is part of the school's provision and this includes sports, visits to places of cultural interest, a one-day excursion to Ronda, Granada or Seville and evening activities such as bowling. Contact the school for enrolment details.

Escuela de Idiomas "Nerja" S.L.

Almirante Ferrándiz, 73, Apdo Correos 46, 29780 Nerja (Málaga)
Tel: +34 95 252 1687
Fax: +34 95 252 2119
Website: www.idnerja.es
Established: 1980
Level: None
Nearest Station: Málaga
Nearest Airport 'Picasso'
Contact: Luis Carrión or Renate Urban

A resort on the Costa del Sol, Nerja is not as much of a magnet for British tourists as other places in this infamous and much-maligned part of Spain. It has a number of British-run pubs and English bookshops which, provided you show some will power and avoid them, should not have a detrimental effect on your attempts to learn Spanish. Escuela de Idiomas Nerja is situated in the centre of the town, in a pretty whitewashed building surrounded by gardens that provide an informal setting for lessons. The school has 12 classrooms, a library and cafe. All teachers are graduates in *filología* (Spanish language and literature).

The school offers seven different courses including a most unusual option: courses for people in retirement. These are aimed at the growing market of non-Spaniards (Germans and British people) who have chosen to spend their retirement in the sun. The course lasts two weeks and includes thirty lessons, a one-day excursion to Granada, a Spanish cookery class, a lesson in sevillanas, a showing of a Spanish film and medical insurance. It costs 49,000ptas.

The Intensive course costs from 46,000ptas for two weeks to 300,000ptas for 24 weeks and is a general language and culture course with twenty hours of classes per week. Beginners start on particular dates; those with prior knowledge of Spanish can start on any Monday. The Intensive one-to-one course is geared towards professionals who need to learn Spanish in one short, intensive burst. You can study from one to four weeks, for four, six or eight hours daily (Courses C, B and A). For two weeks, Course A costs 320,000ptas, course B costs 240,000ptas and course C costs 160,000ptas. The Grupo 5 course is an intensive course for university students and professionals who need to acquire the language fast. The emphasis of the classes is on conversation, with thirty hours of classes a week in groups no bigger than six. Courses cost from 80,000ptas for two weeks to 520,000ptas for 24 weeks. Beginners start on particular dates; those with prior knowledge of Spanish can start on any Monday. The refresher course for teachers begins once a month from March to September and costs 53,000ptas for thirty hours of classes. The Business Spanish course is designed for those who already have a certain level of Spanish and provides students with the opportunity to sit the Exams of the Spanish Chamber of Commerce. There are four course start dates in March, May, June and October, in line with the four different exam dates. The course lasts two weeks, with thirty hours of lessons a week and a maximum of ten students in each group. The cost for the course is 85,000ptas; the exam fee is 14,000ptas. The school's DELE preparation course involves the intensive course (four hours a day) plus one hour of individual tuition per day. The course costs the equivalent of the Grupo 5 course.

All fees include course materials, a level test at the start of each course, activities, continuous assessment, certificates and diplomas. At the school you can watch Spanish films, take flamenco lessons and take part in lectures and parties. Health insurance is also included. Accommodation can be arranged either with Spanish families or in flat shares with other students.

Contact the school for enrolment details.

Escuela Mediterráneo

Marqués de Guadiaro, 4, 29008 Málaga
Tel: +34 95 221 3448
Fax: +34 95 222 9903
Established: 1985
Level: None
Nearest Station: Málaga
Nearest Airport: 'Picasso'
Contact: Pilar Martín Martínez

Less of a tourist magnet than other places on the Costa del Sol, Málaga was founded about two thousand years ago. This school is located in a pedestrianised area in the old part of the city, which is only ten minutes away from the beach by bus. It is small, with 150 students annually, the majority of them northern Europeans. There are five classrooms, all on one floor, and there are about five students (on average) in every lesson.

The school offers 'General' courses (four hours of tuition) at four levels (beginners to superior) and the prices for these range from 33,500ptas for two weeks to 190,000ptas for 16 weeks (additional week, 14,000ptas). There are specific start dates for each course in every month of the year. You have the option of paying for the course on its own or the course plus accommodation. There are four possibilities available ranging from a one person sharing a double room in an apartment (53,500ptas for two weeks, including the course) to a single room in a Spanish family (71,500ptas for two weeks, including the course).

The other course options available are Super Intensive courses and the Commercial Spanish course. The Intensive course (six hours a day) alone costs 60,000ptas for two weeks and 108,000ptas for four weeks. With accommodation the prices range from 82,000ptas for one person sharing a double room in an apartment for two weeks to 177,000ptas for a single room in a Spanish family for four weeks. The Commercial Spanish (four hours) course alone costs from 44,000ptas for two weeks to 75,000ptas for four weeks. With accommodation the prices range from 66,000ptas for one person sharing a double room in an apartment for two weeks to 144,090ptas for a single room in a Spanish family for four weeks. Private lessons cost 2,750ptas per hour.

The school organises holiday courses, which take place during the various fiesta dates throughout the year (e.g. Easter (Semana Santa) or the Feria de Málaga) and which also offer the opportunity to relax in the sun and enjoy a bit of a break. Contact the school for more information.

Other activities offered by the school include flamenco lessons – 5,000ptas for nine hours, and excursions from 3,500ptas. There is a 10 per cent discount for students in possession of a valid student card.

Instituto de Español Picasso

Plaza de la Merced, 20, 29012 Málaga
Tel: +34 95 221 3932
Fax: +34 95 221 5003
instituto.picasso@ingenia.es
www.ingenia.es/instituto.
picasso
Established: 1982
Level: None
Nearest Station: Málaga
Nearest Airport: 'Picasso'
Contact: Regina Streuli or Ursula Holthausen

Pablo Picasso was a Malagueño, a fact that often eludes people because Barcelona, with its Picasso Museum located in the artists' former home there, seems to have (wrongly) assumed the honour of being his hometown. This school, as its name indicates, is situated next to Málaga's own Picasso museum, in an old building with seven large, bright classrooms. The school is attended by about 550 students annually, the majority of them Europeans.

The school has a provision of five courses, as well as one-to-one lessons offered at a cost of 3,000ptas per hour (reduced to 5,500ptas for two consecutive hours and 7,500ptas for three consecutive hours). The 'Basic' course (four hours a day), costs from 34,000ptas for two weeks to 200,000ptas for 16 weeks. The 'Extra Basic' course (four hours a day plus two one-to-one lessons a day) costs 79,000ptas for two weeks. The Intensive course (6 hours a day: four hours plus two hours in mini-groups) costs 57,000ptas for two weeks. The Extra Intensive course (Intensive course plus 2 hours of one-to-one per day) costs 102,000ptas for two weeks. The Mini-group course (so called because the number of participants ranges from a minimum of three to a maximum of five) involves three hours of lessons and an hour-long activity per day and costs 38,000ptas for two weeks and 65,000ptas for four weeks. All courses last from two to twenty weeks, Monday to Friday.

All students sit a level test on the first day of their course. Certificates are awarded for regular attendance and those who successfully pass the school's exam will receive it's own diploma. Preparation for the DELE exams is also available and this involves enrolment four to six weeks prior to the exams (which take place in May and November).

Accommodation is available in shared apartments, with host families and in mini-apartments. Prices range from 15,000ptas for one person sharing a double room in a shared apartment for two weeks to 90,000ptas for two people sharing a mini-apartment for four weeks.

Contact the school for enrolment details.

Lexis Instituto de Idiomas

Paseo de Reding, 19, 29016
Málaga
Tel: +34 95 222 4006
Fax: +34 95 260 1598
Email: lexis@ingenia.es
Website: www.pta.es/lexis
Established: 1993
Level: None
Nearest Station: Málaga
Nearest Airport: 'Picasso'
Contact: Isabelle Thevenet
Located close to the centre of Málaga,

in a modern building on a tree-lined street, this language school provides language classes at all levels as well as specialist classes (for advanced speakers only) in different professional and vocational areas such as Legal Spanish and Spanish for Tourism. The school is attended by between 250 and 300 students who come from Germany, Italy and the UK, among others and the maximum number of students in one class is eight. Students have access to the school's library, video library and newspaper archive and the emphasis of classes is on oral communication. The centre is air conditioned in the summer.

'General Spanish' Courses fall under two categories: four hours of lessons per day and six hours of lessons per day, and can be taken for a minimum of two weeks. They are suitable for candidates who wish to prepare for the DELE exams and begin every Monday. The fees range from 32,000ptas for four hours a day for two weeks to 90,000ptas for six hours a day for four weeks. An additional will cost 15,000ptas (four hours) or 21,000ptas (six hours). One-to-one lessons cost 3,500ptas per hour.

The Specialist Spanish courses require an advanced level of Spanish and begin every Monday with a duration of one or two weeks. The courses include Legal Spanish, Spanish for Economics, Technical Spanish, Spanish for Tourism, Business Spanish and Literature. One week at six hours a day costs 42,000ptas and two weeks at four hours a day costs 56,000ptas.

Two new courses have recently been introduced: Spanish and sport and Spanish, art and culture. The Spanish and sport course involves one sporting activity combined with a course of

Spanish lessons. The provision of sports is varied and includes diving, sailing, potholing, climbing, abseiling, horse-riding and skiing in the Sierra Nevada. Depending on the course you choose, the activity will take place for one day of the course or over a period of time (from one weekend up to three weeks). Prices range from 58,000ptas (Introduction to Diving or Boat Trip, plus 40 hours of language tuition) to 84,000ptas (horse-riding, two week course, plus 30 hours of language tuition). Golf is available, from 68,500ptas for one weekend plus thirty hours of language tuition. A course called Las Mil y Una Noches will cost you from 78,500ptas for two days plus 60 hours of language tuition.

For more information, please contact the school.

Lexis can offer a variety of activities such as cookery classes, video-debate sessions, fiestas and excursions. There are also four accommodation options: living with a family (half board in single or double room), in an apartment (single or shared double room), in hall of residence (full or half board) and various categories of hotels (according to your budget).

Contact the school for enrolment details.

Spanorama International
Spanish training in Spain, los Cedros, 12, PO Box 523, 29017 Málaga
Tel: +34 95 220 1245
Fax: +34 95 2201600
Level: None
Nearest Station: Málaga, Almuñecar, Sevilla, Granada, Madrid, Salamanca, Barcelona (depending on which centre you attend)

Contact: Rita Fäh

For those who like to let someone else do the organising for them, Spanorama is ideal. This group (part of a German organisation) has language centres in seven major cities in Spain: Málaga, Almuñecar, Sevilla, Granada, Madrid, Salamanca and Barcelona, and they will see to all aspects of your trip to Spain, including advice on cheap flights and airport transfers. Accommodation is included in all fees. There are eight courses on offer, not all of which are available at every centre and prices vary according to the city and type of accommodation you have opted for (either in an apartment or with a Spanish family).

The 'Standard' course is available in Málaga, Almuñecar, Granada, Barcelona and Salamanca and the cost for two weeks ranges from 46,200ptas for one person sharing a double room in an apartment in Málaga to 85,800ptas for a single room with a Spanish family in Granada or Almuñecar. The course can last up to twenty weeks and involves twenty lessons per week with class groups of eight to ten students. The 'Intensive' course is available in every centre apart from the one in Barcelona and the cost for two weeks ranges from 56,200ptas for one person sharing a double room in an apartment in Málaga to 133,680ptas for for a single room with a Spanish family in Madrid. The course lasts up to sixteen weeks and involves thirty lessons a week with class groups of ten students. The content of the course is essentially identical to the 'Standard' course, the only difference being that you are taken through it at a faster pace. The 'Intensive Plus' is a combination of the Intensive course and an additional 5 hours of one-to-one tuition. The price of an hour's individual tuition varies according to the centre and ranges from 3,600ptas in Salamanca to 4,900ptas in Madrid.

The 'Business' course is available in Málaga, Almuñecar, Sevilla and Salamanca and the cost for two weeks is the same in every centre, ranging from 122,200ptas for one person sharing a double room in an apartment to 159,000ptas for a single room with a Spanish family. The course involves 30 lessons per week with an additional two hours daily based purely on topics dealing with economics and business. The duration of the course is from two weeks, with a maximum of 10 students in each class. The Individual course is available in every centre except Barcelona and the price per week (for twenty hours a week) ranges from 70,200ptas for one person sharing a double room in an apartment in Almuñecar or Granada to 124,000ptas for a single room with a Spanish family in Madrid. You can attend the course from one week onwards and it can involve from 10 to 30 hours a week of tuition; you will not have the same teacher for all your lessons. Minigroup courses are also available. These are for a maximum of six students and involve six hours of daily tuition, Monday to Friday.

DELE preparation is also available and there is a refresher course for teachers of Spanish. All courses begin every Monday, with absolute beginners starting on the first Monday of every month.

All students, apart from beginners, will sit a level test on the first day. All schools offer a programme of afternoon activities such as excursions, film shows, sports and so on. For enrolment details, contact the office in Málaga.

Universidad de Málaga en Ronda – Programa Internacional de Estudios de Español

Palacio de Mondragón, PO Box 332, 29400 Ronda
Tel: +34 95 287 3265/9089
Fax: +34 95 287 3265
Email: spanishstudies@um. ronda.redestb.es
Website: Under construction
Established: 1990
Level: None
Nearest Station: Aeropuerto
Nearest Airport: 'Picasso' (then by bus to Ronda)
Contact: D Joaquin Hita Iglesias

The University of Málaga was founded in 1972 and has set up the International Programme of Spanish Studies in collaboration with the city of Ronda. Unlike certain other university programmes, this does not allow language students to mix with Spanish students from the university itself as these courses do not take part on a university campus. Ronda is spectacularly situated about 75km inland from Málaga, high up on an isolated ridge, and is divided by a gorge formed by the river Tajo.

There are three course options available on the 'Programa Internacional de Estudios de Español', which is attended by just under five hundred students annually, the majority of them Swedish, American and German. Classes have an average of about eleven participants. The summer courses, which last from one to three months with 20 class hours a week cost from 45,000ptas for one month to 125,000ptas for three months. The 'Intensive' course, which lasts between one and eight months, involves twenty hours of tuition a week and costs 70,000ptas a month. Two- or three-week Intensive courses are also available, at a cost of 45,000ptas and 58,000ptas respectively. The Programme of Hispanic Studies (only suitable for those with intermediate level Spanish or above) is available for one or two semesters and costs 140,000ptas for one semester and 257,000ptas for eight months. Topics studied as part of this course include history, art, literature and politics. Certificates and diplomas will be awarded for attendance or successful completion of the relevant exams.

Additional activities are organised for students by the Secretary of the centre. Accommodation is available with a Spanish family (from 38,000ptas a month for bed and breakfast to 60,000ptas per month for full board) or in student residences (summer only, half board, 50,000ptas a month for one person sharing a double room and 55,000ptas a month for a single room).

NAVARRA

Universidad de Navarra – Instituto de Lengua y Cultura Españolas (ILCE)
Campus Universitario, Edificio Central, E-31080 Pamplona (Navarra)
Tel: +34 948 425 600
Fax: +34 948 425 619
Email: rgoni@central.unav.es
Established: 1956
Level: None
Nearest Station: Pamplona station
Contact: Dona Raquel Goñi

The capital of Navarra for the past thousand years, Pamplona is home to the Fiestas de San Fermín, one of Spain's most famous festivals. It is on these few days of the year (one week in July) when the running of the bulls occurs and the place comes to a halt to enjoy a continuous party. For the rest of the year, Pamplona is a university town with the variety of historical monuments and attractions that you would expect of a provincial capital with such a long history.

The University of Navarra was founded in 1952 and the language courses were established only four years later. ILCE is attended by about 120 students every year, the majority of them from Germany, Taiwan and Japan. Classes can allow for a maximum of forty students – which is quite considerably larger than most other schools – though there are usually fewer participants in each lesson. The aim of the courses is to help you to improve your Spanish in a university environment, with the assistance of all the facilities that that can provide, such as the university library, cafeterias, the IT centre and welfare service.

The courses on offer are: 'Cursos de Verano de Lengua y Cultura Españolas' (Summer Language and Culture courses), an 'Intensive Course for Teachers of Spanish' and three academic year courses – 'Language and culture', 'Hispanic studies' and Business Spanish. The summer courses run only throughout the months of August and September, which is unusual in Spain and must be due to the fact that the famous fiestas take place right in the middle of July. These programmes cost from 45,000ptas for two weeks to 100,000ptas for six weeks. For one week's orientation prior to the academic year course, the cost is 15,000ptas. There are 25 hours of classes per week and the minimum number of students in each class is eight. Those who sign up for a more than two weeks of courses have preference over those sign up for two only (which is the minimum). All students will receive a certificate on completion of the course and there is an optional end-of-course exam.

The three academic year courses are aimed at giving the student a more in-depth view of Spanish language and culture. The Language and Culture course (164,000ptas) includes modules in Language, Introduction to Spanish literature and History of Spanish music. The Hispanic Studies course (190,000ptas) has a similar content, but is aimed more at helping the student to master the language. The Business Spanish course (190,000ptas) includes modules such as Administrative Spanish and Spanish for Deals. The course will allow you to sit the DENE (Diploma de Español de los Negocios), for which the student has to pass the module in Spanish language and achieve 'Notable' (or a higher grade) in a general examination of all the other modules in this course. The 'Intensive course for Teacher's of Spanish' takes place at the end of July and runs for two weeks at a fee of 65,000ptas.

Those students requesting it will be given help in finding it. Please note: the university is closed throughout the Fiestas de San Fermín (July 6 to July 14).

SALAMANCA

Amadís de Gaula

José Jáuregui, 7, Oficina 4, 37002 Salamanca
Tel: +34 923 21 31 21
Fax: +34 923 21 31 21
Email: gaula@arrakis.es
Website: www.arrakis.es/~gaula
Established: 1996
Level: None
Nearest Station: Salamanca station
Contact: Mariluz Iglesias Mellado or Francisco Javier Martín López

Situated in the centre of Salamanca, very near the city's magnificent Plaza Mayor, this school opened its doors in 1993 as a language school and a training centre for air stewardesses. In 1996 it opened its doors to foreigners wishing to learn Spanish. These classes have an average of about nine students and the majority of their participants come from France, Germany and England.

Teachers are all graduates in Spanish Philology and have had a great deal of experience in teaching Spanish to foreigners. The range of facilities offered by the school include excursions and cultural activities, as well as family homestays (from 1,800ptas a day sharing a double room with half board to 2,200ptas a day in a single room with full board). The school can organise conversational exchanges with Spanish students, film shows and excursions at the weekends with guides from the school.

The school offers four core courses. The 'General course in Spanish language', with a minimum duration of two weeks costs 52,000ptas a month for four hours a day and 65,000ptas a month for five hours a day. The Intensive course, with a minimum duration of two weeks, costs 65,000ptas a month for five hours a day. The Language and Civilization course costs 52,000ptas a month and involves at least three hours of classes per day. The Culture course looks at topics such as art, literature and history and also costs 52,000ptas a month.

There are courses for specific purposes,

which include preparation for the DELE examinations (from 56,000ptas per month), business Spanish (from 30,000ptas per month), one-to-one courses and courses for groups (5 people minimum). A certificate of assistance will be given to all those students who have attended ninety percent of their classes. Students who have successfully completed the school's optional exams will receive a diploma in 'Spanish Studies' ('Diploma de Estudios de Español').

As well as family homestays, the school can also organise for you to share a flat (with your own room or sharing a double) with other students. The cost for this ranges from 20,000ptas a month for one person in a double room to 25,000ptas a month for a single room.

Contact the school for enrolment details.

Colegio Lorca – Cursos Internacionales de Lengua y Cultura Españolas

María Auxiliadora, 21 entre-planta, 37004 Salamanca
Tel: +34 923 259 952
Fax: +34 923 249 298
Email: cloraca@readysoft.es
Website: www.readysoft.es/
home/lorcaweb
Level: None
Nearest Station: Salamanca station
Contact: Alejandro Marcos Bartolomé

Frederico García Lorca is one of Spain's most famous poets so it should come as some surprise that this is the only language school that we have so far encountered bearing his name. The school is based on two sites that are a short walk away from one another on two of the main roads behind the Plaza Mayor. The school can arrange accommodation in families and claims that ninety seven percent of its students choose this option as it is without a doubt the best way to improve your language skills in as short a time as possible. The school prides itself on the fact that class sizes are small so as to ensure that each student receives the maximum amount of attention from their teacher. All teachers have degrees in Spanish philology and plenty of experience teaching Spanish to foreigners.

The school runs nine courses. The monthly Spanish language course (every month of the year except for July, August and September) costs from 35,000ptas for two weeks (40 classes) to 64,000ptas for four weeks (80 classes). The Spanish Summer course runs for the three months not covered by the monthly course and costs from 30,000ptas for two weeks (40 classes) to 58,000ptas for four weeks (80 classes). One-to-one courses are available in blocks of 40 (140,000ptas) and 60 (195,000ptas), after which special prices apply. In July, August and September you have to sign up for a minimum of 20 classes and for two students of the same level enroling simultaneously, each will receive a twenty five per cent discount off the total price of the course. The Easter course lasts for two weeks (forty classes) and costs 35,000ptas. The academic year course involves classes classes daily for 30 weeks between the beginning of October and the end of May; it costs 450,000ptas. Group courses can be arranged and the price depends on the size of the class and the number of lessons required; contact the school for more information. Optional courses can be taken in conjunction with summer courses. For a total of 10 lessons (one a day) in 'Literature', 'History', 'Cinema' and 'Customs' the cost is 10,000ptas. The 'Business Spanish' course is also only available as part of the summer courses and costs 10,000ptas for ten classes. The DELE preparation course takes place about two months before the exams (May and November) though the school will send you a test in order to assess your level and advise you on exactly how much time you will need to prepare. The price of the course depends on the number of weeks of study, the minimum being eight weeks.

Staying with a family will cost from 1,800ptas a day for one person sharing a double room with half board to 2,400ptas for a single room with full board. A washing and ironing service is available for an additional 1,500ptas per week. A flat-share with other students will either cost 4,000ptas for one person sharing a double room or 6,500ptas for a single room (prices are given per week).

All the teaching staff take part in the extra-curricular activities which include sports, excursions and cultural activities (fiestas and so on) which means that you get to practice your Spanish outside of the classroom.

Contact the school for enrolment details.

Cursos Internacionales, Universidad de Salamanca:
Patio de Escuelas Menores s/n, 37008 Salamanca
Tel: +34 923 29 44 18
Fax: +34 923 29 45 04
Email: internat@cursos.usal.es
cursos.usal.es
Established: 1963
Level: None
Nearest Station: Salamanca

Contact: Personal de Secretaría

In 1997 El País, Spain's foremost national newspaper, awarded Salamanca University's Cursos Internacionales the ultimate seal of approval, calling it the "sello de calidad en el Espanol" (the mark of quality in Spanish language). Its diverse courses range from 'Spanish language for absolute beginners' to the 'Curso Superior de Filología Hispanica', which is open to both foreign and Spanish students alike and involves lectures (in Spanish!) by respected Spanish authors.

Salamanca University was founded in 1218, making it one of the oldest universities in Spain. It will come as no surprise then, to learn that the town is now home to a plethora of Spanish language schools, the most well-known (and probably largest) of which is Cursos Internacionales. The town centre is packed with the intricate and imposing architecture of the university buildings and narrow, cobbled streets lead to the Plaza Mayor, one of the largest and most breathtaking of Spain's famous central town squares (it is even said to rival the one in Madrid). Classes take place in a building, on the beautiful and central Plaza de Anaya, which is flanked by a cathedral and the Palacio de Anaya. In the summer, the town is filled with students of all ages and nationalities (CI alone has 5,000 students annually, mainly from the USA), who spend the nights bar-hopping around town, lured from one place to the next by the promise of a free "copa".

At CI in July and August, you have the option of choosing a course lasting two, four or six weeks, studying from three to six hours a day. Prices range from 53,000ptas for three hours a week for two weeks to 130,000 for five hours a week for six weeks, to which an extra 25,000ptas can be added for a daily hour of conversation (usually in a cafe) for four weeks. From intermediate level onwards, the course contents can include a variety of options such as 'Business Spanish' and 'History of Spanish Art'. At the most basic level (Nivel inicial), the options are limited to aspects of language learning only. From January to June and September to December, language courses can last from one to ten weeks (hours as above), with the option of staying on for longer at a reduced price, should you wish to complete another term or month of study. Initial prices range from 28,000ptas for three hours a week for one week to 185,000ptas for five hours a week for a term. In July and August, in addition to the statutory language classes, you can take guitar lessons, attempt to learn some typical Spanish dances or attend a cycle of some of Spain's best-known films. A special programme, Programa Individualizado de Lengua Espanol, has been created for those who need a more personalised programme to help them learn Spanish properly but quickly. Cursos Internacionales also have options for more advanced Spanish speakers, including the 'Diploma de Estudios Hispanicos' (one year), which has modules in 'Spanish literature', 'History', 'History of art', 'Geography' and 'Economics' and 'media' and the 'Programa Especial Integrado' (1 year), which allows students to study from two to five subjects of their choice at the university of Salamanca, along with Spanish students. There are courses for teachers of Spanish as a foreign language (including a Masters).

Cursos Internacionales offers help in finding accommodation, either with a family in Salamanca or in one of the university's halls of residence (July, August and September only). Prices range from 2,150ptas per person per day in a double room with a family, to 85,500ptas for a university double room for a month. The CI brochure includes an application form. A deposit of 25,000ptas, deductible from the total, must be made on application.

Don Quijote

Placentinos, 2, apdo 333,
37080 Salamanca
Tel: +34 923 268 860
Fax: +34 923 268 815
Email: donquijote@
offcampus.es
Website: www.teclata.es/
donquijote
Established: Salamanca:1989
Summerschool Salamanca:
1990
Barcelona and Granada: 1991
Level: None
Nearest Station: Salamanca:
Salamanca
Barcelona: (Metro) Plaza de
Catalunya/
Train Paseo de Gracia
Granada: a number of buses
stop outside the school
Contact: Sue-Ann Lard

Don Quijote is an established group of language schools whose centres are attended by about 4,000 students annually. These come from over forty different countries and the majority are German, American, French, Dutch and English. All of the schools are centrally located in their respective cities in traditional buildings that have been modernised.

The school in Salamanca is an example of this; you will find it in a renovated 16th century convent. All have libraries, television rooms and computer facilities. The schools are large enough to cope with between 160 and 200 students at any one time.

There are schools in three locations in Spain – Salamanca, Barcelona and Granada – and all offer a different combination of courses. At all three, students can take one of six courses: 'General Intensive' (four hours a day, 11 weeks, all levels, all year round); 'Super Intensive' (six hours a day, two to 11 weeks, all levels, all year round at Salamanca, seasonal at Barcelona and Granada); 'Spanish for Life' (four hours a day, 12 to 36 weeks, all levels, all year round); 'DELE Preparation' (two, three and four weeks, advanced level, May and November); 'Refresher Courses for Teachers' (see below) and 'Individual Tuition' (on a one-to-one basis up to eight hours a day, all levels).

At Barcelona and Granada, Spanish for Life and Specialisation courses are available. These last for 12 weeks, begin on certain dates and are suitable for intermediate level students and above. This course involves four hours daily with an additional two hours a day for the specialised courses in 'Business and Tourism'. At the Barcelona centre only students can take the Intensive Business Course (intermediate level students and above only, certain start dates). A summer school is organised in Salamanca in July and August. Courses are suitable for students of all levels and last from between two and eight weeks (four hours of tuition per day).

The courses for Teachers of Spanish are available for groups (beginning on certain start dates) or individually (starting any Monday except group start dates). Group lessons involve four hours of tuition a day and courses last for two weeks. You can take a special Flight Attendant course at Salamanca over two weeks for four hours a day at certain times of the year.

Included in the course prices at the ¿? don Quijote schools, in addition to course books and study material, is a welcome dinner, dancing and singing lessons, and the use of bicycles and tennis rackets. Students also benefit from an extra hour every day for general group discussions on themes published by the school every month. There is no obligation for students to attend these lessons. Excursions are organised to places such as Madrid, the Sierra de Béjar-Candelario, Córdoba, Seville and other areas of Andalucía. ¿? don Quijote have recently opened their first student residence at their centre in Granada.

Contact the school for enrolment details.

Escuela Oficial de Idiomas de Salamanca

Peña de Francia, 46, 37007
Salamanca
Tel: +34 923 241 461
Fax: +34 923 225 831
Established: 1982
Level: None
Nearest Station: Salamanca
bus station
Contact: Vega Llorente Pinto

This is the one "official" language school in a city which, due to its academic heritage, attracts a vast number of language school set-ups. For 'official' do not read 'best', as this title is not an absolute guarantee of quality. It merely means that the courses are given under the auspices of the Ministry of Education and that, if nothing else, they will be cheaper than elsewhere, though the forfeit for less inflated prices may be more swollen class sizes. Don't expect any of the frills that you would get with other language schools in an attempt to justify their fees – all that the price includes here are classes. Other languages are taught here and have been since 1982; the department of Spanish for Overseas students was set up in 1988. The school has a total of 3,500 students, with four hundred in the Spanish division.

The course provision here is identical to that of all other Escuela Oficial de Idiomas (Official Language Schools) and is composed of two cycles, the Ciclo Elemental (Elementary Cycle) and the Ciclo Superior (Superior Cycle). The first takes place from October to February and is composed of three modules and the second takes place from February to June and is composed of two modules. The courses consist of two hours of classes daily from Monday to Friday (alternate Fridays only). In 1997/98, the fee for the first cycle was 9,350ptas and for the second cycle it was 16,130ptas.

The courses are entirely language based, and include topics such as practicalities (telephone formalities, conventions when writing letters), grammar, phonetics and phonology (listening and speaking) with some literary content at the more advanced levels. Students will be evaluated at the end of every module in each cycle. Up to the highest level (ie from levels one to four) the tests will involve exercises intended to demonstrate grammatical and communicative competence. At the highest level, students will have to complete a piece of written work under timed conditions and take an oral examination in the presence of a panel, for which the student must sum up, analyse and commentate on a piece of literature or journalism from the 20th century. 'The Diploma del Ciclo Elemental' will be awarded to students successfully completing the first three modules. 'The Diploma del Ciclo Superior' will be awarded to students successfully completing the last two modules.

Prior to the course, those students with previous knowledge of Spanish will sit a level test to place them in a class suitable to their level. Students who already have the DELE certificate will start in the 'Upper Intermediate' course. The school can offer information regarding accommodation and is closed during the month of August.

Contact the school for enrolment details.

Hispano Continental SL

Zamora, 61, 37002 Salamanca
Tel: +34 923 212 344
Fax: +34 923 212 344/264 832
Email: hispancon@helcom.es
Website: www.helcom.es
/hispacon
Established: 1989
Level: None
Nearest Station: Salamanca
train or bus stations
Contact: María Marco Sánchez

Located right in the centre of Salamanca, near the imposing buildings of the University of Salamanca and the city's magnificent cathedral, Hispano Continental offers a fairly standard provision of courses. The exception to this is the 'Preparation course for the certificate of Business Spanish' from the 'Cámara de Comercio de Madrid' (the Chamber of Commerce in Madrid) which few centres cater for.

The school is attended by about 300 students annually, the majority of them from Germany, the USA and the UK.

Average class sizes are about seven out of season and ten dur-ing the high season. All classrooms are equipped with television, video and projector.

There are six courses on offer. The 'Individual' course is tailor-made to the student's requirements and is a fairly expensive option at 3,000ptas per hour. The 'Standard' course ('Curso Normal') in Spanish Language costs 40,000ptas for two weeks for four hours of tuition daily. The Intensive course costs 45,000ptas for two weeks for five hours of tuition daily. The Special Language and Culture courses cost 45,000ptas for two weeks for three hours of tuition a day, 50,000ptas for two weeks for four hours of tuition a day, 60,000ptas for two weeks for five hours of tuition a day. All examination preparation courses (DELE and Business Spanish) cost 85,000ptas for four weeks (100 hours) or 230,000ptas for 12 weeks (three hundred hours). Optional courses (three students minimum) in Spanish Literature, History, Art, Theatre and Cinema, 'Translation' and Business' cost 20,000ptas for 20 lessons. Business courses can be arranged according to demand; contact the school for more information. Courses take place throughout the year and can last from two weeks up to one year. Courses begin on set date every month.

Accommodation is available with families or in flatshares. Living with a family will cost from 2,200ptas per day for one person sharing a double room to 2,400ptas for a single room. Laundry will cost an additional 6,000ptas per month. Flatshares cost from 22,000ptas to 26,000ptas per month. Attendance certificates will be awarded to all those who have attended their classes regularly; a Diploma of Spanish studies will be awarded to all those who successfully complete the optional exam at the end of their course.

Every weekend the school arranges excursions to palaces such as Toledo,

Hispano Continental S.L.

Madrid and further afield to Portugal and Andalucía. Other activities include guided tours around Salamanca, showings of Spanish films, seminars and something that the school calls 'gastronomic excursions'.

Contact the school for enrolment details.

ISLA – Instituto Salmantina de Lenguas Aplicadas

Jesus, 20, 37001 Salamanca
Tel: +34 923 210 394
Fax: +34 923 260 627
Email: isla@helcom.es
Website: www.netattack.com/ isla/isla.htm
Established: 1991
Level: None
Nearest Station: Salamanca station
Contact: Amanda McCarthy

ISLA's glossy and confident brochure acknowledges the presence of an already healthy number of language schools in Salamanca, but claims that its individuality lies in the fact that its courses are aimed at providing the kind of high quality tuition that the city still lacks. Whether or not this is the case, only you can decide. However, one impressive statistic is that not only have all ISLA students sitting the DELE exams passed successfully, they have done so with results around the 90 per cent mark. Another incentive to study here is the fact that you will receive extra tuition, free of charge, should your teacher feel that you need a bit of encouragement.

There are six different courses available. The 'Intensive Spanish Language' course can last from one week to twenty four and it involves four hours of classes per day with a maximum of nine students in each group. You can take the Power-house course for up to 12 weeks and this requires six hours of tuition per day with modules in 'Grammar, Skills and Vocab' and 'Power', which involves practising your Spanish in real life situations, in role-plays and in radio shows or putting together the school newspaper. The Masterclasses (six people per group; from one to eight weeks) offer an interesting option for those who can already handle the language fairly well and who are ready to speak fluent Spanish (these are recommended for DELE, preparation). 'Commercial Spanish' (nine people per group; from one to eight weeks) is suitable for those with low to interm ediate Spanish. One-to-one tuition is available as a separate entity or in combination with a group course – contact the school to discuss details of the course that you require. Closed group courses are also available and ISLA already offers programmes for school and university groups. You take a combination of courses for up to32 weeks.

Prices for courses range from 33,000ptas for two weeks on the Intensive course to 234,000ptas for 12 weeks on the 'Power' course. One-to-one classes are available from 3,500ptas for up to 10 hours; thereafter, the rate is discounted to 2,900ptas per hour. Discounts are available for returning students, and groups of five or more students. Acc-ording to the number of weeks that you sign up for, you will receive an 'ISLA treat'. This involves either: a free one day trip for stays of eight to 15 weeks or a free weekend excursion for stays from 16 to 23 weeks or two free weekend excursions for stays from 24 up to32 weeks. Fees includes access to email and CD-ROM facilities, loan of camping and sports equipment, discounts on books, at the gym and on photo-developing, exchanges with Spanish students and accident insurance, as well as guided tours and fiestas.

ISLA – Instituto Salmantina de Lenguas Aplicadas

Accommodation is available in two categories: with or without meals. Under the first category you can choose a student flat (from 10,000 a week for one person in a double room), a private apartment (from 30,000ptas for a week) and a hotel (from 20,000ptas per week for a single or for one person sharing a double room). Under the second category you can choose either to stay with a family (from 2,100ptas a day for one person sharing a double room, half board) or a residence (from 2,400ptas a day, full board, for one person sharing a double room).

Contact the school for enrolment details.

Salminter – Escuela Salmantina de Estudios Internacionales

Toro, 34-36 2, 37002
Salamanca
Tel: +34 923 211 808
Fax: +34 923 260 263
Email: info@salminter.eurart.es

Website: www.eurart.es/emp
/salminter
Established: 1986
Level: None
Nearest Station: Salamanca
Contact: Angelines Herrero
Redondo

Located on the first floor of a beautiful restored building in the centre of Salamanca, (above a branch of one of Cortefiel), this is one of the larger private language schools that you will come across, with over 1000 students attending its courses every year. The majority of students are European, followed by pupils from Japan and the USA. Other nationalities account for twelve percent of the rest of students. Class sizes are average, with a norm of about ten. The school was founded over a decade ago with the aim of introducing students to a different and more authentic Spain than the stereotype of it that is usually exported to other countries. The school has twelve classrooms and a small reference library. Some classrooms have television and video facilities.

There are nine courses. The 'Intensive' language course costs 56,000ptas a month (eighty hours of tuition) or 34,000ptas for two weeks or for the same number of lessons (40) spread over a month. The Language and Civilization course costs 144,000ptas per term. The 'Spanish Culture' course, involving topics such as literature, art and Spain today, cost 13,000ptas for ten hours per month. The 'Business and Administrative Spanish' course costs 29,000ptas for the month (20 lessons) or 79,000ptas for a term (60 lessons). The DELE preparation course costs 72,000ptas for 85 hours. 'Translation' (using literary, legal and business texts) costs 17,000ptas for 20 hours per month. One-to-one courses cost 2,800ptas per hour with a reduction of twenty five percent for each student for up to three students taking the lessons as a group. The 'Speaking practice' course costs 27,000ptas for 20 hours a month. Special programmes for groups are also an option and in the past, these have been arranged for University of the West of England, Bristol and Hull University. The school is open all year round and students will be given a placement test on the first day of their course. For the different start dates of each course, consult the prospectus.

Accommodation is available with families or in flatshares. The cost of living with a Spanish family ranges from 1,900ptas per day for one person sharing a double room with half board to 2,400ptas for a single room with full board; there is a handling charge of 1,500ptas for this service. Flatshare costs range from 19,000ptas for one person sharing a double room for a month to 24,000ptas for a single room per month. The school arranges cultural activities and excursions as well as a monthly party and can also arrange conversation exchanges with local students.

For more enrolment details, consult the school.

Universidad Pontificia de Salamanca – Cursos Intensivos de Lengua y Cultura Españolas para Extranjeros
Compañía, 5, 37002 Salamanca
Tel: +34 923 218 316
Established: 1983
Level: None
Nearest Station: Salamanca
Contact: Mercedes de Sande

The Universidad Pontificia de Salamanca, not to be confused with the University of Salamanca, was originally formed as an offshoot of that establishment. It was founded in 1617 as an extension of the university's old ecclesiastical faculties and is located in the centre of the city in a magnificent old building. Today its provision is vocational in its emphasis – not unlike the former polytechnics in the UK. Its courses for foreigners are, in certain cases, quite specialised (as opposed to the more general provision offered at the University of Salamanca). They include a course for embassy workers and EEC civil servants and a programme specifically designed for specialists who have to work in Spain or another Hispanic country.

Other courses include preparation for the DELE examinations, Spanish for interpreters and translators, Courses for teachers of Spanish, Business Spanish and Courses for Executives and Business people. All courses include the same basic daily content: two hours of grammar (theory and practice), an hour of conversation, an hour of varied activities such as translation. The courses are set at four levels of competence: ele-mentary, intermediate, superior and advanced. Additional activities include lectures, excursions, conversation with Spanish students, guided visits, Spanish films and a use of the videolaboratory. Musical activities and concerts take place in conjunction with the university's choir and 'tuna' – student music groups who dress up as 17th-century minstrels.

Courses take place on set dates every month and prices are decided according to the duration of a course rather than course type. Fees range from 26,650ptas for one week to 56,900ptas for three weeks and from 70,950ptas for one month to 462,500ptas for nine months. The cost includes all materials, diplomas and certificates. Students who have attended all but three of their lessons will receive a Certificado de Asistencia and those who successfully complete the end of course exam set by the university will receive a Diploma.

Accommodation can be arranged for those students requiring help. Options include hotels and hostels, flatshares with Spanish students and living with a family in Salamanca. Prices vary and range from 900ptas for a room only (with access to a kitchen) to 2,300ptas for full board.

Contact the university for enrolment details.

SAN SEBASTIAN

inlingua idiomas
Larramendi, 23, 20006 San Sebastian
Tel: +34 943 463 636
Fax: +34 943 431 730
Email: San-Sebastian@

inlingua-es.com
Website: www/inlingua-es.com
Established: 1960
Level: None
Nearest Station: San Sebastian
Contact: Javier Altolaguirre

San Sebastian is an elegant town on the north east coast of Spain and is famed for its beautiful Concha beach and for the International Film Festival that it hosts every year in September. Guipuzcoa is the name of the province (incidentally, the smallest in Spain) of which it forms a part. Its northernmost point touches the French border. The weather here is famed for being wet and windy, which means that the vegetation is in direct contrast to the rest of Spain. Whereas the south is dry and desert-like, the north is very lush and green. If you're coming out of season, bring your umbrella with you!

Inlingua is a large and well-known group of language schools. Based in Switzerland, it has 200 centres in 23 countries world-wide, with 65 centres in Spain alone. The one in San Sebastian is based on two sites in the centre of the town and, as well as Spanish courses for foreigners, it also offers English, French and German courses to local students and companies on a long term basis. This means that you will be studying in the same environment as native Spanish speakers, also struggling to learn a foreign tongue! Spanish courses are offered on demand and usually take place at the premises on c/Larramendi (the others being at c/Hernani). Both of these sites are within easy walking distance of the main beach. The majority of students on these courses are from Europe, mainly from Germany and Switzerland, and classes are relatively small.

There are four courses on offer at

Inligua in San Sebastian, as well as alternative options which vary according to the individual. The fixed courses include: Mini Groups of three-six students, who take 20 classes (each lasting 50 minutes) a week. These cost 25,000ptas a week and are usually only available in the period from June to September. The minimum stay is two weeks and beginners usually start on the first and third Monday of each month. CIP-120 are individual courses designed according to fit the needs of the student. These start every Monday and the minimum length is two weeks. Prices range from 80,000ptas to 160,000ptas a week, depending on the number of classes taken per week. Discounts are available for closed groups of two,three or four. Long term courses, which allow the student to spread their work over a period of time to suit them, are available for groups (for example, people who combine work with Spanish classes) or on a one-to-one basis. Prices for the one-to-one long term are 4,500ptas per class; for groups, please enquire.

The school can help you to find a room in a hostal or a pension and will send you a list of hotels on request. Homestay with a Spanish family is not available. Accommodation costs are not included in the price of the courses, for which a 15 per cent deposit must be made on confirmation of your reservation. The remainder must be paid before the start of the course. The school is open all year round, except for two weeks at Christmas and 11 days at Easter.

For enrolment details contact the school.

SANTIAGO DE COMPOSTELA
Universidad de Santiago de Compostela

Oficina de Cusos
Internacionales (Fac de
Ciencias Políticas), Campus
Universitario Sur, 15706
Santiago de Compostela
Tel: +34 981 597 035
Fax: +34 981 597 036
Email: cspanish@uscmail.usc.es
Website: www.uscmail.es/
spanish/welcome.htm
Established: 1942
Nearest Station: Santiago de
Compostela
Contact: Amparo Porta or Rosa
Spinola

Founded in 1495, this university has an excellent academic reputation, having produced alumni who have made significant contributions to western history, culture and science. In the sixties it grew rapidly, taking on a greater number of students as well as expanding its provision. This led to the fragmentation of the university, whose campuses in La Coruña and Vigo became independent of the main campus in Santiago de Compostela, which is situated downtown and not in the beautiful, historical part of the city. Santiago de Compostela itself is famous for its shrine to Saint James the Apostle, a site much visited by medieval pilgrims and modern day tourists alike.

The university has been offering Spanish courses to foreigners for well over fifty years and the programme is a simple one. There is one type of course, which is available at elementary, intermediate and superior levels and for each of which the timetable is identical. Language classes take place from 9.30am to 11am and from 11.30am to 1.30pm and complementary cultural activities begin from 5pm onwards. These are a series of lectures and discussions on different aspects of Spanish culture such as art, history and literature, given by various professors, specialists in these fields, from the university. The course includes film shows, guided visits and excursions every Saturday. The university's libraries and sports facilities are at the disposition of all students on these courses.

The course, available only in July, August and September, lasts four weeks and a 15,000ptas fee must be paid on enrolment, the balance of which (60,000ptas) can be paid on site. For an additional 2,000ptas medical insurance is also available. It is also possible to sign up for two or three weeks. Four types of accommodation are available: from Tipo B-2, the cheapest at 27,000ptas for four weeks for one person sharing a double room (bed and breakfast) to Tipo A-1, 53,000ptas for four weeks for one person sharing a double room (bed and breakfast). Half board and full board are also available, the most expensive option being full board in a single Tipo A-1 room (90,000ptas for four weeks).

Contact the university for enrolment details.

SEGOVIA

Universidad Internacional SEK – Curso de Lengua y Cultura Españolas

Santa Cruz la Real, Cardenal Zuñiga s/n, 40003 Segovia
Tel: +34 921 444 716/727
Fax: +34 921 445 593
Email: usek@gsv.servicom.es
Website: www.sek.edu
Established: 1998
Level: Basic (courses begin at intermediate level)

Nearest Station: Segovia station
Contact: Secretary

Having started out as a college of further education in Madrid in 1892, the current SEK centre in Spain (in Segovia) was officially decreed a private university in 1997. It is one of several branches of the Universidad Internacional SEK, which also has sites in Ecuador (Quito), Chile (Santiago), Argentina (Buenos Aires) and the UK (Berkshire), among others. The setting for SEK in Spain is a convent in the elegant town of Segovia (about an hour and a half's drive outside of Madrid), which is famous for the Roman aqueduct that still stands majestically, although rather incongruously in the city centre.

In 1998, for the first time in its history, SEK has organised a summer Spanish language and culture programme for overseas students, though it already provides summer courses for Spanish students. Unlike most courses of this kind, participants will need to have an already basic understanding of the language, as the two levels of competence towards which the courses are geared are Intermediate and Advanced. Only sixty students will be accepted, with thirty at each level. You can opt to study in July or August and the each course lasts for four weeks with 30 hours of tuition per week.

Each level has a specific daily schedule. At intermediate level this always starts with two hours of language from 9am to 11am. Thereafter, you can choose between a variety of cultural topics. These comprise modules in Spanish literature, art, cinema, history, theatre and music – all focused on the 20th century, a module in Spanish journalism and one on information technology and the media in Spain today. At advanced level, the first two hours are also devoted to language. The modules that follow include a more detailed look at certain subjects such as 'Spanish literature from 1898 to 1927', 'Contemporary Spanish cinema: the latest generation of directors and Contemporary history: from the Transition up to now'. Other topics cover journalism, theatre, music and art.

Once a week, both groups will participate in a series of lecture/classes given by a series of university lecturers and experts in their fields. Two will focus on linguistic themes and two will concentrate on literary topics. On Tuesday and Thursday afternoons, a variety of activities have been planned. These include a guided tour of the city, videos and concerts, and excursions to Madrid, Aranjuez and other places of interest in and around Segovia.

The price of the course includes accommodation in a hall of residence. The enrolment fee is 120,000ptas, in addition to which the cost of single room is 99,000ptas and the cost for one person sharing a double room is 89,000ptas. Students sit a level test on the first day of their course and will receive a 'Diploma Acreditativo' from the Universidad Internacional SEK (UISEK).

Contact the school for enrolment details.

SEVILLA

CLIC – Centro de Lenguas e Intercambio Cultural
Santa Ana, 11, 41002 Sevilla
Tel: +34 95 437 4500
Fax: +34 95 437 1806
Email: clic@arrakis.es

Website: www.clic.es
Established: 1983
Level: None
Nearest Station: Santa Justa
Contact: Eva White

Semana Santa (Holy Week) is the time of year for which this city, the capital of Andalucía, is best known. Spaniards and foreigners alike come from far and wide to watch the famous procession of the Virgin Mary through the city streets, which makes it impossible to find a bed in the city for love or money. The rest of the year is less hectic, but be warned – Sevilla in the summertime is only for those who can stand the intense heat! CLIC, recently affiliated to International House, is located in the heart of the city (the capital of Andalucía) in a house typical of the area. CLIC has another centre in Isla Cristina – a fishing village fifteen kilometres from the Portuguese border – which is more suitable for those who wish to combine language learning with a proper break. (Contact CLIC for more information.) CLIC allows students of Spanish the opportunity of meeting Spaniards, as the centre also provides courses in English, French and German to residents in Sevilla.

There are seven courses on offer at the school, including the chance to live with a Spanish teacher and study with them as their only pupil. This lasts for a minimum of one week, the cost of which is 128,000ptas, including full board in a single room and airport transfer. The standard course (20+2 hours a week) costs from 36,000ptas for two weeks to 110,000ptas for eight weeks. Classes are held in the mornings from Monday to Friday and every group (maximum of twelve students) has two teachers. The long term course is identical to the standard course, the only difference being that it is suitable for those who wish to study for a term or a full academic year. Prices range from 162,000ptas for 12 weeks to 418,000ptas for 32 weeks. The Intensive course involves the same hours as above, but classes are smaller, with three to six students. Prices range from 50,000ptas for two weeks to 275,000ptas for 12 weeks. The Super Intensive course involves 10 more hours per week and costs from 68,000ptas for two weeks to 370,000ptas 12 weeks. A course in business Spanish (eight lessons a week) and a course in Spanish conversation can be added to the first three courses (not Super Intensive); two weeks cost 22,000ptas and 20,000ptas respectively. One-to-one classes cost from 78,000ptas for 20 lessons to 116,000ptas for 16 lessons. The meaning of '+2' is that students can choose from a variety of cultural courses, at no extra charge, to complement their language course. Courses run at eight different levels of competence, from beginners through to proficiency ('Perfeccionamiento'). CLIC offers a special cultural programme during Semana Santa.

Examination preparation courses are also available. DELE preparation lasts for the twelve weeks prior to the exam and involve 26+2 hours of lessons a week; the fee is 225,000ptas. The Chamber of Industry and Commerce of Seville (Business Spanish) exam costs 190,000ptas and includes 28 plus two hours of classes per week for eight weeks.

Four accommodation options are available. Flatsharing with young Spaniards costs from 22,000ptas for two weeks. A room in CLIC own hall of residence costs from 25,000ptas for one person sharing a double room for two weeks and from 32,000ptas for a

single room for two weeks. Living with a Spanish family (half board) costs from 32,000ptas for two weeks. Your own apartment will cost from 60,000ptas for two weeks. A one way transfer to/from Sevilla airport will cost you 5,000ptas.

Giralda Center

Mateos Gago, 17, 41004 Sevilla
Tel: +34 95 422 1346
Fax: +34 95 422 1346
Established: 1983
Level: None
Nearest Station: Sevilla Santa Justa
Contact: Maria del Mar Llamas

Located in the Barrio de Santa Cruz, a characterful and central area of Sevilla filled with narrow winding streets, this language school offers Spanish courses all year round. You will find it in a typical, turn of the century, whitewashed house above a newsagent's, a hundred metres away from the city's famous Cathedral. The provision here is limited, with only two types of course on offer – 'Intensive' and 'Superintensive' – and class sizes are small, with a maximum of six students in each class. There are six classrooms, a room to study in and a cafeteria. There are no activities included in the price of the courses other than exchanges with native Spanish speakers, use of the video library and access to daily papers and magazines. The school, however, can provide information about what's on in Sevilla.

The 'Intensive' course lasts from two to twelve weeks and involves twenty lessons of 55 minutes every week, from Monday to Friday. The 'Superintensive' course involves 25 lessons of 55 minutes every week, Monday to Friday. Both can begin on any Monday, whether you are a beginner or an advanced student.

Giralda Center

The fees range from 17,000ptas for one week of the 'Intensive' course to 90,000ptas for four weeks of the 'Super-intensive' course; these prices include all teaching material and a level test at the start of the programme.

Accommodation can be arranged in families (half board) and flatshares. Staying with a family will cost between 30,000ptas for one week and 49,000ptas for four weeks. Flatshares will cost between 20,000ptas for two weeks and 30,000ptas for four weeks. This price includes a single room in a flat with Spaniards, with access to a kitchen.

Contact the school for enrolment details.

Lengua Viva S.L.
Viriato, 24, E-41003 Sevilla
Tel: +34 95 490 5131
Fax: +34 95 490 5123
Email: info@lenguaviva.es

Website: www.eel.es/ lenguaviva
Established: 1989
Level: None
Nearest Station: Sevilla Santa Justa
Contact: Christian Kratzer or Encarna Martín

The city of Sevilla has given its name to one of the most famous of typical Spanish dances – 'sevillanas' – and at Lenguaviva, one of the extracurricular courses on offer provides you with the opportunity of learning how to dance them. The school is located in the centre of the city and its exuberant motto is 'Vivir el Español' – literally, 'Live the Spanish Language'. Lessons are taught with the aim of getting you to speak the language as quickly as possible. Class sizes are average, with a maximum of ten students in each. The school offers three General courses and three Special courses.

General Spanish involves four lessons a day from Monday to Friday and costs from 38,000ptas for two weeks to 240,000ptas for 20 weeks; Intensive Spanish (six lessons per day) costs from 49,000ptas for two weeks to 216,000ptas for 12 weeks. 'General Spanish Plus' (four lessons per day plus one or two lessons of one-to-one tuition daily) costs from 72,000ptas for two weeks (with one lesson a day of one-to-one) to 188,000ptas for four weeks (with two lessons a day of one-to-one).

Mini group courses involve reduced class sizes (from two to five pupils only) for faster results and more personalised tuition, with four lessons a day; the cost for this starts at 52,000ptas for two weeks. One-to-one courses, involving 5, ten or twenty lessons a week starts at 19,000ptas for five lessons a week. The DELE preparation course lasts for four weeks, with four lessons a day, and costs 78,000ptas. There are two start dates for this course – in April and in October – to coincide with the four weeks prior to the examinations. You will have to pay an additional 11,000ptas for the exam fee.

Students from about twenty different countries attend the school, the majority of them from Denmark, Germany and Japan. You can choose between a wide range of accommodation options. What the school refers to as 'Common Household' involves living with other students in an apartment selected by them; the cost for this starts at 22,000ptas for a single room or for one person sharing a double room for two weeks. 'Living with Spanish people' will allow you to share a flat with young Spanish people and will cost from 20,000ptas for a single room or for one person sharing a double room for two weeks. You can live with a Spanish

family, the cost for which varies between 36,000ptas for a single room or for one person sharing a double room for two weeks (half board) and 46,000ptas for a single room (full board). Hostal "Galatea", close to the school, will cost from 32,000ptas for a single room or 29,000ptas for a double room for two weeks. A flat at Aparthotel Santa Cruz will cost from 50,000ptas for one person for two weeks and from 36,000ptas for two people for two weeks. These last two charge extra during Sevilla's busiest times Semana Santa in March and the Feria de Abril (in April).

The centre organises a variety of cultural activities and excursions outside of Sevilla. Contact the school for enrolment details.

Escuela Hispalense

Calle Teide, 1, E-11380, Tarifa
Tel: +34 956 68 09 27
Fax: +34 956 68 09 27
Email: hispalense@tnet.es
Website: tarifa.net/hispalense
Established: 1989
Level: None
Nearest Station: Algeciras
Contact: Irene Weiss

Tarifa is located at the tip of southern Spain, which is separated from north Africa by such a slim stretch of sea that on a map the two almost seem to be touching. On a clear day, you can see the coast of Morocco from this small town, where all but a few locals speak nothing but Spanish. Escuela Hispalense's location therefore offers an attractive alternative to the larger language schools found in big Spanish towns and cities, such as Salamanca. Constant coastal winds have made Tarifa a true wind-surfers paradise, [and have earned it the ambiguous title of 'La Capital del Viento' ('The Capital of Wind'!)] and should you tire of studying, there are plenty of beaches to provide a relaxing break. Other distractions include a variety of sporting activities (volleyball, climbing) and opportunities to learn Sevillanas and Flamenco, the dances for which this region of Spain is famous. Escuela Hispalense must attract many keen surfers, as students at the school will receive a discount at Surf School Spin Out when renting surf equipment.

The school offers four types of courses: 'Standard', 'Intensive', 'Evening' and 'Private'. 'Standard' (four hours a day, 1-16 weeks) and Intensive (six hours a day, up to two weeks) courses take place between Monday and Friday. In all but the private programmes, the fees include tuition and educational material (textbooks, etc…). Fees range from 19,000ptas for one week (Standard course) to 213,000ptas for 16 weeks (Standard course). For the Intensive course fees are 26,000ptas for one week and 51,000ptas for two. Private lessons cost 2,500ptas per hour. The school is small, with an annual intake of about 150 students (minimum age 16), the majority of whom are from western Europe.

Accommodation can be arranged by the school, according to your budget. Options include hotels, hostels, rooms with a Spanish family or camping. The school can also offer complete learning and holiday packages including Spanish lessons, lodging, surf lessons, rent of surf materials, rental cars or transfer from the airport.

For further information, contact the school. It is closed on local and national holidays and courses take place throughout the year. There is an application form and the school advises you to apply early if you wish them to arrange accommodation for you (eight weeks beforehand for July and August; four weeks for the rest of the year).

TARIFA

Centro de Estudios TAME S L

Avda Gregoria Gea, 61b, 46920 Valencia
Tel: +34 96 359 7244
Fax: +34 96 350 3317
Email: tame@cece.es or tame@combios.es
Website: www.tamein formacion.com
Established: 1980
Level: None
Nearest Station: Valencia (Estación del Norte)
Contact: Amparo Navarro Porcar

Based on two sites in Valencia – one in the city and another just outside, in Mislata – this is a school in which teaching Spanish to foreigners is only one department. The subject has been taught here since 1984, though the school has specialised in languages (among other things) since its foundation in 1980. The majority of foreign students at the school are from Germany and the UK and all courses (including the International Secretarial course) are suitable for those with the minimum requirement of a university degree.

Four courses are taught here, at all levels of competence and all but one (the Tailor-made course for professionals) includes full board accommodation with a Spanish family. The 'General Spanish' language course runs from June to September and costs 50,000ptas a week, for three hours of tuition a day and afternoon activities. The 'Intensive Spanish' language course runs from June to September and costs 60,000ptas a week for four hours of tuition a day. The 'International Secretarial' course runs from October to May at a cost of 150,000ptas a month for five hours of tuition a day (minimum duration of three months). The Tailor-made courses run all year round at a cost of 50,000ptas (accommodation according to your requirements – hotels, hostels, etc – is not included). All courses include 20 hours of tuition per week (except the secretarial course), with a maximum of 10 students per class and transfer from the airport to host families.

The price includes full-board accommodation with a family, airport transfer to the family, course materials, a diploma and a full day's excursion once a week. All courses (except for the secretarial course) have a minimum duration of two weeks. The language courses all contain modules in literature, culture, translation, oral expression and reading comprehension, among others.

All teachers at the centres are specialists in *filología* (Spanish language and literature) and the humanities. Contact the school for enrolment details.

CILCE Centro Internacional de Lengua y Cultura Española

Almirante, 1-2, 46003 Valencia
Tel: +34 96 391 0463
Fax: +34 96 392 1981
Email: cilce@iglobal.es
Website: www.iglobal.es/empresas/cilce/home
Established: 1969
Level: None
Nearest Station: Valencia
Contact: Carmen Payá

A city on the east coast of Spain, Valencia is famous for its weather, its food (this is the home of Paella) and its March fiesta – Las Fallas. The third largest city in Spain, it was founded by the Romans and has its own language – Valenciano – a dialect of Catalan. CILCE (not to be confused with CLIC in Sevilla) is located in the city's historical centre and is only fifteen minutes away from the beach, by bus. The school can offer a range of cultural activities including optional lessons in Spanish cooking and ceramics and, should the mood take you, tennis rackets or guitars are available to borrow.

With about six hundred and fifty students a year and about ten students per class, this is an average sized school, whose students come from the UK, France, Germany, Japan and the USA. Most of the teachers have been at CILCE for more than fifteen years and the two women who run the centre are both graduates in modern languages from the University of Valencia. One of them, Inmaculada Payá, is the author of the textbooks used in the classes.

Six courses are on offer. The 'Intensive' course (20 hours of classes a week) is available on its own, or with accommodation (half board with a Spanish family). Fees range from 42,860ptas for two weeks (course only) to 700,760ptas for twenty weeks (accommodation included). The 'Combined' course offers Intensive course classes and one-to-one tuition so, in addition to the Intensive course fees the price for five hours of one-to-one a week will be 21,500ptas (43,000ptas for 10 hours a week). Mini stays are courses suitable for groups accompanied by a teacher and involve a full package including accommodation and day trips. The Person-to-person course allows the student to choose between four, five or six hours of personal tuition a day and is available only from September to June. The cost starts at 86,000ptas for four hours of classes a day for one week. Courses begin on different dates during most months throughout the year. Courses for groups of professionals can be organised by the school; contact them for details. Courses for groups of younger students accompanied by an adult are also available. The school also has links with the Queen Mary and Westfield College, London and the University of Essex in the UK.

There are five different accommodation options available. Lodging with a Spanish family will cost from 15,000ptas per week for bed and breakfast. A hostel in town will cost from 1,300ptas a day for a single room without a shower. Studio flats in town cost about 45,500ptas for one or two people per week. Flatshares in town cost about 60,000ptas per person per month. If you want to share a flat with a group of Spanish or foreign students further out of the centre, the cost per person per month will be 30,000ptas.

As its name implies, CILCE also offers an ample programme of cultural activities including excursions, visits to museums and fiestas. All students will receive a certificate of attendance and progress.

Escuela Oficial de Idiomas – Generalitat Valenciana

Llano de la Zaidía, 46009 Valencia
Tel: +34 96 340 5022
Level: None
Nearest Station: Valencia
Contact: Escuela Oficial de Idiomas

The city's official language centre, this offers the basic academic provision that you will find in any other Escuela Oficial de Idiomas in Spain – the Ciclo Elemental (three levels) and the Ciclo Superior (two levels). This is applicable to any one of the languages taught at the school, which include English, French, Russian, Italian and Arabic as well as Valenciano and Spanish. The foreign students at this school come from Europe, Morocco, Syria, Egypt and China. Class sizes are larger than average, with a minimum of fifteen and a maximum of 35 in each one. The price of courses has not been made available yet, but they are certainly among the cheapest that you will find as they offer no extras whatsoever. All that the fee includes are one or two hours of classes a day from Monday to Friday and classes every other Friday. There are two course options: the semester course (two hours daily) or the academic year course (one hour daily). The school is closed in August.

Contact the school for more details and enrolment information.

Universitat de Valencia Estudi General

Vice-Rectorat de Relacions Exteriors, Gabinet d'Estrangers, Senda Senent, 11, 2ᵀᴹ planta, 46071 Valencia
Tel: +34 96 386 4180
Fax: +34 96 393 3021
Email: isabel.lopez@uv.es
Website: www.uv.es
Level: None
Nearest Station: Valencia (Estación del Norte)
Contact: Isabel López Soriano or Inés Fernandez Bas

The Universitat de Valencia's history began in 1245 though it wasn't founded until 1500. You can attend Spanish language courses here in the summer months (July and September) only. The provision here is basic – four weeks (eighty hours) of theoretical/practical tuition and Spanish conversation. The courses are taught at three levels of competence – beginners, intermediate and advanced – and at the two higher levels, modules in contemporary Spanish literature and history of art and Valencian culture are introduced.

The course fee (70,000ptas for four weeks) includes extra-curricular activities in the afternoons (with the participation of teachers), sports, course materials, medical and accident insurance and cultural visits.

If you wish to find accommodation with a Spanish family or in a flat, you should contact Fernando at the Universitat de Valencia on: +34 96 382 2278. For accommodation in the university hall of residence, write directly to the halls at either: Colegio Mayor Luis Vives, Blasco Ibañéz, 23, 46010 Valencia (Tel: +34 96 386 4190, Fax: +34 96 386 4195) or Colegio Mayor Rector Peset, Playa del Forn de Sant Nicolau, 4, 46001 Valencia (Tel: +34 96 391 0340, Fax: +34 96 392 2729). Halls of Residence are usually the most expensive option.

To enrol, you must fill in the application form and send it to the address above, along with two passport photographs and receipt of payment of the fees into the relevant account. You cannot pay by cheque. Contact the university for more information and further enrolment details.

VALLADOLID

Paramo – Academia de Español

Relatores, 1-4A y B dcha, 47011 Valladolid
Tel: +34 983 264 143
Fax: +34 983 264 143
Email: paramo@vasertel.es
Established: 1988
Level: None
Nearest Station: Estación del Norte – Valladolid
Contact: Clemente Sanchez Pelaez

Valladolid, situated at the heart of what is known as 'Old Castile', once rivaled Madrid for the crown as the capital of Spain and today it still retains some monuments to its glorious past. The school is situated in the heart of the historic centre of the city and is attended by about two hundred students every year, the majority of them from Germany, Japan and Switzerland. Class sizes are small, with a maximum of five students in each. There are five classrooms and a dining room/living room where students can eat breakfast and lunch.

This school really offers a package with its courses. As well as comprising the cost of accommodation and tuition, fees include breakfast and lunch at the academy, two day-long excursions and ten cultural activities a month (including museum entrance fees), classes in Spanish cookery, songs and folk music, wine tasting, a Certificate of Attendance and a course Diploma. There is also a school library with videos. The range of cultural activities and excursions is impressive and well-thought out – they aren't just a limp afterthought tacked on to the end of the language courses. You will have the opportunity to visit places such as the National Sculpture Museum, the house of Cervantes and the wine 'bodegas' for which this part of Spain is famous. There will also be lectures on various topics such as Spanish etiquette and customs as well as evening outings. Excursions will take you to, among other places, Salamanca, Segovia, Madrid and on the route of Isabel of Castile (a white wine trail).

Three courses are available. The Intensive Course in Language and Culture (suitable for all levels) is open all year round, beginning on the first and sixteenth of every month. The cost ranges from 90,000ptas for two weeks to 410,000ptas for twelve weeks, with the possibility of staying on for longer. The 'Immersion course in Spanish' (suitable for intermediate and superior levels only) is available all year round and lasts two weeks, beginning on the first and third week of every month. The course costs 110,000ptas and involves six hours of tuition a day for the fortnight. The DELE preparation course lasts one or two months (at a cost of 165,000ptas or 300,000ptas respectively), beginning in April and or May and October and/or November. Prices include accommodation with Spanish families - the school works with a number of such families all year round. Should the student wish to stay in a hotel, they will have to make up the difference in price.

You can take part in any course without the extras (food, excursions and so on); contact the school for further details. Also available are refresher courses for teachers, translators and professionals, courses for groups from overseas centres (eg from universities) and private classes.

For more information and enrolment details, contact the school.

Warwick House
López Gómez, 18-2 dcha, 47002 Valladolid

Paramo – Academia de Español

Tel: +34 983 200 999
Fax: +34 983 304 825
Email: warwick@dragonet.es
Established: 1981
Level: None
Nearest Station: Estación del
Norte – Valladolid
Contact: María Luisa del Val

A small school dedicated mainly to teaching English to Spanish students, Warwick House's Spanish courses are attended by about 65 overseas students annually, the majority of whom come from the UK and Japan. The fact that so few non-Spanish speakers are taught here (classes are small, with four to five students) could be an important factor for those who want to avoid speaking their native tongue as much as possible while in Spain. Valladolid – a city in the north of Spain – is also one of the best places to learn the language as it is supposedly here that the purest Castellano is spoken.

Two options are available at this school. One-to-one tuition tailor-made to the needs of the student costs 2,500ptas; the fee is reduced to 2,250ptas if you sign up for a minimum of ten hours or more. It is up to you to choose the duration and intensity of your course. The tuition is centred around grammar, functional Spanish and oral and written comprehension. In addition, lectures on cultural themes, excursions and visits will also be included in whatever programme you devise. An example of an intensive course (Monday to Friday) organised for one particular student goes as follows: grammar and conversation from 9am to 11am every day, a half hour coffee break and then a combination of videos, lectures, written comprehension, oral comprehension, pronunciation and role plays for two hours.

The weekend is set aside for excursions and sightseeing. After lunch and a break, homework from 5pm to 7pm and a cultural outing from 7pm to 9pm, followed by dinner. This is clearly a very intensive example of what is available and such a relentless programme may not suit you or your requirements. Consult the school for further details.

The other option are the Holiday courses for British schools – short courses tailor-made for groups for a period of five to ten days, including ten to forty hours of Spanish lessons. Excursions are optional. The school can arrange for students to live with a Spanish family (2,500ptas per night), though course participants usually stay in a local hotel.

Contact the school for further information and enrolment details.

VIZCAYA

Universidad del País Vasco

Vicerrectorado de Investigación
y Relaciones Internacionales,
Universidad del País Vasco,
Edificio Rectorado, 48940
Leioa (VIZCAYA)
Tel: +34 94 464 7700 ext2089
Fax: +34 94 480 1590
Established: 1970
Level: None
Nearest Station: Bilbao
Contact: Mónica Aróstegui

According to its short brochure, the presence of Erasmus/Socrates students at the University of the Basque Country is what acted as a spur for the Spanish language and culture courses that it now offers for overseas students. So if you do go there, expect to be surrounded by exchange students from all over Europe, in particular from England, France and

Germany. At the university you can learn Castellano as well as the language of the Basque Country, Euskera (Basque).

The university is situated in Bilbao, an industrial town in the north of Spain, and on two other campuses, one in San Sebastian, the other in Vitoria. All of these are in the region known as the Basque country, which lies on the border of France. Bilbao has recently hit the headlines due to the fact that an enormous and very unusual looking new modern art museum (the Guggenheim Museum) has been built there.

Around 200 students attend the Spanish language and culture courses at the university and average class sizes are between 15 and 20 students. You don't need any prior knowledge of Spanish and the only prerequisite is that you must be over 16 years of age. There are classes during the month of August.

Courses are offered on three levels: advanced, intermediate and elementary (only available at the campus in Vitoria as long as more than ten or more students can attend). A test will take place on the first day in order to place you in the class most suitable for you. There are two types of course: 'Intensive' and 'Spring and Autumn'. The 'Intensive' courses last a fortnight and there is no registration fee for Erasmus/Socrates students. For non-Erasmus students the cost is 11,250 ptas. The course consists of three hours of classes daily, with emphasis on Oral understanding, Oral expression and Written expression.

The spring and autumn courses last three months and include six hours of classes weekly. The registration fee for Erasmus students is 5,000ptas, for non-Erasmus students it is 22,500. Course modules are similar to the 'Intensive' course but are based mainly on Oral expression and understanding.

You will be presented with a certificate from the university on successful completion of your course exams. It is also possible to accumulate credit points (four for the 'Intensive' course, eight for the autumn and spring courses respectively).

The university can help find accommodation for overseas students. For details, contact the above address.

ZARAGOZA

Hispalengua
San Miguel, 16, 50001 Zaragoza
Tel: +34 976 221 810
Fax: +34 976 212 010
Email: Hispalengua.Oxford@ Jet.es
Website: www.Jet.es/~Hispalen
Established: 1975
Level: None
Nearest Station: Zaragoza station
Contact: María Alegre

Zaragoza, situated half way between Barcelona and Madrid in what was the old kingdom of Aragon, is a beautiful city whose famous fiestas (a celebration of both religion and culture) in honour of Nuestra Señora del Pilar take place in the month of October. This school is situated in the heart of the city and prides itself on the personalised attention that it devotes to each student. It is attended by about six hundred students annually (mainly French, German and Japanese) and classes have an average of about six students in each.

There are four courses on offer. The Intensive Spanish course involves 20 lessons a week and costs 45,000ptas a week including full board accommodation. The Mini group course, which involves 25 lessons per week in a group of no more than five, costs 65,000ptas a week including full board accommodation. Specialist classes (Business Spanish, Secretarial Spanish, Spanish for the Tourism and Leisure Industry) are organised via the school and cost (a very steep) 4,500ptas for 50 minutes, as does one-to-one tuition.

Accommodation in a Spanish family selected by the school will cost 24,000ptas for half board and 24,600ptas full board, per week. The school can also find you hotel accommodation starting from a rate of 3,000ptas a day. One cultural activity takes place every week and students can use the facilities in the nearby sports centre. Excursions outside the town will cost extra, as will the textbook to be used in class and medical insurance.

Contact the school for enrolment details.

LANGUAGE SCHOOLS APPROVED BY THE SPANISH MINISTRY OF EDUCATION AND CULTURE

COURSES ORGANISED BY UNIVERSITIES AND STATE-RUN INSTITUTIONS

Centro de Estudios Norteamericanos de la Universidad de Alcalá
Libreros, 13-1a,
28001 Alcalá De Henares (Madrid),
SPAIN
Tel: +34 91 885 4375
Fax: +34 91 885 4383
Email: cenuah@cenuah.alcala.es

Universidad de Alcalá, Vicerrectorado de Extensión Universitaria

Cursos de Lengua y Cultura Españolas para Extranjeros,
Vicerrectorado de Extensión Universitaria,
Plaza de San Diego, s/n
28001 Alcalá De Henares (Madrid)
SPAIN
Tel: +34 91 1-885 4089
Fax: +34 91 1-885 4089/4126

Council on International Educational Exchange
Universidad de Alicante
Resident Director CIEE,
Cursos Internacionales,
Universidad De Alicante,
San Vicente del Raspeig (Alicante),
SPAIN
Tel: +34 96 (34-6) 590 3437
Fax: +34 96 (34-6) 590 3464

Escuela Oficial de Idiomas (Alicante)
Marqués de Molins, 56-58,
03004 Alicante,
SPAIN
Tel: +34 96 514 4269
Fax: +34 96 514 4085

Sociedad de Relaciones Internacionales de la Universidad de Alicante
Universidad de Alicante,
San Vicente del Raspeig, s/n,
Campus San Vicente,
03690 Alicante,
SPAIN
Tel: +34 96 590 3793
Fax: +34 96 590 3794

ESADE, Escuela de Idiomas
(Fundación ESADE),
Avda Espugues, 92-96,
08034 Barcelona,
SPAIN
Tel: +34 93 495 2095
Fax: +34 93 495 2075

Escuela Oficial de Idiomas
Barcelona-Drassanes,

Avda Drassanes, s/n,
08001 Barcelona,
SPAIN
Tel: +34 93 329 2458
Fax: +34 93 441 4833

Universidad de Barcelona
Estudios Hispánicos,
Pza Universidad,
08071 Barcelona,
SPAIN
Tel: +34 93 318 4266
Fax: +34 93 302 5947

Escuela Oficial de Idiomas (Bilbao)
Pza de San Pedro,
48014 Bilbao (Vizcaya),
SPAIN
Tel: +34 94 475 2980/
447 2198/475 4972
Fax: +34 94 476 2236

University Studies Abroad Consortium
– Asociación de Estudios para
Extranjeros
Facultad de Ciencias Sociales y de la
Información,
Universidad del País Vasco/UPV,
Apartado 644,
48080 Bilbao,
SPAIN
Tel: +34 94 464 8800 (ext. 3088)
Fax: +34 94 480 2103

Universidad de Toulouse-Le Mirail y
Ministerio de Educación y Cultura, en
colaboración con la Universidad de
Braunschweig (RFA)
Sr. Director de los Cursos de Verano
de Burgos,
Universidad de Toulouse-Le Mirail, 5,
Allée Antonio Machado,
31058 Toulouse,
FRANCE
Tel: +33 61 504 985
Fax: +33 61 504 910

Universidad de Cádiz, Vicerrectorado

de Extensión Universitaria y
Relaciones Institucionales
José Paredes Monge, 1,
11002 Cádiz,
SPAIN
Tel: +34 56 220 802
Fax: +34 56 220 877

Universidad de Córdoba – Servicio de
Lenguas Modernas y Traducción
Técnica
Edificio de Servicios Múltiples, 5a
planta,
Avda Menéndez Pidal, s/n,
14071 Córdoba,
SPAIN
Tel: +34 57 218 132/218 133/218 996
Fax: +34 57 218 996
Email: si3goluj@uco.es

Universidad de Oviedo
Secretaría General de los Cursos de
Verano de la Universidad de Oviedo
Cátedra Jovellanos de Extensión
Universitaria,
Begoña, 25,
33206 Gijón,
SPAIN
Tel: +34 98 518 2218
Telefax: +34 98 510 3930
ALSO AT:
Negociado de Extensión Universitaria
Pza del Riego, 9
33003 Oviedo
SPAIN
Tel: +34 98 510 3930

Centro de Lenguas Modernas de la
Universidad de Granada
Cursos para Extranjeros,
Placeta del Hospicio Viejo, s/n,
(Realejo)
E-18071 Granada,
SPAIN
Tel: +34 58 220 790
Fax: +34 58 220 844

LANGUAGE SCHOOLS

Universidad de Zaragoza
(From August 20 to June 30)

\Servicio de Lengua y Cultura
Españolas para Extranjeros
Edificio Interfacultades – 3a Planta
Pedro Cerbuna, 12,
50009 Zaragoza,
SPAIN
Tel: +34 976 761 047
Fax: +34 976 762 050
(From June 30th to August 20th)
Residencia Universitaria,
Calle Universidad, 3,
22700 Jaca (Huesca),
SPAIN
Tel: +34 974 360 196
Fax: +34 974 355 785

Escuela Oficial de Idiomas
Departamento de Español para
Extranjeros
Pepín Rivero, s/n,
La Coruña,
SPAIN
Tel: +34 981 279 100
Fax: +34 981 279 116

Escuela Oficial de Idiomas de Las
Palmas
Departamento de Español,
Fernando Guanarteme, 51,
35007 Las Palmas de Gran Canaria,
SPAIN
Tel: +34 928 266 056/228 912
Fax: +34 928 276 940

Universidad de León
Avda Facultad, 25,
24071 León,
SPAIN
Tel: +34 987 291 650
Fax: +34 987 291 693

Universidad de La Rioja
Unidad de Relaciones Internacionales
La Cigüeña, 60,
26004 Logroño,

SPAIN
Tel: +34 941 299 100
Fax: +34 941 299 146

Sección Cursos
Instituto de Cooperación
Iberoamericana
Agencia Española de Cooperación
Internacional,
Avda de los Reyes Católicos, 4,
28040 Madrid
SPAIN
Tel: +34 91 583 8241

Instituto de Formación Empresarial de
la Cámara de Comercio e Industria de
Madrid
Pedro Salinas, 11,
28043 Madrid,
SPAIN
Tel: +34 91 538 3838
Fax: +34 91 538 3803

Centro de Estudios Hispánicos
Universidad Antonio de Nebrija
Pirineos, 55,
28040 Madrid,
SPAIN
Tel: +34 91 311 6602
Fax: +34 91 311 661
Email: cehi@dii.unnet.es

Universidad Complutense de Madrid
Fundación General Donoso Cortés,
65-6a planta,
28015 Madrid
SPAIN
Tel: +34 91 394 6437/41
Fax: +34 91 394 6411

Departamento de Español
Escuela Oficial de Idiomas
Jesús Maestro, s/n,
28003 Madrid,
SPAIN
Tel: +34 91 554 4492
Fax: +34 91 533 5331

Servicio de Idiomas de la Universidad
Autónoma de Madrid
Ciudad Universitaria de Cantoblanco,
28049 Madrid,
SPAIN
Tel: +34 91 397 4633
Fax: +34 91 397 4620

Secretaria de los Cursos para
Extranjeros
Facultad de Filosofía y Letras
(Edificio A),
Universidad Complutense,
Ciudad Universitaria,
28040 Madrid,
SPAIN
Tel: +34 91 394 5325/36
Fax: +34 91 394 5336

Universidad Pontificia de Comillas
(Inés Gil)
Alberto Aguilera, 23,
28015 Madrid,
SPAIN
Tel: +34 91 542 2800
Fax: +34 91 559 6569

Escuela Oficial de Idiomas de Málaga
Secretaría Cursos de Español
Paseo de Martinicos, 26,
29009 Málaga,
SPAIN
Tel: +34 95 227 4398/2502
Fax: +34 95 227 2007

Universidad de Málaga
Cursos para Extranjeros,
Avda Andalucía, 26-1a planta,
29071 Málaga,
SPAIN
Tel: +34 95 227 8211
Fax: +34 95 227 9712

Escuela Oficial de Idiomas
Travesía Herta de los Cristales, 7,
29600 Marbella,
SPAIN
Tel: +34 95 277 7739

Fax: +34 95 277 8295

Servicio de Promoción Educativa
Vicerrectorado de Extensión
Universitaria,
Universidad de Murcia,
30071 Murcia
SPAIN
Tel: +34 968 363 319/20
Fax: +34 968 363 603

Estudio General Luliano de Mallorca
San Roque, 4,
07001 Palma de Mallorca,
SPAIN
Tel: +34 971 711 988
Fax: +34 971 719 105

Departamento de Español
Escuela Oficial de Idiomas
Aragón, 59,
07005 Palma de Mallorca,
SPAIN
Tel: +34 971 411 314
Fax: +34 971 411 208

Secretaría de ILCE
Edificio Central,
Campus Universitario,
Universidad de Navarra,
31080 Pamplona,
SPAIN
Tel: +34 948 425 600 ext 2404

Programa Internacional de Estudios
de Español
Universidad de Málaga,
Palacio de Mondragón,
PO Box 332,
24900 Ronda (Málaga),
SPAIN
Tel: +34 95 287 3265
Email: spanishstudies@um.ronda.
redestb.es

Departamento de Español
Escuela Oficial de Idiomas,
Peña de Francia, 46,

37007 Salamanca,
SPAIN
Tel: +34 923 241 461/098
Fax: +34 923 225 831

**Cursos Internacionales de la
Universidad de Salamanca**
Patio de Escuelas Menores, s/n,
37008 Salamanca,
SPAIN
Tel: +34 923 294 418
Fax: +34 923 294 504
Email: curespu@gug.usal.es OR
kolb@gugu.usal.es

Universidad Pontificia de Salamanca
Cursos de Lengua y Cultura Españolas
Compañía, 5,
37002 Salamanca,
SPAIN
Tel +34 923 218 316
Fax +34 923 218 316

Escuela Oficial de Idiomas
Avda Castiella, 8,
11360 San Roque (Cádiz),
SPAIN
Tel: +34 956 781 082
Fax: +34 956 781 021

**Asociación de Estudios para
Extranjeros**
University Studies Abroad
Consortium,
Escuela de Arquitectura,
Universidad del País Vasco/UPV,
Plaza de Oñati, 2,
20009 San Sebastián,
SPAIN
Tel: +34 943 218 466 ext 222
Fax: +34 943 311 623

Escuela Oficial de Idiomas
Rubén Marichal, s/n,
38004 Santa Cruz de Tenerife,
SPAIN
Tel: +34 922 283 711
Fax: +34 922 249 360

**Secretaría del Servicio de Idiomas de la
Universidad de La Laguna**
Avda Trinidad, s/n,
Edif de Becas, 2a planta,
La Laguan,
Santa Cruz de Tenerife,
SPAIN
Tel/Fax: +34 922 603 345

**Centro de Idiomas de la Universidad
de Cantabria**
Avda de los Castros, s/n,
39005 Santander,
SPAIN
Tel: +34 942 201 313
Fax: +34 942 201 316
Email: ciuc@gestion.unican.es

**Universidad Internacional
Menendéz y Pelayo**
MADRID   Isaac Peral, 23,
              28040 Madrid,
              SPAIN
              Tel: +34 91 592 0600/
              544 8374
              Fax: +34 91 543 0897

SANTANDER UIMP "Las Llamas",
              Avda de los Castros,
              s/n 39005 Santander,
              SPAIN
              Tel: +34 942 360 055
              Fax: +34 942 280 816

**Secretaría de los Cursos
Internacionales
Universidad de Santiago de
Compostela**
Facultad de Ciencias Políticas,
Campus Universitario,
15706 Santiago de Compostela,
SPAIN
Tel: +34 981 597 035
Fax: +34 981 597 036

Universidad de La Rioja
Unidad de Relaciones
Internacionales,

La Cigüeña, 60,
26004 Logroño,
SPAIN
Tel: +34 941 299 100
Fax: +34 941 299 146

Secretaría de los Extranjeros
Facultades de Filología y Geografía e
Historia,
Palos de la Frontera, s/n,
41004 Sevilla,
SPAIN
Tel: +34 95 455 1492/3
Fax: +34 95 456 0439

Universidad de Sevilla
Instituto de Idiomas,
Palos de la Frontera, s/n,
41004 Sevilla,
SPAIN
Tel: +34 95 455 1155/56
Fax: +34 95 455 1450

Fundación José Ortega y Gasset
Callejón de San Justo, s/n,
45001 Toledo,
SPAIN
Tel: +34 925 212 908
Fax: +34 925 226 548

Escuela Oficial de Idiomas
Llano de Zaidía, 19,
46009 Valencia,
SPAIN
Tel: +34 96 340 5022
Fax: +34 96 349 2547

Universidad de Valencia
Estudi General,
Vicerrectoral de Relaciones
Exteriores,
Gabinete de Extranjeros,
Senda Senent, 11,
46023 Valencia,
SPAIN
Tel: +34 96 386 4180
Fax: +34 96 398 3021

Cursos Internacionales-Cursos para Extranjeros
Universidad de Valladolid,
Casa del Estudiante,
Real de Burgos, s/n,
47071 Valladolid,
SPAIN
Tel: +34 983 423 600
Fax: +34 983 423 234/51

Universidad del País Vasco
Vicerrectorado del Campus de Álava,
Manuel Iradier, 46 bajo,
01005 Vitoria-Gasteiz,
SPAIN
Tel: +34 945 265 722
Fax: +34 945 267 822

Escuela Oficial de Idiomas no.1
Departamento de Español,
Domingo Miral, s/n,
50009 Zaragoza,
SPAIN
Tel: +34 976 357 289
Fax: +34 976 568 034

Servicio de Lengua y Cultura
Españolas para Extranjeros,
Edificio Interfacultades, 3a planta,
Pedro Cerbuna, 12,
50009 Zaragoza,
SPAIN
Tel: +34 976 761 047
Fax: +34 976 762 050

Courses organised by private centres

Escuela Internacional
Central de Reservas,
Talamanca, 10,
28807 Alcalá de Henares (Madrid),
SPAIN
Tel: +34 91 883 1264
Fax: +34 91 883 1301

Centro Cooperativo de Idiomas
Gran Vía, 64-1a planta y 66-9a

planta,
28013 Madrid,
SPAIN
Tel: +34 91 541 3902
Fax: +34 91 541 2801

Colegio de España
Aspe, 31,
03012 Alicante,
SPAIN
Tel: +34 96 524 3262

Colegio de España
Compañía, 65,
37008 Salamanca,
SPAIN
Tel: +34 923 214 788
Fax: +34 923 218 791

Anglo Orbe
José del Hierro, 42,
28027 Madrid,
SPAIN
Tel: +34 91 367 8870
Fax: +34 91 367 8403

Centre de Estudios y Vacaciones Almuñecar
Santa Isabel la Real, 11,
Granada,
Tel: +34 958 275 424
Fax: +34 958 275 015
Email: ceva@valnet.es

Instituto Mediterráneo
Vélez, 21,
18690 Almuñecar (Granada),
Apartado de Correos no. 569,
SPAIN
Tel/Fax: +34 958 880 584

CF Idiomas
Isilla, 3,
09400 Aranda de Duero,
SPAIN
Tel/Fax: +34 947 505 117

American British College –

Centro de Estudios de Español
Guillem Tell, 27,
08006 Barcelona,
SPAIN
Tel: +34 93 415 5757
Fax: +34 93 415 4814

**Barna House –
Centros de Estudio
de Español**
Roger Llúria, 23,
08037 Barcelona,
SPAIN
Tel: +34 93 488 0080
Fax: +34 93 488 0169

Gala Internacional
Passeig de Gracia, 69,
Barcelona,
SPAIN
Tel: +34 93 487 8725
Fax: +34 93 487 5369

Inlingua Idiomas
Rambla de Catalunya, 33,
08007 Barcelona,
SPAIN
Tel: +34 93 487 5580/4401
Fax: +34 93 488 0040

Don Quijote
Central Promotion Office,
Placentinos, 2,
Apartado de Correos no. 333,
37080 Salamanca,
SPAIN
Tel: +34 923 268 860,
Barcelona +34 93 412 4849
Fax: +34 923 268 815,
Barcelona +34 93 412 3712
Email: donquijote@offcampus.es
Website: www.teclata.es/
donquijote

Institutos Mangold
Rambla de Catalunya, 16 pral.,
08007 Barcelona,
SPAIN

Tel: +34 93 301 2539
Fax: +34 93 412 1879
Email: *mangold@mhp.es*

International House
Trafalgar, 14 Entlo.,
08010 Barcelona,
SPAIN
Tel: +34 93 268 4511
Fax: +34 93 268 0239
Email: *spanish@bcn.ihes.com*
Website: *www.ihes.com/bcn*

Kingsbrook Idiomas
Traversera de Gracia, 60-1°-3a,
08006 Barcelona,
SPAIN
Tel: +34 93 209 3763
Fax: +34 93 202 1598

Metrocultura Idiomas
Ronda Sant Antoni, 100,
08001 Barcelona,
SPAIN
Tel/Fax: +34 93 301 4634

La Puerta al Español
Burdiñate, 5 bajo,
20570 Bergara (Guipuzcoa),
SPAIN
Tel: +34 943 763 001
Fax: +34 943 760 032

Castrum Lenguas, Cultura y Turismo
Carretera de Rueda, 33,
47008 Valladolid,
SPAIN
Tel: +34 983 222 213
Email: *castrum@vasertel.es*
Website: *www.vasertel.es*

Second Language Acquisition Services
Egaña, 6-2°C,
48010 Bilbao,
SPAIN
Tel: +34 94 444 8062/6
Fax: +34 94 444 8066

Escuela de Español de las Alpujarras
Natalio Rivas, 1-4°,
18001 Granada,
SPAIN
Tel: +34 958 201 087
Fax: +34 958 275 015

Estudios Subbética
Martín Belda, 56,
14940 Cabra (Córdoba),
SPAIN
Tel/Fax: +34 957 525 151

Escuela Lusitania
Pza de Caterías, 11,
10003 Cáceres,
SPAIN
Tel: +34 927 214 619

Escuela Internacional de Español
Pérgolas, 5,
Box 31,
11007 Cádiz,
SPAIN
Tel/Fax: +34 956 260 557

Hemeroscopea-Centro de Idiomas
José Antonio, 18-1°,
03710 Calpe (Alicante),
SPAIN
Tel/Fax: +34 96 579 2398

Academia Andaluza de Idiomas
Carretera del Punto, 9,
11140 Conil de Frontera (Cádiz),
SPAIN
Tel/Fax: +34 956 440 552

Centro de Idiomas KLACK
Intercultural Córdoba
Manchado, 9 (Esq. Realejo),
14002 Córdoba,
SPAIN
Tel/Fax: +34 957 491 303

Los Geranios-Centro de Estudios
Santa Ana, 6,
41700 Dos Hermanas (Sevilla),

SPAIN
Tel: +34 95 472 0503
Fax: +34 95 566 6976
Email: geranio@cece.es

Trinity School,
Ave del Paraíso, 6,
11500 El Puerto de Santa María,
(Cádiz)
SPAIN
Tel: +34 956 871 926
Fax: +34 956 541 918

Academia Internacional Frigiliana
Avda Príncipe de Asturias, 9,
29788 Frigiliana (Málaga),
SPAIN
Tel/Fax: +34 253 3499

Hemeroscopea-Centro de Idiomas
Plaza 18 de Julio, 23-1°,
03740 Gata de Gorgos (Alicante),
SPAIN
Tel: +34 96 575 7051
Fax: +34 96 579 2398

Genana
Ermita Nova, 3,
46110 Godella (Valencia),
SPAIN
Tel: +34 96 364 1949
Fax: +34 96 390 0740

Carmen de las Cuevas
Cuesta de los Chinos, 15,
Albaicín,
18010 Granada,
SPAIN
Tel: +34 958 221 062
Fax: +34 958 220 476
Email: carmen.cuevas@grx.servicom.es
Website: www.eel.es/cuevas/

Centro de Estudios Hispánicos
Aljibe del Gato, 1,
Carmen de los Gatos-Albaicín,
18010 Granada,
SPAIN

Tel: +34 958 205 863
Fax: +34 958 277 240
Email: castila@redestb.es
Website: www.eel.es/castila

CEGRÕ-Centro Granadí de Español
Sacristía de San Matías, 12,
18009 Granada,
SPAIN
Tel: +34 958 228 602
Fax: +34 958 228 657

Colegio Nueva Universidad de
Granada
Información e Inscripción,
Parra Alta, 7,
18012 Granada,
SPAIN
Tel: +34 958 275 418
Fax: +34 958 275 015

Escuela Montalbán
Conde Cifuentes, 11,
18005 Granada,
SPAIN
Tel/Fax: +34 958 256 875

Don Quijote Granada
Azhuma, 5,
18005 Granada,
SPAIN
Tel: +34 958 254 212
Fax: +34 958 265 158
Email: donquijote@redestb.es

Instituto Mediterráneo
Cuesta de la Alhacaba, 31,
18010 Granada,
SPAIN
Tel/Fax: +34 958 293 732

Sociedad Hispano Mundial
Palacio de Exposiciones
y Congresos,
Paseo del Violón, s/n,
18006 Granada,
SPAIN
Tel: +34 958 246 892

Fax: +34 958 246 893

CLIC-Centro de Lenguas e Intercambio Cultural
Santa Ana, 11,
41002 Sevilla,
SPAIN
Tel: +34 95 437 4500/300
Fax: +34 95 437 1806

Hemeroscopea Centro de Idiomas
Dr Borrull, 4,
03730 Jávea
(Alicante),
SPAIN
Tel/Fax: +34 96 579 2398

Corus, Centro de Lengua Español
Central Office,
27 Wytham Street,
Oxford
OX1 4SU
UK
Tel: +44 1865 249 558

Centro de Enseñanza de Español La Herradura
Urb. El Camping no.3 bajo,
18697 La Herradura
(Granada),
SPAIN
Tel: +34 958 640 528
Fax: +34 958 640 491

ALBA, Language Consulting
Avda de Pío XII, 3,
28016 Madrid,
SPAIN
Tel: +34 91 359 6016
Fax: +34 91 359 4981
Email: 101764.2473@compuserve.com

Escuela Benedict
Edificio Mercurio I, 5º piso,
35100 Playa del Inglés
(Gran Canaria),
SPAIN
Tel: +34 928 761 830
Fax: +34 928 766 351

Gran Canaria School of Languages
Ruiz de Alda, 12,
35007 Las Palmas de Gran Canaria,
SPAIN
Tel: +34 928 267 971
Fax: +34 928 278 980
Email: gcschool@intercom.es
Website: www.canary.step.es/gccourses

Academia Victoria
Gran Vía, 3,
26002 Logroño
(La Rioja),
SPAIN
Tel/Fax: +34 941 242 038

Centro Internacional San Millán
Calvo Sotelo, 13-1ºD,
26003 Logroño (La Rioja),
SPAIN
Tel: +34 941 241 332
Fax: +34 941 259 794

ALCE
Paseo de la Habana, 170-1JD,
Madrid,
SPAIN
Tel/Fax: +34 91 350 9859

Aliseda-Escuelas Internacionales de Español
Goya, 115-3º,
28009 Madrid,
SPAIN
Tel: +34 91 309 1176
Fax: +34 91 401 0673
Email: chester@bitmailer.net
Website: www.chester.es/aliseda

Asesoría Lingüística Thamesis
Castelló, 224 bajo B,
28001 Madrid,
SPAIN
Tel: +34 91 431 9635
Fax: +34 91 575 6597

British Language Center
Bravo Murillo, 377-2º,

28020 Madrid,
SPAIN
Tel: +34 91 733 0488/0739
Fax: +34 91 314 5009

CEE Idiomas
Carmen, 6,
28013 Madrid,
SPAIN
Tel: +34 91 531 5881/913/522 0472
Fax: +34 91 531 9308

Centro Cultural Hispano Europeo
Dr Castelo, 32-5ºD,
28009 Madrid, SPAIN
Tel: +34 91 574 3713

Centros de Idiomas Sagasta
Sagasta, 30-3º izda
28004 Madrid
SPAIN
Tel: +34 91 446 6982
Fax: +34 91 447 2223

DIDASCON
Corazón de María, 35-1ºA,
28002 Madrid,
SPAIN
Tel: +34 91 519 9574
Fax: +34 91 519 9290

ENFOREX-Escuela de Lengua Española
Alberto Aguilera, 26-2º dcha,
28015 Madrid,
SPAIN
Tel: +34 91 594 3776
Fax: +34 91 594 5159
Email: enforex@mad.servicom.es
Website: www.servicom.es/

Escuela Madrid Plus
Arenal, 21-6º,
28013 Madrid,
SPAIN
Tel: +34 91 548 1116/043
Fax: +34 91 559 2904

Estudio Internacional Sampere
Castelló, 50,
28001 Madrid,
SPAIN
Tel: + 34 91 431 4366
Fax: +34 91 575 9509
Email: estudiointer.sampere@
mad.servicom.es
Website: www.worldwide.edu/spain/eis

Eureka "Academia de Español"
Areanl, 6-4º,
28013 Madrid, SPAIN
Tel: +34 91 521 8275
Fax: +34 91 531 4948
Email: eureka@adv.es
Website: www.adv.es/eureka

Eurocentres/Idiomas Vivos España
Paseo de la Castellana, 194,
28046 Madrid,
SPAIN
Tel: +34 91 345 3512
Fax: +34 91 345 3513
Email: 100632.126@compuserve.com

Inlingua Madrid
Arenal, 24-1º izda,
28013 Madrid,
SPAIN
Tel: +34 91 541 3246/7

Instituto Hernán Cortés
Diego de León, 16-5a planta, puerta 4,
28006 Madrid,
SPAIN
Tel: +34 91 563 4601
Fax: +34 91 563 4526

Instituto Vox
Gran Vía, 59-3º izda,
28013 Madrid,
SPAIN
Tel: +34 91 547 1559
Fax: +34 91 547 2753

Institutos Mangold
Gran Vía, 32-2º,

28013 Madrid,
SPAIN
Tel: +34 91 522 8300
Fax: +34 91 521 5803

International House Madrid
Zurbano, 8,
28010 Madrid,
SPAIN
Tel: +34 91 310 1314
Fax: +34 91 308 5321
Email ihmadrid@mad.servicom.es

Language Studies International
Luchana, 31-1,
28010 Madrid, SPAIN
Tel: +34 91 446 0999
Fax: +34 91 593 3685

Linguacenter
Rafael Calvo, 8,
28010 Madrid,
SPAIN
Tel/Fax: +34 91 447 0781

Listen & Learn
Narvaéz, 14,
28009 Madrid,
SPAIN
Tel/Fax: +34 91 576 2528

Tándem Escuela
Internacional
Luis Vélez de la Guevara, 8,
28012 Madrid,
SPAIN
Tel: +34 91 369 1625/0932
Fax: +34 91 1032

Al-Andalus
Herrera, 12,
29017 Málaga,
SPAIN
Tel: +34 95 229 1741
Fax +34 95 220 3785

Centros de Estudios de Castellano
Avda Juan Sebastián Elcano, 120,

29017 Málaga,
SPAIN
Tel/Fax: +34 95 229 0551

Cervantes
Escuela Internacional de
Estudios de Español
Juan Sebastián Elcano, 69
29017 Málaga,
SPAIN
Tel: +34 95 229 5378
Fax: +34 95 229 9047

CILE-Centro Internacional
de Lengua Española
Cister, 4,
29015 Málaga,
SPAIN
Tel/Fax: +34 95 222 4122

DEBLA
Cañada de los Ingleses, s/n,
29016 Málaga,
Apartado de Correos 15799,
SPAIN
Tel: +34 95 260 3885
Fax: +34 95 260 2197

Escuela Hispana
Granada, 59-2º,
29015 Málaga,
SPAIN
Tel/Fax: +34 95 221 2689

Escuela Mediterráneo
Marqués de Guadiaro, 4,
29008 Málaga,
SPAIN
Tel: +34 95 221 3448
Fax: +34 95 222 9903

Instituto Flomar
Beatas, 12,
29008 Málaga,
SPAIN
Tel: +34 95 221 7777
Fax: +34 91 260 2418
Email: flomar@vnet.es

LANGUAGE SCHOOLS

Website: www.wnet.es/flomar

Instituto Internacional Alhambra
Avda Juan Sebastián Elcano, 78,
29017 Málaga,
SPAIN
Tel: +34 95 229 1509
Fax: +34 95 220 1600

Malaca, Instituto Internacional de Estudios de Español
Cortada, 6,
29018 Málaga,
SPAIN
Tel: +34 95 229 3242/1896
Fax: +34 95 229 6316

Malacitana, Instituto Internacional de Idiomas
Cañón, 3-1°,
Apartado de Correos 4025,
29080 Málaga,
SPAIN
Tel/Fax: +34 95 221 6292

Málaga Plus
Pasaje Antonio Barceló Mudaño, 8,
29017 Málaga,
SPAIN
Tel: +34 95 229 9330/8849
Fax: +34 95 229 7000

Miramar, Español para Extranjeros
Antonio Trueba, 4,
Apartado de Correos 6095,
29017 Málaga,
SPAIN
Tel: +34 95 229 8695
Fax: +34 95 229 3836

Hispánica, Colegio Internacional
Prolongación de Carabeo, 24
apartada 14,
Nerja (Málaga),
SPAIN
Tel +34 95 252 2096
Fax +34 95 252 2309

Centro Británico/Centro Español
Cervantes, 25,
33004 Oviedo (Asturias),
SPAIN
Tel/Fax: +34 98 527 4732

Hispalingua
Genearl Yagüe, 3-entlo,
33004 Oviedo (Principado de Asturias), SPAIN
Tel/Fax: +34 98 424 3186
Email: si@interplanet.es
Website: www.cyberastur.es/hispalingua

Tándem-Naturlengua
Campoamore, 11-entlo A,
33001 Oviedo,
SPAIN
Tel/Fax: +34 98 520 3984

Club de Amigos de Alemania
Felipe Prieto, 2-1°D,
34001 Palencia,
SPAIN
Tel: +34 979 744 312

Trans Words Idiomas
Gran Vía, 138-entlo 3°,
08330 Premiá de Mar (Barcelona),
SPAIN
Tel/Fax: +34 93 752 3907

Estudio Internacional Sampere
Cielo, 40,
El Puerto de Santa María,
11500 Cádiz,
SPAIN
Tel: +34 956 868 630
Fax: +34 956 874 109
Email: estudiointer.sampere@
mad.servicom.es
Website: www.worldwide.edi/spain/eis

Salminter, Escuela Salmantina de Estudios Internacionales
Toro, 34-36 2°,
37002 Salamanca,

SPAIN
Tel: +34 923 211 808
Fax: +34 923 260 263

Aula de Español Fonseca
Gran Vía, 19-3º,
37001 Salamanca,
SPAIN
Tel/Fax: +34 923 213 777

British School Salamanca y Colegio
Amadís de Gaula,
Zamora, 54-3º,
37002 Salamanca,
SPAIN
Tel/Fax: +34 923 213 121

Colegio de Estudios Hispánicos
Bordadores, 1,
37002 Salamanca,
SPAIN
Tel: +34 923 215 607
Fax: +34 923 214 837
Email: ce.hispanic@eurart.es

Colegio "Frederico García Lorca"
Paseo Carmelitas, 23-1º,
37007 Salamanca,
SPAIN
Tel: +34 923 259 952
Fax: +34 923 249 298

Colegio Hispánico Miguel de Unamuno
Rúa Antigua, 5,
37002 Salamanca,
SPAIN
Tel: +34 923 212 055
Fax: +34 923 271 418
Email: chismu@iponet.es
Website: www.iponet.es/chismu

Colegio Ibérico
Pozo Amarillo, 26-1º,
37002 Salamanca,
SPAIN
Tel/Fax: +34 923 267 288

Eurocentres/Idiomas Vivos España
Vera Cruz Primera, 2,
37008 Salamanca,
SPAIN
Tel: +34 923 271 881
Fax: +34 923 271 727
Email: 106001.3655@compuserve.com

Hispano Continental School
Zamora. 61,
37002 Salamanca,
SPAIN
Tel/Fax: +34 923 212 344

Idiomas Castilla
Vázquez Coronado, 9-2º,
37002 Salamanca,
SPAIN
Tel: +34 923 217 435/266 654
Fax: +34 923 266 654

ISLA (Instituto Salamantina de Lenguas Aplicadas)
Plaza de los Basilios, 8,
37002 Salamanca,
SPAIN
Tel: +34 923 210 394
Fax: +34 923 260 627

Oxford Academy-Academia de Idiomas
Edificio Goya Salón-Bajo,
30740 San Pedro del Pinatar (Murcia),
SPAIN
Tel/Fax: +34 968 180 297

Lacunza-Escuela Internacional
Moraza, 5-bajo,
20006 San Sebastián,
SPAIN
Tel: +34 943 471 487
Fax: +34 943 463 061

Tándem Donostia
Plaza de Gipuzkoa, 2-1º izda,
Apdo de Correos 1075,
20080 San Sebastián,

SPAIN
Tel: +34 943 425 157
Fax: +34 943 425 292

Inlingua Santander
Avda Pontejos, 5,
39005 Santander,
SPAIN
Tel: +34 942 278 465
Fax: +34 942 274 402

Unilang Idiomas
Rulasal, 5-4 izda,
39001 Santander (Cantabria),
SPAIN
Tel/Fax: +34 942 224 294
Email: unilang@redestb.es

Unilang Idiomas
Gerardo Diego, 21,
39200 Reinosa (Cantabria),
SPAIN
Tel: +34 942 754 965
Email: unilang.reinosa@via.goya.es

Iria Flavia Idiomas
Preguntorio, 9-1°,
15704 Santiago de Compostela,
SPAIN
Tel/Fax +34 981 572 032
Email: iria@encomix.es
Website: www.encomix.es/-iria

Giralda Center
Mateos Gorgo, 17,
41004 Sevilla,
SPAIN
Tel/Fax: +34 95 422 1346

IELE-Instituto de Estudios de la Lengua Española
García de Vinuesa, 29,
41001 Sevilla,
SPAIN
Tel: +34 95 456 0788
Fax: +34 95 456 4257

Instituto San Fernando de la Lengua Española

Recardeo, 21-1°-2,
41003 Sevilla,
SPAIN
Tel: +34 95 498 8151
Fax: +34 95 498 8152

Lenguaviva
Viriato, 24,
41003 Sevilla,
SPAIN
Tel: +34 95 490 5131
Fax: +34 95 490 5123
Email: info@lenguaviva.es
Website: www.lenguaviva.es

Linguarama Ibérica
Luis de Morales, 32,
Edificio Forum, 1a planta,
41018 Sevilla,
SPAIN
Tel: +34 95 453 4534
Fax: +34 95 453 4754

Escuela Hispalense
Teide, 1,
11380 Tarifa,
SPAIN
Tel/Fax: +34 956 680 927

Hemeroscopea-Centro de Idiomas
Avda del Mediterráneo, 183,
03725 Teulada (Alicante),
SPAIN
Tel: +34 96 574 1212
Fax: +34 96 579 2398

Academia Plaza
Avda de Fontes, 15 bajo,
30700 Torre Pacheco (Murcia),
SPAIN
Tel/Fax: +34 968 578 837

CILCE
Almirante, 1-2°,
46003 Valencia,
SPAIN
Tel: +34 96 391 0463/1678
Fax: +34 96 392 1981

Centro de Estudios TAME
Barrio la Luz, 13,
Valencia,
SPAIN
Tel/Fax: +34 96 383 0301

Colegio Ausias Marche y FICDE
Secretaría de los Cursos de Español,
Tancat de L'Alter, s/n,
Picassent (Valencia),
SPAIN
Tel: +34 96 123 0566
Fax: +34 96 123 4729

Hispania Universalitas
Santa Teresa, 6-5a puerta,
46001 Valencia,
SPAIN
Tel: +34 96 391 5011

Inlingua Idiomas
Colón, 18-3a,
46006 Valenciaq,
SPAIN
Tel: +34 96 352 9773
Fax: +34 96 352 5915

Hidalgo 2000
Independencia, 5,
47007 Valladolid,
SPAIN
Tel/Fax: +34 983 293 111
Email: hidalgo@adenet.es
Website: www.edent.es/hidalgo

Páramo-Academia de Español
Relatores, 1-4º A-B dcha,
47001 Valladolid,
SPAIN
Tel/Fax: +34 983 264 143

Colegio de Español La Janda
Sagasta, 7,
Apartado de Correos 28,
11150 Vejer de la Frontera,
SPAIN
Tel: +34 956 447 060
Fax: +34 956 447 378

Email: lajanda@arrakis.es
Website: www.arrankis.es/-lajanda

Iberlingua
Paseo de la Mina, 13,
50001 Zaragoza,
SPAIN
Tel: +34 976 237 514
Fax: +34 976 237 095

NB: The addresses given are those of the main headquarters/general enquiries. Some schools have branches in parts of Spain other than the address given here.

Miscellaneous

The schools profiled in this chapter cover a diverse range of interests, the common factor between them being that their course provision includes something distinctly Spanish – be it playing the flamenco guitar, learning how to make paella or horseriding. The range of subjects require varying levels of spoken Spanish and this we have specified in the fact box at the start of every entry. The acting classes and the courses in coffee and wine tasting will appeal to those with the highest level of Spanish, while for dressmaking and music the basics in Spanish comprehension are all that you will need – enthusiasm for the subject is probably more important.

We have tried to seek out schools with courses on Spanish themes. The most obvious were wine-tasting courses, but unless you want to become a professional wine-taster/oenologist, it would seem that there is little catering for the enthusiastic amateur. As far as we are aware, there are no wine-tasting courses in English.

The schools/centres vary in size, with one of the largest being *Centros Culturales Nicolás Salmernón* (a centre run by the municipality of Madrid) and the smallest being *Coffee Consulting*. Some of these places will be accustomed to taking in foreign students (the dressmaking schools, the cookery courses and some of the music colleges) while others will have had less, if any, experience of non-Spanish pupils

(Centros Culturales Nicolás Salmerón, Ensayo 100). Levels of English spoken by staff and teachers will vary, though in general, as is usually the case with most Spaniards, it is poor.

We have visited most of the schools in this section, which means that we have personally vetted their suitability for our readers. A number of other schools were also visited. These have not appeared in the guide because, although they sounded suitable on paper, in practise they did not offer the right provision for non-Spanish students. If you know of, or have been to, a school that you feel would be of interest to other readers, please let us know, as we are always on the lookout for unusual/interesting schools offering courses for Spaniards and non-Spaniards alike.

BULLFIGHTING

If you are a bullfighting aficionado and would like to take some sort of introductory course in the subject, you will be disappointed to learn that there are no courses for amateurs. Given the dangers involved in the sport, this is probably hardly surprising. There is, however, a club in London, the Club Taurino de Londres, for bullfighting aficionados. Tel: 0181 995 5668 to find out more about events and information. You can also contact the *Peña Taurina el Puzayo* in Madrid (Avda Ciudad de Barcelona, 51, 27007 Madrid, Spain, tel: +34 91 433 9709 or the *Peña Taurina el 7*, also in Madrid (Doctor

Esquerdo, 3, 28006 Madrid, Spain, tel: +34 91 726 0794).

The *Universidad Complutense de Madrid* runs a course in the summer on the more theoretical and intellectual side of bullfighting. The course usually takes place in an hotel in Almería in the south of Spain and a high level of Spanish is required (few non-Spaniards attend this course). For more information, contact the Universidad Complutense de Madrid, Docente de Cursos de Verano, faxing them on +34 91 395 6433 (for contact details see the Universidad Complutense de Madrid see the University chapter on *p239*) or contact Brian Harding, secretary of the Club Taurino in London.

If you are aged between 10 and 18 you can learn to become a bullfighter. The bullfighting school in Madrid is the *Escuela de Tauromaquia de Madrid*, Venta del Batán, 28011 Madrid, (tel: +34 91 470 1990). To enrol, you will need parental consent (if you are younger than 16 years of age) and you must present a photocopy of your birth certificate, a medical certificate, six photographs, an analysis of your blood group and, where relevant, a photocopy of your DNI (*Documento Nacional de Identidad*). It costs 500ptas to enrol at the school, together with a monthly payment of 300ptas. The course lasts one academic year, though students tend to stay on at the school from three to five years, depending on age and level of apprenticeship.

ACTING
Ensayo 100
Raimundo Lulio, 20, 28010 Madrid
Tel: +34 91 447 7905
Fax: +34 91 447 9486

Email: ensayo100@iponet.es
Website: www.iponet.es /~ensayo
Established: 1996
Level: Intermediate to high
Nearest Station: (Metro) Iglesia, Alonso Martinez
Contact: Carmen Vals Marcos

A private acting school located in one of Madrid's most authentic *barrios* (neighbourhoods), this has only been going for two years and so its first set of students have yet to graduate. The school itself is also a theatre venue, so there is a stage permanently at the disposal of students, as well as a bar, the top of which is prettily decorated in slightly "Gaudiesque" fashion with shards of broken pottery. There is a basic, minimalist feel to the place and there are no fixed classrooms, just rooms that are partitioned off during class hours. The school started four years ago with the monothematic afternoon courses and expanded to include the in-depth, four year course.

It will be obvious that a high level of Spanish is required, particularly in the analysis and theory classes. There have been overseas students (from America, Denmark and Sweden) and these have been people either studying something else simultaneously or working in Madrid. There are six teachers at the school, all of whom are actors. One of the teachers has a degree in Fine Arts and another studied at RESAD ('Real Escuela Superior de Arte Dramatico').

There are three different courses available. The first is 'Formación Integral del Actor' which is for students looking to pursue acting as a career and which tends to be attended by students of more or less undergraduate age (18 to 22). This lasts four years, runs from Monday to Thursday from 10am to 1pm and offers a complete training including the voice, the body, the history of Theatre on the Stage works and mime (amongst others). The course begins in October and ends in June, the enrolment fee is 10,000ptas and the fee per month is 25,000ptas. At the end of the four-year course students on this course are given a certificate of studies. The final year will be devoted to putting together a play from start to finish, including learning about costumes, lights, make-up and so on, as well as the acting itself. The culmination of this will be the performance of the play itself.

The other two courses are the monothematic workshops in acting techniques and a youth theatre for children and teenagers. The monothematic workshops last a year and take place once a week in the afternoons. The sessions last from two and a half to four hours and the fee is 12,000ptas per month, with a matriculation fee of 5,000ptas. Subjects covered are interpretation, physical training and the voice.

The founders of the school are striving to create an atmosphere of work and collaboration. They want it to be clear that this is a place of learning and not of competition. I sat in on one class ('The History of Theatre on the Stage') which involved the teacher attempting to illustrate to students what it would have been like to attend a showing of Moliere's Tartuffe in Moliere's era. To do this, some of the students acted the parts, while the others sat around playing the part of the audience. The atmosphere was good-natured and enthusiastic. However, perhaps inevitably, I was aware of one person rather selfishly trying to absorb most of the teacher's attention on a point that was not worthy of the time that was eventually spent on it.

As most students come from outside of Madrid, they tend to live in residences or rent flats together. The school, however, cannot help with accommodation. To enter, the basic requisite is to be at least 18 years of age and to have COU or the equivalent (ie A level).

The school is closed from June to October. For enrolment details please contact the school.

TAI – Escuela Superior de Artes y Espectaulos

Serrano Anguita, 10, 28004 Madrid
Tel: +34 91 447 2055
Fax: +34 91 447 2317
Email: EscuelaTAI@dirfo.es
Website: www.dirfo.es/ EscuelaTAI
Established: 1975
Level: Intermediate to High
Nearest Station: (Metro) Alonso Martínez
Contact: Inés Hidalgo

Located in one of the trendiest parts of Madrid, at the centre of what on Friday and Saturday nights becomes the magnet for the capital's bar-hopping youth, this school began in 1975, as the Taller de Artes Imaginarias – TAI – (Workshop for the Imaginary Arts). Concentrating on the teaching of cinema and TV, it was a first for Spain in this field and today it is still probably the highest-ranking school of its kind in the country.

About 10 per cent of the students at TAI are from overseas, the majority of them from South America, while the rest are from other European countries. It is also worth noting that many of the

MISCELLANEOUS

school's Spanish students are not from Madrid – as the school offers something that is virtually unique in the rest of the country, it attracts anyone with an interest in cinema and TV throughout the Iberian peninsula. This unrivalled provision is encapsulated in six different degrees, none of which exist in the "official" (ie state) university syllabuses. Cinematography and the Audio-visual Arts (with emphasis on Cinematography); this comprises five areas in which the student can choose to specialise from their second year onwards. In the first year all students do the same thing. The course costs 595,000ptas per year and lasts for two or three years, depending on what you choose to specialise in. The course in the Art of the Photographic Image lasts two years and costs 425,000ptas per year. Multimedia Design and Communication lasts three years, costs 495,000ptas per year and you can specialise in either Graphic Design, Multimedia Communication (Comunicacion Multimedia) or Advertising Design and 2D and 3D Animation. Stage Design and Building takes two years to complete. The Theatre course (425,000ptas) lasts three years and comprises two specialisms: performing or directing. Finally Creative Literature, a two-year course costing 395,000ptas, includes three areas in which the student can choose to specialise: Narrative Literature, Drama or Screenplays for Cinema and TV. There is no extra cost for materials.

The school building is essentially a place to study and all practical work usually takes place outside of it. There are also visits to sets, to TVE (Televisión Española) and so on. The school has its own film production company and students can, from time to time, participate on the sets. TAI has about 80 teachers, all of whom have solid background in their fields. As these subjects are not yet considered to be official degrees in Spain, teachers tend to have a great deal of experience, rather than academic qualifications.

The school's philosophy is that students mustn't just be good at what they do – they have to be able to do the very best they can and the belief at TAI is that in order to do this, the student's artistic creativity must be brought out. The teachers try to form students culturally, so that they have an idea of the history of what they are doing as well as its future. For this reason, students must attend classes such as the History of Cinema and are expected to have an idea of the basics of classical literature.

The level of Spanish for all of these varies. In photography, for example, you could probably get away with a fairly elementary knowledge of the language while for theatre, you will need an excellent standard. You should bear in mind that you will have to do written exams, so perhaps it is worth asking yourself how comfortable you would feel sitting an exam in a foreign language knowing that no concessions will be made just because it is not your first language. The school, however, will conduct an oral exam in certain cases.

Competition to get into the school is high and in some subjects, students have to sit an entrance exam. In others, they must be 17 or over and have done BUP or its equivalent (ie GCSEs). There is a maximum of 24 students per subject in each year (14 in Photography). Most students are aged between 18 and 25. TAI has a list of student residences, halls of residence (most expensive option) and hostels (cheapest option) to which it has sent students in the past. Financial aid is available to those who cannot afford the fees. The school has an employment office and it receives a number of offers of work every year. Obviously, a student's success in finding work once they leave the school is very much up to them. However, the school is known throughout the country and the prestige of its name can help at interviews.

The school is extremely well equipped. Facilities include a theatre, two sets for film and TV, a computer room, a room for video projections, a montage room for film and TV (AVID), a photography laboratory, a video postproduction room, a radio studio and a performance classroom. For further enrolment details contact the school.

Other schools of interest
(a high level of Spanish will be required on all courses).

BARCELONA
La Casona Formación e Investigación Teatral de Barcelona, Burgos, 55, 08014 Barcelona,
Tel: +34 93 422 6922
Fax: +34 93 422 6922
email lacasona@ambbit.es
website www.lacasona.es

Estudi de Teatre "L'Escala"
Carrer del Bou de Sant Pere, 7 (baixos), 08003 Barcelona
Tel: +34 93 310 3237

Escola de les Arts Interpretatives
Aribau, 44 baixos 1ª, 08011 Barcelona
Tel/Fax: +34 93 453 1549

Institut del Teatre Sant Pere Mes baix 7, 08003 Barcelona
Tel: +34 93 268 2078
Fax +34 93 268 1070

email institut@redestb.es
www.diba.es/iteatre

"El Timbal" Escola d'Arts Escèniques, Portaferissa, 13 pral, 08002 Barcelona
Tel: +34 93 302 7347, +34 93 301 0788

MÁLAGA

Escuela Superior de Arte Dramatico, Plaza Maestro Artola, 2, 29013 Málaga
Tel: +34 95 225 7454/2111
Fax: +34 95 225 7454

ALTERNATIVE HOLIDAYS
Cortijo Romero
"Little Grove", Grove Lane, Chesham, Buckinghamshire, HP5 3QQ, UK
Tel: +44 1494 782 720
Fax: +44 1494 776 066
Email: bookings@cortijo-romero.co.uk
Website: www.cortijo-romero.co.uk
Established: 1986
Level: None
Nearest Station: Málaga or Granada
Contact: Janice

Guests do not come to Cortijo Romero for a conventional package holiday in beautiful surroundings, they come for what the brochure describes as "rest and renewal". This is achieved through the 'Personal Development Courses' that take place during most weeks here: the essential part of the Cortijo Romero experience. According to the brochure, these are intended to "provide opportunities, methods and support for you to explore, develop and realise some of your potentials." There is a structure to the days, which include yoga and meditation sessions, singing, learning a bit of Spanish or whatever other activities form part of the course that you are attending. Cortijo Romero is located in a well-known area of natural beauty in the south of Spain – the Alpujarras – situated at 1,300ft in a fertile valley surrounded by the mountains of the Sierra Nevada in an area designated as a Biosphere Reserve by UNESCO.

Essentially, courses here are devoted to helping you "find yourself", a new-age term that may put some people off. However, what Cortijo Romero offers is an opportunity to relax, take a step back from your life and perhaps even change your outlook on the way you live. You will also have the opportunity to meet new people in the form of your fellow guests, as all of you will be participating together in the courses. Food is vegetarian and supposed to be excellent. You can find out for yourself beforehand by sending off for 'The Cortijo Romero Book of Recipes'.

One course takes place each week at Cortijo Romero. 'Being Here' is a less intensive course than the rest. This is designed to introduce you to the Cortijo Romero experience if you have never been before, or to give you a chance to stay on and see more of the place if you have just completed one of the more concentrated courses. 'Being Here' takes place several times during the year. Other courses include 'You and the Alhambra', 'Holistic Massage', 'Christmas Week' (an alternative way to celebrate the festive season), 'Go Sane in Spain' and 'Coming Home to Yourself: Expanding Mind, Body and Soul'. See the brochure for the full list.

Prices range from £265 to £365 per week and are all-inclusive. This means that you get full board, the course and a full day outing. Optional extras include sessions of holistic massage, shiatsu, Thai yoga,

acupuncture and others. The cost of these is £15 to 25 per session. Accommodation is in an original converted farmhouse (cortijo means farmhouse) whose bedrooms are furnished in the local style. A maximum of 24 people attend the courses at any one time. Contact the above for a copy of the brochure and a booking form.

COOKERY
Alambique

Plaza de la Encarnación, 2, 28013 Madrid
Tel: +34 91 547 4220/8827
Fax: +34 91 559 7802
Established: 1972
Level: Basic
Nearest Station: (Metro) Opera
Contact: Tania Ruiz

Founded 22 years ago by four women, Alambique is an enormous kitchen shop, with a demonstration kitchen at its far end. It was established with the aim of introducing Spanish women to unusual cooking techniques and providing them with a shop dedicated entirely to their cookery needs. The shop is basically like a Spanish version of the London shop, Divertimenti, and is just as enticing with its stacks of dishes and knick-knacks for every conceivable type of cooking technique. Three of the original partners have since been bought out by the fourth, whose daughter, Ines Llamas, now runs the administrative side of the courses and gives some of the classes while she gives lectures around the world.

The demonstration kitchen is the focal point of classes. This is a long rectangular wooden table, surrounded on three sides by wooden stools. In the centre of the table is a cooker with an enormous extractor fan looming above it. There is a small kitchen in the wall behind the table. At the end of every class the dishes, accompanied by some good Spanish wine, are sampled by all those who have taken part in the demonstration, either simply watching or participating.

Students come to the classes from all over the world as do qualified teachers and chefs who teach not only Spanish cookery, but cookery from around the world. One student, a Japanese woman who attended the courses for two years, has since opened up her own Spanish restaurant in Japan. The youngest student is 13-years old and participants range from professional chefs (there are certain courses that cater specifically for them) to those who simply want to expand their reper-toire. Language is not a barrier – as Ines says, cooking is something that is almost entirely visual – and some students have even been known to photo-graph demonstrations because they couldn't write notes. There are about 500 to 600 students per year and many of the teachers are guest teachers who come to give a short series of classes or a one-off demonstration. The school has one teacher from England – John Reeder – a professor at the University of Madrid, Complutense, who runs the wines and beverages classes at Alambique. The price of each course varies according to its length.

Cookery for beginners, a two month course which takes place every Monday from 6.30pm to 8.30pm, costs 35,000ptas; the Curso de Mayordomo (a Butler's or Maid's Course) costs 100,000ptas for three hours every Monday for three months. Shorter courses include En el Mundo del Café, a two and a half-hour class costing 4,000ptas. Other courses include: Basque Cookery: yesterday and today (18,000ptas for a four day course from 11am to 1.30pm daily); Spanish Cookery (12,000ptas for a class lasting two and a half hours once a week for three weeks); Rice (8,000ptas for a two hour lesson once a week for two weeks) and Cooking fish and seafood (18,000ptas for a four day course from

Estudi de Teatre "L'Escala"

11am to 1.30pm daily). There is an enrolment fee of 3,000ptas for first-time participants. For enrolment details, contact the school.

The school also runs courses in image and social protocol. The cost of theses ranges from 10,000ptas (The Art of Receiving Guests, Personal Image) to 25,000ptas (courses in the image that you portray at work).

Escuela de Hostelería Arnadi (Hofmann)

Argentería, 74-78,
08003
Barcelona
Tel: +34 93 195 889
Fax: +34 93 195 889
Established: 1983
Level: Basic
Nearest Station:
The school is situtated
in the centre of town
Contact: José Ma Vargas
(from 4pm to 8pm,
Spanish time)

Situated in the oldest part of Barcelona – the Barrio Gótico – in a beautifull renovated old palace, this school is probably best described as the Spanish equivalent to the Cordon Bleu cookery schools.

The facilities are all brand new and courses offered range from the serious, 28-month long Curso de Hostelería (specialising in cookery or cookery and pastry-making) to short two-day courses (17,000ptas per course or 29,000ptas for the four-day course in July) in particular aspects of cookery (Basque cookery, rice, cod). A special four-month course in the basics and techniques of cookery was introduced in April 1998.

Learning for Pleasure

Aptdo 150, 29650 Mijas
(MÁLAGA)
Tel: +34 95 248 6210
Fax: +34 95 248 6210
(UK bookings can be made
through the Learning for
Pleasure representative at 2
Spring Cottages, London Rd,
Crowborough, Sussex, TN6
1UT, tel/fax: 01892 668 090)

Learning for Pleasure offer a most unusual and interesting range of courses geared towards those who want to take educational holidays in beautiful surroundings. Cookery courses are provided by, amongst others, Janet Mendel, an American journalist who has lived in Andalucía for 20 years. She runs a four day course in Spanish Cooking (72,000ptas or 83,000ptas, depending on the dates). Cookery programmes in the past have included Frances Bissell in Spain (Frances Bissell writes for The Times newspaper in the UK and is the official The Times Cook). Leith's School of Food and Wine, a prestigious cookery school in the UK, runs a custom-made course at Learning for Pleasure's head-quarters – Las Limas – a beautiful farmhouse in Cádiz, situated on the edge of a National Park.

Programmes are not solely based around cookery courses and have included Gardening in Spain, Herbalism in Spain (Herbal medicine through walks and talks), the Colours of Spain (painting, lectures) and Bird and Nature Watching in Spain, as well as walking holidays, horseback tours and even a computer literacy course. Prices include accommodation, tuition, all meals and excursions during the course. Other courses on other topics can be organised on request.

Saltsan
Kurutziaga, 40, 48200 Durango
(VIZCAYA)
Tel: +34 94 620 0427
Fax:+34 94 620 0427
Level: Basic

This school/delicatessen offers two-week long courses for a maximum group of ten people. The course begins once a group of ten has been formed, so for those with enough friends who would be interested in taking it, the course could turn out to be a fun group holiday. Classes take place for four hours a day, from 4.30pm to 6.30pm and from 8pm to 10pm, from Monday to Thursday. The course is very practical, as students follow whatever the teaching is doing. The course involves the composition of about 20 dishes and students can take the food home with them. The course is flexible and you can choose the dishes that you would like to make. The course costs 20,000ptas with everything included (food, utensils, etc).

CULTURE/
MISCELLANEOUS
Club de Oro
Ayala, 66-1 izda, Madrid 28001
Tel: +34 91 431 0557
Fax: +34 91 435 7353
Established: 1995
Level: Intermediate
Nearest Station: (Metro)
Velázquez or Goya
Contact: Purificación Martínez
or Pilar Alonso

This is a social club located in the wealthy and central district called Salamanca, a residential area known for its exclusive shopping street – Serrano. It was founded by two women who saw a gap in the market for a private centre offering cultural and leisure activities in Madrid and, more specifically, in this part of the capital. The club is basically a converted apartment, the focal point of which is a large bright room filled with bridge tables covered with colourful cloths. This can be used in many different ways and can be hired for parties or simply used as a meeting place for friends to come and have a coffee and a chat. At one end of it is a raised dais on which sits a piano and its walls are used to exhibit works of art that are also available to buy.

Courses at the Club de Oro include Yoga, Tai chi, Creative Art, Floral Art, Bridge, Cookery, Mus (a Spanish card game), Graphology and Make-up. There is also History of Art, which is popular among visiting American and English students from a nearby language school called ELE Madrid. Other overseas students include women in their thirties whose husbands have been posted to Madrid for business purposes. The club also offers beauty treatments and three times a week a doctor of homeopathic medicine holds a clinic there. This is very much in line with the ethos of the club, whose aim is to provide an environment to counter-act everyday stress, as well as a place to meet like-minded people. The founders had originally thought that they would mainly attract housewives, but as it turns out, most of the club's members are people who work. As a result, most courses take place between the hours of 7pm and 9pm, though the club is very flexible and you can request the timetable to suit you.

The school is open between 10.30am and 2pm and 4.30pm and 9.30pm. Club membership costs 5,000ptas and thereafter you have to pay 5,000ptas per term. There are two types of course prices – for members and non-members. You can take part in any course without becoming a member. Prices for courses range from 6,000ptas per month (7,000ptas per month for non-members) for tai chi to 22,000ptas (25,000ptas for non-members) for the complete three month course in Floral Art. Most courses cost in the range of 7,500ptas (add about 1,000 ptas more for non-members). The cost of lectures is about 1,000ptas per lecture. Other activities include cultural excursions.

This is probably the place to come to if you are looking for an activity to complement something that you are already doing in Madrid. The atmosphere is relaxed and friendly and it is an ideal place to just unwind after work. Of particular interest may be the cookery course. This involves the preparation of a three course meal which you then get to eat at the end of the class. In a way it is more like a home economics class as the teacher also provides fact sheets on food health and safety and serving protocol. Very little English is spoken here. Contact the school for enrolment details.

Centros Culturales Nicolás Salmerón:

Mantuano, 51, 28002 Madrid
Tel: +34 91 413 5564/5664
Established: 1983
Level: Varies according to the course you have chosen.
Nearest Station: (Metro)
Concha Espina (line 9) and
Prosperidad (line 4); buses: 7,
16, 29, 51 and 52
Contact: Javier Alvarez Padilla

Of the 65-odd cultural centres in Madrid, this is the largest and most well-known and it is located towards the north east of the city in a huge building that was once a school. Today, as well as the various classrooms that are now home to cultural activities, it houses a public library. As this is a cultural centre that is funded by the local equivalent of a borough council (in this case, the Junta Municipal de Chamartín), classes are extremely cheap, the total cost for three months of classes ranging from 2,100ptas (for OAP yoga) to 8,000ptas (for the Cinema course). As a result, classes are always full.

The building is on three floors, each with four or five classrooms devoted to different activities. The centre is known for offering a wide range of courses. There are in fact 32 different topics, generating about 100 classes every week, (therefore an average of about three classes per topic). The centre is open from 9am to 2pm and from 4pm to 9pm, Monday to Friday and classes last from one and a half to two hours. Courses have three start dates per year: October (ending in December), January (ending in March) and April (ending in June). In June and July there are intensive courses in *baile de salón* (tango, merengue), painting, drawing and French, for those who do not have the time to attend courses during the rest of the year (fees are the same as for normal classes). The centre is closed in August and there are no courses during that month and September. Extra costs incurred by pupils depend on their course. In painting, for example, you have to bring your own canvas and in Glass art, you have to bring your own glass. Obviously, for the *sevillana* classes, you will have to bring your own shoes.

There have been overseas students, although the majority of the 2,100 people attending courses here are from

Madrid (and of these, men are heavily outnumbered by five to one). Of greatest interest to these overseas students have been the more unusual courses such as marquetry (inlaid work in wood), glass-making (the Tiffany technique) and a particular kind of lace-making. Anyone aged 18 or over may enrol for courses at this centre (there is a centre for children nearby), though the majority of participants tend to be older. There are about 30 teachers at the centre (one per class), all of whom have either got degrees in their subject or who have trained professionally in it (eg *sevillanas*). Not much English is spoken here, however, for most courses a grasp of the basics of Spanish is all that you will need. It is worth bearing in mind that the centre also caters for deaf students.

As well as courses, the centre is also an exhibition centre (there is an exhibition hall where anyone may exhibit for free and there is usually a showing by a new artist every fortnight) and a venue for concerts and plays (the centre possesses a theatre/auditorium). The theatre is occasionally used for works in English, performed by the students at the University of St Louis in Madrid. For enrolment details please contact the school. There is an enrolment fee of 1,000ptas. At the end of their course, students may receive a diploma from the Ayuntamiento de Madrid (the Town Hall of Madrid). Priority of places is given to residents in the area.

DRESSMAKING AND FASHION DESIGN
Academias de Moda ISA
Andrés Mellado, 6, 28015
Madrid
Tel: +34 91 544 6887
Fax: +34 91 544 7018
Established: 1980

Level: Intermediate
Nearest Station: (Metro) Argüelles/Moncloa
Contact: Isabel Marcos Blázquez

There are three Academias de Moda ISA in Madrid as well as centres in Spain and worldwide practising the ISA system. This [patented] system was devised by Isabel Blázquez Navas in order to cope with what she felt was a gap in the market in terms of the way that dressmaking was being taught in Spain. Having attended a succession of courses in her native Salamanca and in other towns in Spain, she realised that the provision available at that time was simply not touching on some important aspects of dressmaking. She devised a system that specifically addressed these issues, as well as the more traditional aspects of dressmaking. Isabel Blázquez Navas has written three books outlining her system.

The 'Curso Completo' costs between 20,000ptas and 77,000ptas per month, depending on how many hours you do daily (Monday to Friday). This covers Fashion and Design, Industrial and Scaled Pattern design, Industrial Dressmaking, Textile Technology and Pattern design on Computer. The courses in Fashion and Design, Industrial and Scaled Pattern Design and Dressmaking and the accelerated course in Design' and/or 'Industrial and Scaled Pattern design' cost between 9,000ptas and 18,000ptas depending on the course and the number of class hours per month. The computer-assisted course in Design, Industrial and Scaled Pattern design, which uses the latest technology (Invesmark and Invesmark NT systems) costs 150,000ptas for 90 hours and 250,000ptas for 150 hours. Other courses include Costume Design

MISCELLANEOUS

for theatre, film and television, Tailoring by hand, Haute Couture Dressmaking, Accelerated Dressmaking, Embroidery in Precious Stones, Fabric Painting, 'pecial techniques for Fabric Painting and Embroidery in Precious Stones, Hats and hair accessories. Students have the opportunity to create an entire collection. They are free to choose the theme – suits, swimwear, lingerie, casualwear, bridal wear, etc – and are encouraged to design a collection that reflects their own personality.

The school has an employment bureau as well as links with companies to whom it sends students for work experience. At the Semana Internacional de la Moda, ISA rents a stand where student's work is displayed. There is a fashion show at the end of the academic year where students can show off their collections. As students must buy all their own materials, the participants in these shows are limited to those who can afford the cost. There are about 450 students in all three centres in Madrid put together, most of them women aged between 18 and 30. Students include people in management positions in the clothing industry who need to learn about the craft in order to be able to run their businesses effectively.

Students must buy their own materials themselves (including the ISA system textbooks). The cost varies according to the course that you are doing. For students on the course in Industrial Pattern Design, for example, the cost for the year will be between 15,000 ptas 20,000ptas. At the branch in Arguelles, pens, paints, thread and various other bits and pieces are availalbe to buy from the

The only pre-requisite is a basic education (BUP – the equivalent of

GCSEs – is not essential). Students must attend history of art classes, so a certain level of comprehension of Spanish is necessary. At the end of their course, students on the Fashion Design, Industrial and Scaled Pattern design courses receive a certificate and diploma recognised by the ministry of education under article 35. This means that students are qualified to give classes in private schools, official (ie state) schools or on their own, should they wish to. Students on all other courses will receive a certificate of studies.

The school can give students a list of residences and homestays with Spanish families (a popular option as it is probably the cheapest). Excursions, such as a trip to Barcelona for the Muestra de Maquinaria or the Exhibition of Cloth in Paris are organised by the school, provided students show enough interest.

Vélez Per

Doctor Esquerdo, 8, Local 3, 28028 Madrid
Tel: +34 91 356 2020
Fax: +34 91 402 8030
Established: 1958
Level: None
Nearest Station: (Metro)
Manuel Becerra, O'Donnell, Sainz de Baranda
Contact: Sagrario Vélez Perea

Veléz Per has recently moved to new, larger premises just off a busy main road to the east of the centre of Madrid. To get into building number eight, you have to walk into what looks like (and is) the entrance to a car park and in front of you, you will see a building and a sign directing you to the school in the right hand corner. As the foundation date of the school suggests it has been around for some time. Its owner, Sagrario Vélez Perea, has been involved in dressmaking since the age of 13. Even well before that age, she knew that she wanted to be in fashion. She tells a story of the time when, at the tender age of eight, she swapped a ring that had been handed down to her by an aunt in return for a box of colourful rags.

The school is used to having overseas students, many come from South America but others have come from further afield. For example, the school counts the wife of the Emir of Qatar, the Ambassadress of Nigeria and the Consul of Colombia among its alumni. Students come with all levels of expertise, though generally those coming from abroad are of a high standard. As far as language in concerned, the school has apparently had quite a bit of experience of non-Spanish speakers who have ended up learning the language simply by attending classes.

The main course offered by the school is Pattern-making and Computer-Aided Design, (80 hours – 170,000ptas, 250 hours – 510,000ptas; there is an enrolment fee of 10,000ptas). Other courses include: Intensive Industrial and Scaled Pattern-making and Fashion Design (from 176,000ptas for 30 days to 720,000ptas for nine months), Dressmaking and High Fashion

Student Story

"I came here to be with my boyfriend, who is a Spanish journalist. I had been a dancer and had always wanted to get into fashion. But in Switzerland, where everyone is either a banker or a doctor, it's not that easy to do courses in "artier" subjects. So, moving to Spain was the perfect opportunity for me to start. I've been at ISA since October and am doing the design course. Before I started I had a very basic knowledge of the subject (from school), but I think that even an absolute beginner would have no problem here as they're good at starting people off from scratch. As far as the language is concerned, you need to have a grasp of basic Spanish, but the school is really helpful and they take care of you, making sure that you know all the technical vocabulary. My best moment so far has been the realisation that I can actually draw! My dream is to work in a big fashion company as a clothes buyer, using my languages (English, Spanish, German) as well as the skills I will have learnt here. I don't really see myself ending up as designer but I am really enjoying my course. The classes are small (6 or 7 people) and the atmosphere is friendly. I've already made some good friends here. Why choose to study fashion in Spain? I think that in a way the answer to that is obvious. You only have to walk down the street to see that the Spanish have an innate sense of style. They just know how to put their outfits together and how to look good!"

Miriam Weyss, Switzerland.

(60,000ptas for one month and 225,000ptas for nine months), Men's Tailoring (10,000ptas per month for two hours a week or 14,000ptas per month for four hours a week). There are also short courses (40,000 ptas each) in Embroidering with Precious Stones, Fabric Painting' and Millinery.

Generally, students work on different stages of the dressmaking process – pattern design, design, dressmaking and so on. However, it is also possible to study all three should you wish to do so. The school has an exhibition space on Duque de Alba which acts as a sort of shop window for the school and is where student's work is put on show. There is also a fashion show at the end of every academic year, where ~ professional models show off the fruits of the student's labour. The school is closedin August, though if there is sufficient demand they will remain open. Intensive Summer courses are also available.

The cost of extras will vary according to your course: between 10,000ptas and 25,000ptas per year, depending on the course. You can buy materials directly from the school or elsewhere. (Beware, it may be more convenient to buy from the school, but is it cheaper?). Ages range from 16 to 60 (predominantly female). In haute couture, the school takes in students as young as 15 and in Design they can be anything from 16 to 40. In Pattern design students are usually between 25 and 50 years old. At the moment there are a total of about 150 students at the school, though there is room for more.

The school can help you to find accommodation and is used to finding suitable accommodation for girls under the age of 16. A decent place to live in the area will cost you in the region of 40,000ptas a month. This is a private school, not an official state school, therefore the diploma that you receive is their own and if you wish to, you may take it to the Notary's office at the Ayuntamiento (Town Council) to have it validated. For enrolment details, contact the school. Before your arrival, if you wish the school to provide you with a certificate of studies for Visa purposes, you will have to send the school 50 per cent of the fee.

Escola d'Arts I Tècniques de la Moda

Passeig de Gràcia, 114 pral.,
Barcelona 08008
Tel: +34 93 416 0000
Fax: +34 93 237 7474
Email: schola@eatm.com
Website: www.eatm.com
Established: 1968
Level: Intermediate
Nearest Station: (Metro)
Diagonal
Contact: Roser Melendres
(Director) or Cristina Garriga

Offering degree-level courses in fashion and design, EATM also has an arrangement with Winchester School of Art in the UK, whereby it can offer a BA (Honours) in Fashion awarded by the University of Southampton. Students come from Spain, South America, Switzerland, Norway and China and it is necessary to sit the university entrance exam – selectividad – if you wish to apply. Courses include seminars by people such as Antonio Miró, work experience, international exchanges and workshops with other schools. The enrolment fee is 150,000ptas and each monthly instalment (there are nine) comes to 50,000ptas.

Instituto Técnico del Vestir (INTEVE)
Tarragona, 49, Barcelona
Tel: +34 93 805 2177
Fax: +34 93 805 5682
Email: escgenny@filnet.es
Website: www.inteve.com
Established: 1972
Nearest Station:
Comprehension
Contact: Vicente Gallego

With a trilingual prospectus (Spanish, English, French) it is evident that this school is more geared up than most for overseas students. It offers made-to-measure courses, including refresher courses, in all aspects of fashion design and dressmaking. Courses are entirely practical, hence the necessity to understand Spanish, but not to speak it. The length of courses varies from degree-length to short, monothematic courses.

GOYMAR/EDIDE
Bravo Murillo, 377, 4°E, 28020 Madrid
Tel: +34 91 733 9997
Fax: +34 91 733 9997
Established: 1980
Level: High
Nearest Station: (Metro) Plaza de Castilla
Contact: Concepción Tormo Crespo
A dressmaking/fashion design and computing school whose students are Spanish and South American.

Kroom Dos Diseño
Goya, 19-1°C, 28001 Madrid
Tel: +34 91 431 1051
Fax: +34 91 262 2832
Established: 1976
Level: Basic
Nearest Station: (Metro) Goya
Contact: Luís García Valencia
This school runs three degree-length courses in fashion design, pattern making and dressmaking and couture, as well as intensive short courses and monothematic courses in the same areas.

TEACHING
Aula Iberoamericana de la Casa de América
Paseo de Recoletos, 2, 28001 Madrid
Tel: +34 91 595 4838/6
Fax: +34 91 595 4827
Email: aula@casamerica.es
Established: 1992
Level: Good written and spoken Spanish
Nearest Station: (Metro) Banco de España
Contact: Myrna Rivera Méndez or Bienvenida Sánchez Alba

The Casa de America, a cultural centre, offers a course for teachers of Latin American studies. The course involves modules culture, environment and so on, with a view to improving understanding of Latin American culture. To participate, you must have a degree or some form of higher education qualification. The course is attended by Spanish, Latin American and European Union students.

ENVIRONMENTAL EDUCATION
The following places offer courses where adults and children can learn about the environment, including nature visits to parts of the Spanish countryside in order to observe wildlife and plants. A high level of Spanish will be required.

CÁDIZ
Amatur Plaza de San Jorge, 1,
11180 Alcalá de los Gazules (Cádiz)
Tel +34 956 413 005
Fax: +34 956 413 228

CÁDIZ
Granja-Escuela "Buenavista"
Junta de los Rios, s/n, 11620 Arcos de
la Frontera – Cádiz
Tel: +34 956 725 950; also Aula de la
Naturaleza El Higuerón de Tavizna
Tel: +34 956 234 211

GRANADA
Aula de Naturaleza "Ermita Vieja",
CIE Huerto Alegre, Apdo de Correos
776, 18080 Granada
Tel/Fax: +34 958 228 496
Tel: +34 958 340 472

GUADALAJARA
Ecoaventura
Pl Boixareu Rivera, 40B, 19001
Guadalajara
Tel/Fax: +34 949 215 036. Sports, environmental education, arts and crafts (pottery, photography), excursions.

MADRID
Centro de Estudios Técnicos y Medioambientales
Fuencarral, 137-1ƒI, 28010 Madrid
Tel/Fax: +34 91 448 4794. All courses last 20 hours and cost 25,000ptas, covering topics such as botany, photographing nature, astronomy and medicinal plants. Some courses take place outside Madrid such as the botanical course for which students travel to the mountains off Léon.

MADRID
Club Eduma
Alcantará, 34 bajo H, 28006 Madrid
Tel: +34 91 402 3053/401 2502
Fax: +34 91 402 3053. This is a private school whose provision includes courses for those who wish to become sports instructors and environmental educators.

ZARAGOZA
Conocer y Proteger la Naturaleza en Aragón (CPN-Aragón), Gascón de Gotor, 3-3°, 50006 Zaragoza
Tel: +34 976 270 238,
mobile 908 262 323

MUSIC
Aula de Música Moderna y Jazz
Montornés, 37, 08023
Barcelona
Tel: +34 93 211 1062
Fax: +34 93 211 2490
Email: 1_aula@seker.es
Established: 1978
Level: Intermediate
Nearest Station: (Metro)
Penitents
Contact: Enric Alberich

Located in the centre of the city and founded twenty years ago as an alternative music school specialising in jazz, pop, rock and other genres within modern music, the Aula de Musica Moderna y Jazz offers classes in flamenco guitar. The aim of the school is to stimulate student's knowledge of these types of music using a combination of theory and practice.

The school is based in a four-storey building with 22 classrooms and a concert hall with a capacity of one hundred. There is also a semi-professional recording studio, a laboratory giving students access to the latest technology, a library, an audio library, a bar and a restaurant. Of the two hundred and seventy students, most are Latin American and Spanish, with a handful of students from elsewhere in Europe.

The flamenco guitar course takes place during the academic year (from September to June) and costs 10,500ptas per month. This course focuses on three different aspects: Flamenco Guitar, Singing Accompaniment and The History and Musical theory of Flamenco. There are also intensive summer courses during the months of June, July and September (Aula is closed during the month of August). These include workshops and seminars on various topics such as Film Scoring, Improvisation, Music and technology, Theory and Composition. Options in Flamenco guitar are not included among these. Fees start at 40,000ptas for the 20-hour course in film scoring.

Aula can offer preparation for the Diploma in Modern Music from the Conservatorio del Liceo. For all you budding Brian Epsteins out there, it also offers a music degree in collaboration with Berkeley College of Music in the USA, which includes modules in 'Film scoring, Music Business Management and Music Therapy. The school participates in a range of exchange programmes with other music schools all over Europe and occasionally hosts lectures given by visiting professors from Berkeley College.

Aula, in conjunction with the Conservatorio del Liceo in Barcelona (one of Spain's foremost conservatoires), has created a department dedicated entirely to the study of Management in the Music Industry. The courses offered here include masterclasses, musical production and editing and specific seminars and cost 16,800ptas per month. For more details contact Vía Músical (tel: +34 93 302 0442).

The school will interview you prior to enrolment and in the case of students with prior musical knowledge, there will be a level test. As yet, the school can't offer information regarding accommodation, but is hoping to do so in the future.

Avinyó Espai Músical
Avinyó, 7 bis, pral., 08002 Barcelona
Tel: +34 93 302 3149
Fax: +34 93 302 3149
Email: avinyo@mx3.redestb.es
Website: personal.redestb.es

Kroom Dos Diseño

/andreag/avinyo/
Established: 1988
Level: Intermediate
Nearest Station: (Metro) Liceo
or Jaume I or Pza Catalunya
Contact: Roger Font Sola

Flamenco guitar and Spanish guitar are amongst the instruments taught at this school in central Barcelona, situated just off the Ramblas. Spanish, French and American students attend classes and fees range from 23,000ptas per academic year for theory lessons to 65,000ptas per academic year to learn an instrument, "combo" and theory. The registration fee for new students is 6,000ptas. The school is affiliated to INCANOP (Institut Català de Noves Professions *(see p235)*.

Escola D'Arts Musicals Luthier (guitar, piano, violin, etc)
Balmes, 53 pral., 08007 Barcelona,
Tel: +34 93 323 3346/451 7130,
Fax: +34 93 215 3984

Escola de Música Joan Llongueres, Institut de Pedagogia Musical I Rítmica Dalcroze (learning through the Dalcroze and Willems methods)
Sénecam 22, 08006 Barcelona,
Tel: +34 93 217 1894,
Fax: +34 93 416 1448

Escola de Música Juan Pedro Carrero
Pintor Fortuny, 18 pral., 08001 Barcelona
Tel: +34 93 301 0718
Fax: +34 93 301 0718
Email: Tempus_Mundi@ rocketmail.com

Established: 1992
Level: Basic
Nearest Station: (Metro) Plaza de Catalunya
Contact: Carmen Passolas Castel

A private school for lovers of classical music, the level of ability required for admission to the courses at this school is high. Of added interest will be the extra-curricular activities organised by the centre including concerts and rehearsals. Students come from Spain, America and Japan. The academic year course, from October to June, costs between 18,000ptas and 35,000ptas per month. Registration costs 23,000ptas. Five day intensive courses can be arranged at a cost of 40,000ptas. Master classes are also available.

In July Carmen Passolas Castel runs an international music course (Curso Internacional Música de Vilaller) for young musicians of all levels. Students who do not wish to participate may also attend. The programme involves music-making, outings in the mountains, sightseeing and sports (including horseriding). Fees are: 75,000ptas for musicians at elementary level, 83,000ptas for musicians at inter- mediate or advanced level and 65,000ptas for non-active participants. The fee includes accommodation, free entrance to all concerts in the Festival de Música de los Pirineos, free transport to all concerts and tour of Alta Ribagorça. To take part in the Chamber Music Course there is an additional fee of 12,000ptas. The festival is followed by a week-long Chamber Music Competition.

Aula de Música Moderna y Jazz

Escola de Música "La Guineu" (guitar, piano, violin, etc.)
Artesania, 102, 08042 Barcelona,
Tel/Fax: +34 93 350 5598,
Email: laguineu@yahoo.com

Escuela de Música de Bellaterra
Plaça del Pí, 5-C, 08193 Bellaterra (Barcelona)
Tel: +34 93 580 4246
Fax: +34 93 454 7268
Email: emb@catworld.net
Established: 1991
Level: None
Nearest Station: Bellaterra
Contact: Montserrat Roig

This is a small music school specialising in jazz and modern music situated 15km outside the city of Barcelona, in the university area. The school attracts mainly Spanish students, but its proximity to the Universidad Autónoma de Barcelona means that there are students from all over the world. The school runs four types of course: children's, adults, special courses and summer courses.

Escuela de Música de Farré
Sta Catalina, 33 bajos, 08014 Barcelona
Tel: +34 93 339 7493/213 5519
Fax: +34 93 202 3514
Email: tess@odllink.com
Website: Under construction
Established: 1971
Level: Intermediate
Nearest Station: Sants
Contact: Joana Farré (Mobile 919 950 767)

Officially recognised by the Conservatori del Liceu (Conservatoire of the Barcelona Liceu), this school provides classes in Canto de Música Español (Spanish Songs), flute, modern music, guitar, drums, violin, piano and other instruments. Students at the school come from Spain, Germany, the UK and Japan. The course in Spanish Songs, which lasts from January to March and from April to June, requires four hours of classes a week in groups of five students. Lasting a total of 48 hours, the course costs 35,000ptas. The school is affiliated to INCANOP (Institut Català de Noves Professions, *see p235*).

Formación Músical (Spanish guitar, etc)
Teodora La Madrid, 38, Barcelona,
Tel: +34 93 418 8874/417 0017

A music school offering courses for those who wish to study for exams (set by the Conservatorio Municipal de Música de Barcelona) and for those who wish to learn simply for the pleasure of it, the provision at Formación Músical includes lessons in Flamenco guitar. Group classes are small, with no more than five students in each. The school was giving away free guitars or violins to people signing up for the 1997/98 courses.

Taller de Musics SA
Requesens, 5, 08001 Barcelona
Tel: +34 93 329 5667

Fax: +34 93 329 7211
Website: www.quasar.es/taller
Established: 1979
Level: Basic
Nearest Station: (Metro) St Antoni/ Train Plaza de Catalunya or Paseo de Gracia
Contact: Xavier Fort

Another music school in the centre of Barcelona which offers courses in Flamenco guitar, Taller de Musics has about 600 students, the majority of whom are from Spain. The school specialises in the teaching of jazz (instrumental, Big band, etc) and modern music (blues, rock, latin pop, brasileira and so on) as well as teaching *flamenc*. This is the term for all aspects of flamenco music – guitar, singing, voice, dancing and theory. The academic year course runs from September to July and there is an intensive course in July ('Juliol Intensiv') as well as masterclasses and special courses throughout the year. Prices vary according to course. You can join a class at any time during the year. The only prerequisite for admission is that you sit a basic

Escola de Música Juan Pedro Carrero

entrance test. Contact the school for enrolment details.

Escuela de Música Fundación Alcalde Zoilo Ruiz-Mateos (guitar and band instruments)
Blas Infante, 14, 11520 Rota (Cádiz),
Tel: +34 93 956 810 411/ 811 211
Fax: +34 93 956 813 450

Cursos Manuel de Falla in Granada
Tel: +34 958 210 429
Fax: +34 958 210 399

Part of the annual festival of dance and music in Granada, these courses cover such themes as photographing music, analysing music, guitar and choral singing.

Universidad de Alcalá, Aula de Música
Vicerrectorado de Extension Universitaria-Fundacion General de Alcalá, Colegio de Basilios, C/Colegios, 10, 28801 Alcalá de Henares
Tel: +34 91 878 81 28
Fax: +34 91 878 92 52
Email: fundaaum@cicom.es
Website: www.cicom.es/ fundacion
Established: 1987
Level: Very high standard of both written and spoken Spanish.
Nearest Station: Alcalá de Henares
Contact: Avelina Lopez-Chicheri

This is a unique place offering year-round courses solely for music professionals who wish to continue their training beyond degree level. It is not funded in any way by the Ministry of Education and is part privately funded and part funded by the University of Alcalà de Henares. Courses are only really suitable for those with a very good grasp of Spanish, particularly on those courses focusing on analysis or theory rather than performance. Student ages range from 20 to 70 and the only prerequisite is that you must be a music professional. Of the 500 or so students at the school last year, only three or four were from overseas. These came from Holland, Latin America and Portugal. However, many students at the school are foreigners now living in Spain, as well as native Spaniards themselves. Annually, the Aula de Música hosts a number of visiting lecturers, many of whom are English speakers. The Aula de Música's facilities include a highly specialised music library, whose collection includes rare and valuable volumes on all aspects of music in English, French and German, as well as in Spanish. The Aula also publishes a special magazine-QUODLIBET-which is aimed at music professionals and features essays on musical analysis, teaching, interpretation and so on. The Aula de Música is located within the university complex of the Universidad de Alcalá, which is a short distance away from the centre of Alcalá de Henares.

The Cursos de Especialización Músical are divided into several categories: analytical theory, theory, composition, conducting, the teaching of strings and piano, musical interpretation and master classes. Prices vary and discounts are available if you are enrolling on more than one course. For the master classes there is a fee of 10,000ptas to be in the audience and

20,000ptas to participate. Otherwise, the fees range from 10,000ptas (Piano techniques; Theory-Practice of conducting contemporary music) to 120,000ptas (John Cage and the consequences). The duration of courses also varies, from a couple of days to several days over the course several weeks. Courses take place all week long, including at weekends.

Accommodation can be arranged for all students at the Aula de Música, whether they are from overseas or from Spain. Options include hostels and university accommodation. It is also possible to rent a flat in the centre of Madrid as it is only half an hour away by train (the train leaves every quarter of an hour from the station in Alcalá de Henares). As one of the school's sponsors is Iberia (the Spanish airline), there is a special rate for course participants when they book to fly with that airline.

For enrolment details, please contact the school.

Escuela de Música "Chamartín"

**Paseo de la Habana, 137,
28036 Madrid
Tel: +34 91 350 7806/
Mobile: 909 210 422
Established: 1990
Level: None
Nearest Station: (Metro)
Colombia or Cuzco
Contact: Ana Estevez**

Located in the residential area called Chamartín in the north of Madrid, you will find this school tucked away by the side of a nail clinic. Founded eight years ago, the school is open to anyone, of any age and of any ability. Student ages range from five to 60 and there are about 150 students at the school in total. What may be of particular interest to overseas students is that the school's week-long summer course in July in Guadarrama, a village in the Sierra Madrileña (the mountains that surround the capital). The course will take place in a special camping complex, which also has room for 100 guests. Facilities include conference rooms, a swimming pool and tennis courts. Teachers are from the Orquesta de Madrid and it is something like a training camp. The mornings are devoted to music and the afternoons will be filled with sporting activities such as horseriding. The course costs 38,000ptas and there is room for about 85 people.

The school is also one of the few centres in Spain which provides training for the Guildhall Music Examinations (See pamphlet for proper official title). Students are prepared for the exams at the school every year for up to eight years (four years at elementary level and four years at professional level) and are assessed in June when an examiner from London comes over to Madrid. All 13 teachers at the school have music degrees and Tomas Zamorana, head of the school since last year, teaches the trumpet.

Most students at the school are from the neighbourhood of Chamartín, but some come from as far as Valladolid in order to take the Guildhall exams and a handful of others have come from overseas. As well as the course that runs from September to June there is also an intensive course in July. This is called the Curso Intensivo de Acercamiento a la Música (Intensive Introduction to Music Course) and it is ratified by the Guildhall. The cost is 15,000ptas for four hours a week, two days a week, for the month. Subjects that can be studied on this course are piano, guitar, violin and singing and it is open to anyone, however minimal their knowledge of music may be.

There are five classrooms and students can come here simply to practice (this will be particularly useful for those who do not have access to a piano in Madrid). Discounts are available to groups and there is a special deal whereby you get a free guitar if, when you matriculate at the school, you also join the guitar club with which it has a link.

The students give a concert at the end of the academic year (June), usually in the local cultural centre (Centro Cultural Nicolás Salmerón). Language is not a problem as most teachers are from other European countries. For enrolment details contact the school.

Instituto de Música y Tecnología (IMT)
Cartagena, 76, 28028 Madrid
Tel: +34 91 356 0977
Fax: +34 91 356 0977
Established: 1991
Level: Basic
Nearest Station: (Metro)
Avenida de America
Contact: Pablo Kahayan

You wouldn't come to this school for its location – a residential and rather charmless area in the north of Madrid. The school is set back from the road and from the outside it looks like a shop, its window filled with guitars and musical accoutrements. The front is an office/shop, which basically serves the students at the school. Behind it and in the basement are the classsrooms/ studios. The school is run by Pablo Kahayan, an affable Argentinian, and Chema Vílchez,

the commercial and musical directors of the school respectively.

This school is interesting primarily because it offers what is, strangely, a rare provision in Spanish music schools: courses in flamenco guitar and percussion. These have only been going for a year and have already attracted a number of foreign students, mainly from Denmark, Brazil, the UK and South America. These classes allow a maximum of two students and take place once a week for up to three hours, though intensive courses are geared towards those from overseas who want to maximise their time in Madrid and at the school. In such cases, students can choose their own timetable.

The complete course involves three stages and is suitable for complete beginners. The aim is to develop the student to the point of reaching a professional level and in the first year (iniciación), pupils study flamenco technique and learn its basic rhythms. The second year (nivel medio) involves more in depth study, concentrating on traditional flamenco guitar with a gradual introduction to more modern flamenco. The focus in this year will be on concert performance, though there will still be work on accompaniment of singing and dancing. The third year (nivel avanzado) will be devoted to concert performance and flamenco improvisation, with a look at other styles, such as jazz and south American music, which have gradually begun to creep into flamenco. The styles of the most contemporary and well-known flamenco guitarists will be studied while your own personal style, an essential characteristic of every flamenco guitarist, will be encouraged and developed. Utmost importance is accorded to the creation and interpretation of pieces. The percussion course is structured in the same way, and include the following topics: rhythms (rumba, sevillanas, tangos, etc), techniques (coordination, warming up exercises, etc.), styles (classical flamenco to jazz and bossa nova), improvisation and the use of different instruments (drums, castanets, etc), among others.

You have to bring your own guitar as it isn't possible to hire one from the school, (though you can buy one from the shop) and the course fee includes scores and various essential recordings on cassette. There is an annual enrolment fee of 5,000ptas. The basic fee for one lesson a week for a month is 12,000ptas. Thereafter, two classes a week for a month cost 22,000ptas, three classes a week for a month cost 32,000ptas and four classes a week for a month cost 40,000ptas. It is possible to do more hours than this.

Contact the school for more details.

You will be given a level test at the start of your course. Various languages are spoken at the school (English, German, Dutch) and help in finding accommodation is available to those who require it. As this is a private school, you will receive its own certificate rather than an official certificate from the Ministry of Education (flamenco guitar is not yet an officially recognised subject). Seminars and masterclasses are held at the school. A recent visitor was Gary Husband, the drummer with Level 42. Well-known figures in flamenco are also brought in to address students on the flamenco courses. IMT is approved by the Musicians Institute of Hollywood. It is the only school in Spain (that we know of) to have this endorsement.

Escuela de Música "Chamartín"

"Orfeo" Escuela de Enseñanzas Artisticas

Pza Luca de Tena, 5 – 3d
Tel: +34 91 539 0360
Established: 1980
Level: Intermediate
Nearest Station: (Metro) Palos de Moguer or Delicias
Contact: Pablo Garzon

Located on the third and ground floors of an old apartment block, above a hairdresser's and a bar called Café Liverpool, this is a tiny, but charming school dedicated mainly to forming professional singers. Climb three flights up a dark wooden staircase and you will come to the entrance of the school, which is basically a small apartment with five rooms next to each other, a waiting room and a minute office. Each room, (for private lessons only), is decorated with posters of famous singers and contains an upright piano and a couple of chairs.

Pablo Garzon, (who runs the school), was taught by Alfredo Kraus for 15 years before becoming a professional opera singer. He sang all over the world and at the age of 25, he and a friend decided to set up this school. It was only ten years later, having spent that time concentrating on his professional career, that he decided to come back to Madrid to teach full time at the school. He has performed with many great opera stars including Pavarotti, Carreras and Montserrat Caballe. He teaches the Lampedi technique of singing at the school and has been sent students by well-known singers including Elizabeth Schwarzkopf.

The school has about 290 students in total, 170 of whom are singers. About 20 to 25 of these are from overseas, mainly from the US, Scotland, Sweden and Germany. Some of the school's alumni have won scholarships to study abroad and a claim to fame is Gema Castaño, the voice of Pocahontas in Spanish. Dance is taught at the school and classes are given in Classical Ballet, 'Classical Spanish Ballet', 'Contemporary and Jazz', 'Ballroom Dancing' and 'Waltzing'. The dance studio is in the basement of the building. Music lessons are also provided.

There are two types of courses: academic year classes and the intensive summer programmes. The enrolment fee is 10,000ptas, with a monthly fee of 23,000ptas, a termly fee of 60,000ptas or an annual fee of 165,000ptas. There are summer courses in Theatre which run for sixteen hours a week and include work on performance, movement and language. There are also ballet classes (three to four hours a week).

The average age of pupils is about 22 and the people who come to study here are almost entirely people who wish to become professionals. As well as requiring a voice with "musicality and colour", students need to have a certain intellectual curiosity, with an interest in reading the classics and getting to know the history behind what they are singing. As a result, students tend to be graduates with degrees in the humanities, though this is not essential.

The school is open from 10am to 1pm and from 4pm to 10pm every day, including Saturday and Sunday. English is spoken at the school, though Pablo Garzón himself speaks only Italian and German, as well as Spanish. Contact the school for enrolment details.

MISCELLANEOUS

Músicaula

Dña María Coronel, 10-1,
41003 Sevilla
Tel: +34 95 422 1333
Established: 1994
Level: Basic
Nearest Station: Sevilla Santa
Justa
Contact: Don Jorge Duarte

Músicaula calls itself Andalucia's first arts centre and offers tuition for a variety of instruments, including flamenco guitar as well as the opportunity to actually learn to dance sevillanas in Sevilla itself. It prides itself on providing excellent teaching, with fully qualified and experienced teachers. Classes are small (or one-to-one) and are suitable for musicians at all levels, from beginners to professionals. All students sit a level test prior to the start of their course. This is one of very few music schools in Spain that offers courses specifically for foreigners, and the provision for overseas students is distinctly Spanish: Flamenco guitar, Sevillana lessons and Classical guitar. These students also have the opportunity to study any of the other instruments offered by the school.

Classes are given in flute, musical theory, piano, keyboard, percussion and drumming and guitar (Flamenco, Classical and Electric) and violin. The course for overseas musicians lasts for three months, with two hours of classes per week. The programme is intended mainly for those students who are already in Sevilla to study (for example, at the university or on a language programme) and Músicaula usually liaises with the international organisations to which these students are linked. However, the school can (and has) make exceptions and deal with individuals who wish to participate on this programme. Usually, the school gives each student on this course a free guitar on which to practice in Sevilla and which they may take home to continue practicing what they have learnt. The modules studied on the course are 'Sevillanas', 'Rumbas', 'Fandangos', 'Punteos' and 'Classical'.

There could be no more appropriate place to study Sevillana dancing. The course covers all aspects of the dance – from movement to clapping and rhythms and includes an introduction to the Rumba. It begins in November and ends in April in time for the Feria de Abril for which Sevilla is renowned. The students are taken on a visit to the focal point of the feria – the Real de la Feria – where the crowds wear typical dress (for the women, the highly coloured dresses and shawls which have come to symbolise Spain's national dress). You can watch groups dancing sevillanas (and even join in yourself) and later, will have the option of attending a bullfight. Prior to the fight, an expert in this field will give students a talk explaining the history and outlining the basic details of this tradition.

The price for flamenco guitar courses is 8,000ptas per month for one hour a week (beginners) and 12,000ptas for one hour of one-to-one tuition per week. Sevillana lessons cost 7,000ptas per month for two one hour lessons per week.

ArteAula is a centre for arts and crafts located in the same place as Músicaula. Classes are given in drawing and painting, decorative painting and furniture restoration. Músicaula is open all year round. For enrolment details, contact the school.

SPORT

FLYING
Aeroclub Cáceres
Campo de Vuelo 'La Cervera',
Alfonso IX, 16, 10004 CÁERES
Tel: +34 927 243 431
Mobile: 908 921 496

Course for pilots, sales, rentals.

Escuela ULM,
Villanueva del Pardillo, 28229
Madrid,
Tel: +34 91 858 9471,
Fax: +34 91 858 9475,
Mobile: 908 111 526.

Courses, sales, hot air balloon
excursions.

**Aeroclub Ultralijeros 'El
Casar' Guadalajara**
Mobile: 907 501 821
Contact: Javier Gª Roldán

School, aerial photography.

GOLF
Costa Ballena Club de Golf
Aptdo. Correos 99, 11520
ROTA (Cádiz)
Tel: +34 56 847 070
Fax: +34 956 847 050

A golf course designed by José María
Olazábal. Lessons are available at the
Andalusian Golf School.

HANG GLIDING
Parapente Draco, Ctra. S.
Nevada km8, 18191 Pinos
Genil (Granada)
Tel: +34 958 488 560/366 146
Fax: +34 958 488 686
Email: parapentedraco@
readysoft.es
Website: www.readysoft.es/

home/draco
Established: 1997
Level: Basic
Contact: Lola Morillas/
Daniel Martínez

This is a school, a flying centre and an
examination centre for hang-gliders.
The teachers here all have qualifications
recognised by FEADA (*Federación
Andaluza de los Deportes Aéreos*,
Andalucian Federation for Air Sports)
and the school itself also has official
recognition from FENDA (Federación
Española de los Deportes Aéreos). The
two-day hang-gliding course costs
45,000ptas per person and it takes
place in the areas of Monachil and
Cenes de la Vega (in Granada),
involving three 550metre flights and
several smaller ones. The price of the
course includes a temporary federal
licence (valid for three months).

HORSERIDING
Cabacci Centro Ecuestre
Ctra. de Lugros, 18500 (Guadix)
GRANADA
Tel: +34 958 662 201/661 706

Children's and adult riding courses,
riding summer camps.

Centro Ecuestre Jerezano
Ctra de Sanlucar Km 0.5, Jerez
de la Frontera
Tel: +34 956 145 137/341 220
Mobile: 970 884 715
Established: 1993
Level: None
Contact: Juan or José Mª
García Molina

Courses for beginners and programmes
in Andalucian dressage and Classical
dressage are offered at this school in a
part of southern Spain famous for

horseriding. Children and adults alike are welcomed here and horseback excursions through the vineyards and short treks can be organised. The price of an hour-long class is 1,650ptas, a five-day course costs 6,600ptas (one hour a day) and a two-week course (also one hour a day) costs 15,400ptas. A half-day trip (including picnic) costs 7,150ptas; a trip lasting a whole days costs 3,300ptas (picnic and snack foods included). Students are predominantly Spanish, English and German and start dates are flexible.

Caballos la Vereda
Crta. N-110 km 113.500, Riaza (SEGOVIA),
Tel: 921 125 114,
Mobile: 908 822 861

Classes and excursions.

Bailo Sport Deporte y Salud
Ctra. Pamplona-Huesca
Tel: 989 703 690

Riding school (short courses, week-long courses) and other sports catered for such as canoeing and walking.

Equitour
PO Box 807, Dubois, Wyoming 82513, USA
Tel: (Wyoming) 307 455 3363
Fax: (Wyoming) 307 455 2354
Email: equitour@wyoming.com
Website: www.ridingtours.com /spain.htm

Equitours offer a series of rides through Spain in regions such as the Alpujarras, Santiago de Compostela and Andalucia.

Hidden Trails
5936 Inverness Street, Vancouver, BC, CANADA, V5W 3P7
Tel: (Canada) 604 323 1141
Fax: (Canada) 604 323 1148
Email: hiddentrails@ hiddentrails.com
Website: www.hiddentrails.com

Hidden Trails organise riding tours, some including lessons, around Spain and the rest of the world.

MISCELLANEOUS
Centro Internacional de Actividades en la Naturaleza "La Vereda"
Villalba de la Sierra, Apdo. De Correos 334, Cuenca
Tel: +34 969 230 052/140 161

This centre offers numerous activities such as horseriding, canoeing, hang-gliding, mountain-biking, orienteering and white-water rafting. Group trips can be arranged around Spain and to other parts of Europe and North Africa.

MOUNTAIN SPORTS (walking, canoeing, white water rafting, winter sports)
Gorgol Guías de Montañas, Tramacastilla de Tena, 22663 Huesca
Tel/Fax: +34 974 487 626
Email: guiasgorgol@qrz.net

Aragón Aventura, Carretera de Ordesa, s/n, 22639 Gavin, (Biescas) Huesca
Tel: +34 974 485 358/495 632
Fax: +34 974 485 348
Mobile: 929 437 669
Email: aragonaventu@ cosin.com

Website: www.rci.es/soaso/
aragonaventura

Transpirineos (Iniciativas Aragonesas de Ocio y Aventura),
Avda PrimerViernes de Mayo, 7, 22700 Jaca (Huesca)
Tel: +34 974 356 385
Fax: +34 974 355 205
Email: transpirineos@
pirinet.com
Website: www.pirinet.com/
transpirineos.

MOTORCYCLE RACING
Kenny Roberts Training Ranch,
Circuit de Catalunya, E-08160
Montmeló, Barcelona,
Tel: +34 91 571 9723
Fax: +34 93 571 9724.

Sessions cost $350 per day with accommodation and food, and include equipment, protection, insurance and medical cover, lunch, transport and use of motorcycles.

RAFTING
Aguas Blancas
Avda Sobrarbe, 4, 22330
AINSA (Huesca)
Tel: +34 974 510 008/500 983

Rafting, kayak and canoeing courses for small or large groups. Weekend, three- and five-day excursions are available.

SAILING
Escuela de Vela Fuerza Seis
Madrid office: Genova, 5,
28004 Madrid
(NB: the courses take place at Puerto Deportivo Luis Campomanes in Altea, Alicante)

Tel: +34 91 319 2828
Fax: +34 91 319 2093
Established: 1986
Level: Intermediate
Nearest Station: Alicante
Contact: Luis Adan Galdeano

You must be aged 18 or over to take part in the sailing courses offered by this school. Four courses are on offer: small sailing boat (beginners and advanced) and cruiser (coastal and sea-going). Courses 55,000ptas to 62,000ptas for one week and 100,000ptas to 112,000ptas for two weeks (accommodation is included in all price categories).

SKYDIVING
Centre de Paracaigudisme Costa Brava
Aeròdrom d'Empúriabrava, Sector Aeroclub, s/n, Apartado de Correos 194, GERONA,
Tel: +34 972 450 0111
Fax: +34 972 450 749

TREKKING
Viajes Trekking
Henríquez Jorquera, 2-8ǀ C, 18011 Granada
Tel: +34 958 150 731
Established: 1994
Level: Basic
Contact: Manuel Morante

For those interested in active holidays in Spain, Viajes Trekking (as the name suggests) offers 2-, 3-, 10- and 15-day walking, cycling, camping, diving and trekking holidays for up to 15 people. Activities take place in the Parque Natural de Sierra Nevada, Parque Natural de Cazorla Segura y las Villas and Parque Natural de Cabo de Gata Níjar (all in the Granada area). Also on offer are excursions into the deserts and mountains of Morocco for two weeks in July, August and September. Prices range from 3,000ptas for a weekend in the Alta Montaña in the Sierra Nevada to 65,000ptas for the nine-day trip along the paths of the Dunes of Erfoud in Morrocco. Trekkers are advised that they may be exploring areas where tourism has not yet had a profound impact, therefore they may have to do without the usual tourist luxuries for some part of the trips.

WALKING
Campo a Través
Alcanara, 3, Madrid
Tel: +34 91 576 2843
Fax: +34 91 578 1785
Mobile: 908 422 945

Walking holidays in and around Madrid, throughout Spain and abroad, lasting from a day to a couple of weeks.

WATERSPORTS (miscellaneous)

CANOEING
Asdon Aventura
Río Miño, 22, 28804 Alcalá de Henares (MADRID)
Tel: +34 91 883 4799
Mobile: 908 610 738

Estación Náutica Alto Tajo
Plaza Pablo Picasso, 4-4ºB, 28529 Rivas Vaciamadrid (MADRID)
Tel: +34 91 666 0006
Fax: +34 91 367 8629
Mobile: 908 020 904

DIVING
Centro de Buceo Albacora
Pto. Deportivo de Barbate, Barbate (CçDIZ)
Tel: +34 956 250 188
Mobile: 908 650 200

Cormorá Divecentre
Club Nautic 10, 17487 Empuriabrava (GIRONA)
Tel: +34 972 452 845
Fax: +34 972 451 005
Mobile: 909 718 913 or 039 027 794
Email: cormora@ifr.es
Website: www.ifr.es/~cormora.
Level: English, French and German are spoken here.

Centro Escuela de Buceo Trek Dive
Pº Andrés de Segovia, 13, bloque, 43, edificio Alvarez, 18697 La Herradura (GRANADA)
Tel: +34 958 640 657
Fax: +34 958 640 649

Dardanus
Centro de Buceo Dardanus, Castell de Ferro, Granada
Tel: +34 958 656 008
Mobile: 908 625 822

Amarras Sub
Lagasca, 33-1º dcha, 28001 Madrid
Tel: +34 91 577 0696

Club Oceano
Orense, 29 bajo dcha, Madrid
Tel: +34 91 556 5361

Deep Sub
Andrés Torrejón, 15 bajo, 28014 Madrid,
Tel: +34 91 433 1789
Fax: +34 91 501 1564
Email: deepsub@mx3.redestb.es

Escuela de Buceo Arrecife
Travesía de las Cañas, 1, 28043 Madrid
Tel: +34 91 519 1191

Sociedad de Exploraciones SES (AD)

Oña, 103, 28050 Madrid
Tel: +34 91 766 3303
Mobile: 909178 010

Avenatour

Ctra. de Benasque, s/n, 22450
Campo (Huesca)
Tel: +34 974 550 177
(Barcelona) +34 93 697 5959
Mobile: 909 338 636

WINDSURFING/SAILING
Surf-3, Shop and School

Escuela de la Vela CYII-Surf 3,
C/Galileo, 31, 28015 Madrid
Tel: +34 91 447 1282

WINE AND COFFEE TASTING

Coffee Consulting

Doctor Vallejo, 24, Madrid
28027
Tel: +34 91 407 0089
Fax: +34 91 407 0349
Email: coffeeco@stnet.es
Website: www.stnet.es/
cafe&vino
Established: 1989
Level: Advanced
Nearest Station: (Metro) Pueblo
Nuevo
Contact: Fructuoso Arranz

Based in an unassuming building in a bustling, residential area of northeast Madrid, this is the only place in Spain, and possibly Europe, where you can learn the art of coffee tasting, an art that until now has been the sole preserve of employees in the coffee industry. Admittedly, you might not want to make a journey to Spain just to come here. However, this is a very unusual course and for those with a genuine passion for coffee, who know what they like and want to find out more, this could be of great interest.

The man who runs the courses, Fructuoso Arranz, worked for two multinational coffee-making companies where he was trained in the art of coffee tasting. Today, apart from courses in coffee and wine tasting, his main business is testing the taste and chemical composition of coffees, wines and herbal drinks for major corporations. He also has a Masters in Viticulture and enology from the Universidad Politécnica de Madrid, the broadest wine-tasting course in Spain. All courses take place in a purpose-built classroom, which has an adjoining cellar. There is also a laboratory and a small kitchen.

There are three courses on offer. Two for coffee and one for wine tasting. The first coffee course (25 hours) is only geared towards people involved in the coffee industry. The second course (nine hours, 18,000ptas) is less in depth, focusing on teaching the difference between what is good and what is bad, and it involves tasting about forty different types of coffee. This is more suitable for people in the hotel and catering industry and anyone else with an interest in the subject. At the end of the course you will be given a booklet outlining all that you have learnt, as well as a diploma.

The wine-tasting course lasts for five hours on a Saturday and is aimed at anyone with an interest in knowing more about what they drink. It's a one-off course designed to introduce people to the methodology behind wine-tasting ('cata', as it is known in Spain) in one day. There are five sections to the course. The first is targetted at orienting your palate and you are taught to identify its different zones (acid, bitter, sweet and salty). Next, you learn how to identify different smells. In the third part of the class, you are taught how wine is made and the different categories of wine (white, red, rose, cava and champagne). The fourth module of the course (the most eagerly awaited?) is when you finally get to try the wines (25 different types within the categories mentioned above). Finally, there is a discussion about wines and you are given a booklet outlining all that you have learnt during the course. The cost of this course is 10,000ptas and there are usually from 10 to 15 people in each class. There is an extended nine-hour course, which costs 12,000ptas and occasionally, there are three-day courses offering a broader insight into the subject. Private courses can be arranged according to the requirements of the person/group. Courses on specific wines such as Rioja, Cavas, etc. can also be organised

Courses are open all year round. Fructuoso Arranz gives courses abroad (contact him for more information) and therefore there are no sessions when he is away. Contact the school for details.

Círculo de Vino Matritense
C/del Pez, 27
Tel: +34 91 522 5307
Fax: +34 508 3507
Email: vinomatritense@nil.es
Website: www.nil.es/
vinomatritense
Established: 1993
Level: High
Nearest Station: (Metro)
Noviciado
Contact: Fernando García

This school offers three courses to suit three different levels of experience in wine-tasting. Levels I (introduction), II (beginner) and III (advanced) last four, five and nine days respectively and cost from 15,000ptas to 51,000ptas. Students come from Spain, Germany and the USA. Weekly seminars also take place here.

FINDING OUT ABOUT OTHER COURSES IN SPAIN
Wherever you are, the local paper will doubtless carry information about courses in the area. You will usually find these under the section entitled *Anuncios Breves* (Small Ads) or equivalent. In larger cities, such as Madrid and Granada, you will find guides entitled *Guía del Ocio*. These are weekly guides to what to do in your free time. They usually cost about 250ptas and contain cinema and restaurant listings as well as articles and reviews. In the Madrid version, there is a section called A Saber, in which courses of all types are advertised. The range is eye-opening, and spans desktop publishing and dancing to courses on how to chat people up (*Aprende a ligar*) and two-day events on improving the way you relate to others.

A magazine geared purely towards courses has recently been launched in Madrid. It is called *Cursos*, (price 250ptas) and is published on a monthly basis. It should be available from most newsstands, but it can be difficult to get hold of. *Cursos* contains course listings and articles about courses. Also in Madrid, the newspaper *Segundamano* (*see p31*, Living in Spain) is a good source for course information. The *Enseñanzas y Clases* section carries about two pages of small ads for people advertising classes in Spanish as a foreign language, music, dancing and ceramics, amongst others.

For more information about courses on various themes in Spain, contact the Instituto Cervantes nearest you. For addresses of the Instituto Cervantes centres all over the world. It may also be worth your while surfing the net. The comunidad *autónoma* of Andalucía has a website in English, with a wealth of information about the region for English speakers and other tourists, including details of a number of courses. You can visit this site at www.andalucia.com/.

INFORMATION ON THE WORLD WIDE WEB

CECE (*Confederación Española de Centros de Enseñanza,* Spanish Confederation of Teaching Centres), which claims to be the first Spanish web server for information about non-university education has links to a number of centres. Be warned, however, that the information is all written in Spanish. You can find CECE on www.cece.es.

For non-regulated (ie private) education in Catalunya, INCANOP (*Institut Català de Noves Professions,* Catalan Institute for New Professions) offers links to 900 schools in that area, offering more than 7,500 courses. Go to www.xtec.es/incanop/guia.htm for the list of subjects with centres affiliated to INCANOP. For lists of the centres in each category, click on the category itself. Below is a list of addresses for some of the categories that may be of interest.

For Spanish for foreigners
(*Castellà per a estrangers*), go to www.xtec.es/incanop/10/c186.htm

For Catalan for foreigners
(Català per a estrangers) go to www.xtec.es/incanop/10/c190.htm

For Spanish dancing
go to www.xtec.es/incanp/16/c274.htm

For flamenco
go to www.xtec.es/incano p/16/c446.htm

For guitar
go to www.xtec.es/incano p/16/c578.htm

For ceramics
go to www.xtec.es/incano p/19/c192.htm

INCANOP recommends that before signing up for classes you should find out:

• What the course is aiming to achieve.

• Hours of practical classes and hours of theory classes on the course.

• Cancellation conditions.

• Facilities available at the school (libraries, etc).

• If the course will qualify you to be awarded the Diploma of the Generalitat de Catalunya (a diploma showing that the course is recognised by the *comunidad autónoma* of Catalunya).

CULTURAL ACTIVITIES IN MADRID – USEFUL ADDRESSES

ARCO (an international exhibition of contemporary art in Madrid). Takes place in January and February at Parque Ferial Juan Carlos, I, 28043 Madrid
Tel: +34 722 5017
Fax +34 722 5798

Casa de America
(exhibitions, plays, courses, etc on

Spanish-American themes)
Paseo de Recoletos, 2, 28001 Madrid
Tel: +34 91 595 4835
Fax: +34 91 595 4827

Casa de Velázquez
(a French cultural institution in Spain)
Paul Guinard, 3, Ciudad Universitaria,
28040 Madrid
Tel: +34 91 543 3605
Fax: +34 91 544 6870

Centro Cultural Círculo de Lectores
(literary soirées, meetings with authors)
O'Donnell, 10, 28009 Madrid
Tel: +34 91 435 3614
Fax: +34 91 435 3949

Círculo de Bellas Artes
(exhibitions, lectures, concerts)
Marqués de Casa Riera, 2, 28014
Madrid
Tel: +34 91 531 7700
Fax: +34 531 0552

Casa do Brasil
(lectures and events on Brasilian
themes) Avda Arco de la Victoria, s/n,
28040 Madrid
Tel: +34 91 544 1404
Fax: +34 543 5188
email 10034.3114@compuserve.
com, website: www: outworld.com-
puserve.com/homepages/CBrasil

Centro de Estudios Judeo-Cristianos Religiosas
Ntra. Sra. De Sion, Hilarión Eslava, 50,
28015 Madrid
Tel/Fax: +34 91543 1251

Comunidad de Madrid, Dirección General de Patriomonio Cultural
(lectures on Spanish and Portuguese
themes) Sala de Exposiciones del Canal
de Isabel II, Santa Engracia, 125, 28003
Madrid. Tel: +34 91 580 2625/445 1000
ext 2505 Fax: +34 91 580 2614

Sala de Exposiciones de Plaza de España (exhibitions)
Plaza de España, 8, 28008 Madrid
Tel: +34 91 580 2492
Fax: +34 91 580 2614

Forum FNAC – FNAC is a major book
and record shop located just off the
Puerta del Sol, its Forum FNAC offers
lectures, presentations and concerts on
a wide variety of themes.

Fundación Arte y Tecnología (exhibitions), Fuencarral, 3, 28004 Madrid
Tel: +34 91 522 6645
Fax: +34 91 531 7106

Fundación Cultural Mapfre Vida
(lectures, exhibitions)
Avda General Perón, 40, 28020 Madrid
Tel: +34 91 581 1596
Fax: +34 91 581 1629

Fundación ICO (exhibitions on
Spanish art)
Paseo del Prado, 4-9 planta, 28014
Madrid
Tel: +34 91 592 1626
Fax: +34 91 592 1597

Fundación Ortega y Gasset
(advanced courses on Spanish and
Latin American themes, and others)
Fortuny, 53, 28010 Madrid
Tel: +34 91 310 4412
Fax: +34 91 308 4007

Fundación Lázaro Galdiano (museum
and library devoted to art and books),
Serrano, 122, 28006 Madrid
Tel: +34 91 561 6084
Fax: +34 91 561 7793, email
apereda@flg.es

Instituto del Patrimonio Histórico Español
Greco, 4, 28011 Madrid

Instituto de México en España
(lectures, films, concerts on Mexican themes), Carrera de San Jerónimo, 46, 28014 Madrid
Tel: +34 91 420 2992
Fax: +34 91 369 3817

Fundación Maraya, Cultura y Pensamient
(cultural organisation offering lectures, literary events), Miguel Angel, 1dpdo. 1º, 28010 Madrid
Tel: +34 91 310 4897
Fax: +34 91 308 7093
Email: fundacionmaraya@ctv.es

Ministerio de Educación y Cultura, Dirección General de Bellas Artes y Bienes Culturales
(exhibitions, lectures), Plaza del Rey, s/n, 28014 Madrid
Tel: +34 91 532 5089 ext 2428/3427

Museo Nacional de Ciencia y Tecnología
Paseo de las Delicias, 61, 28045 Madrid

Museo Romántico
San Mateo, 13, 28004 Madrid

Museo de América
Avda Reyes Católicos, 6, 28040 Madrid

Museo Arqueológico Nacional,
Serrano, 13, 28001 Madrid

Ministerio de Fomento
(architecture)
Sala de Exposiciones de la Arquería de Los Nuevos Ministerios, Paseo de la Castellana, 67, 28071 Madrid,
Tel: +34 91 597 8765
Fax: +34 91 597 8506

Museo Casa de la Moneda
(exhibitions on the theme of money, and other topics)
Doctor Esquerdo, 36, Madrid 28071,

Tel: +34 91 566 6544
Fax: +34 91 504 2943

Museo de la Ciudad
(houses a permanent exhibition about the city of Madrid)
Príncipe de Vergarra, 140, 28002 Madrid
Tel: +34 91 588 6599
Fax: +34 91 588 6554

Museo Nacional Centro de Arte Reina Sofía
(major art museum with permanent collection, temporary exhibitions, lectures, films)
Santa Isabel, 52, 28012 Madrid
Tel: +34 91 467 5061/62
Fax: +34 91 467 3163

Real Academia de Bellas Artes de S. Fernand
(concerts, exhibitions), Alcalá, 13, 28014 Madrid

Residencia de Estudiantes
(films, lectures), Pinar, 23, 28006 Madrid
Tel: +34 91 563 6411
Fax: +34 91 563 8127

Salas de Exposición del Ministerio de Educación y Cultura
Avda Juan de Herrera, 2, 28040 Madrid

Teatro de la Abadía (plays)
Fernández de los Ríos, 42, 28015 Madrid
Tel: +34 91 448 1181/1338
Fax: +34 91 448, 1449
email abadia@ctv.es

Teatro de la Zarzuela
Jovellanos, 4, 28014 Madrid
Tel: +34 91 524 5400
Fax: +34 91 429 7157

Universidad Complutense de Madrid, Actividades Culturales
(film, lectures, music)
Tel: +34 91 394 6933

Universities

The most famous university in Spain is the ancient Universidad de Salamanca. Founded in 1218, it is also the oldest university in the country. Its imposing architecture and revered halls, together with the air of academe that envelops the whole town, place Salamanca on a par with all the oldest and grandest universities in the world. However, unlike most of its contemporaries (Oxford, Bologna, Paris), the Universidad de Salamanca has remained academically stagnant for many years, some would even say centuries.

As if to highlight the dinosaur that Salamanca has become, there has been an enormous rise over the past century, and in particular over the past 25 to 30 years, in the number of establishments granted university status in Spain. In 1890 there were less than 20 throughout the whole of Spain (including her islands), today there are over 55, with the most recent additions being the Universidad de Burgos (founded in 1994) and the Universidad Oberta de Catalunya (distance-learning, founded in 1995).

As is only to be expected, some of the oldest universities in Spain are also those with the best reputations – Granada (1531), Sevilla (1505), Barcelona (1450), Santiago de Compostela (1495) and Universidad Complutense de Madrid (1508; the largest university in Spain with well over 100,000 students). However, others with excellent word-of-mouth reputations include the newer institutions such as Universidad Autónoma de Madrid (1968), Universidad Autónoma de Barcelona (also 1968), Universidad Carlos III de Madrid (1989) and Universidad Pompeu Fabra (1990, Barcelona). The three polytechnic universities – Universidad Politécnica de Cataluña, Universidad Politécnica de Madrid and Universidad Politécnica de Valencia (all founded in 1971) – have also distinguished themselves, as have the Church-affiliated universities (see below).

The provision of a university education in Spain is not the sole preserve of state-run universities: of the 55 universities in Spain, six are private universities and four are affiliated to the church. As in most countries, one of the major differences between a private university education and a state university education relates to cost. At private Spanish universities (this includes church-affiliated universities), students pay the full cost of their tuition at whatever rate has been fixed by that institution. At state Spanish universities, students pay between 10 per cent and 20 per cent of the actual cost of their education. The private universities are: Universidad Ramon Llull, Universidad Alfonso X El Sabio, Universidad Antonio de Nebrija, Universidad San Pablo (CEU), Universidad Oberta de

Catalunya and Universidad Europea de Madrid (CEES). The church-affiliated universities are: Universidad Pontificia de Salamanca, Universidad Pontificia de Comillas, Universidad de Navarra and Universidad de Deusto.

The decision as to whether an institution may be granted the status of university is the responsibility of the individual *comunidades autónomas* (autonomous communities). Each *comunidad* can only make such decisions as to institutions within their own jurisdiction and they must judge eligibility according to specific guidelines. These guidelines apply both to state-run and private centres.

The degrees awarded by private universities, as well as the private teaching centres (*centros privados de enseñanza*) with the power to award certain degrees, are recognised by the *Consejo de Universidades* (The Board of Universities). The prerequisite for any private teaching centre is that it must be integrated within a private university or affiliated to a public university.

Church-affiliated universities function in much the same way. These award both official titles and ecclesiastical titles, some of which are officially recognised as civil degrees, by law, through the *Real Decreto del Consejo de Ministros*.

WHAT TO STUDY

The degree provision in Spain offers little, if anything, that is truly innovative or unusual. Of the 230 degrees (both at vocational training and university-level) on offer, the three that reflect Spanish culture specifically are the *Licenciado en Enología* (Degree in Wine Studies), *Licenciado en Música*

(Music Degree, incorporating flamenco and flamenco guitar) and *Licenciado en Danza* (Dance Degree, with a core requirement in Spanish ballet). The *Licenciado en Enología* has only recently been introduced and is a second cycle subject (in other words, it can only be undertaken once a first cycle subject has been completed, see below). Students with qualifications in biology, chemistry, pharmacy, agricultural engineering and agricultural chemistry, as well as those in possession of the title of technical agricultural engineer, may be admitted onto the course. The two-year course considers various aspects of wine, from the scientific *bioquímica y microbiología enológicas* (the biochemistry and microbiology of wine) to the more practical *economía y gestión de la empresa vitivinícola* (the economics and management of a wine-making business) and *normativa y legislación vitivinícola* (the legislation governing wine).

HOW TO GET IN
SELECTIVIDAD

As outlined in the opening chapters of this guide (*see* The Spanish Education System *p25*), in order to gain a place at a Spanish university to study most subjects, regardless of whether or not you are Spanish, you will have to take the Spanish university entrance exam – *selectividad*. The only subjects and qualifications for which *selectividad* is not a prerequisite are diplomas, technical engineering and technical architecture. It goes without saying that the fundamental requirement for anyone wishing to undertake this test is that they must be able to speak, write and comprehend Spanish fluently. Although every year a proportion of places (5 per cent) at Spanish universities are set aside for overseas students, it is worth bearing in mind that the majority of these students will be from South America and Spanish will be their first language. If Spanish is not your first language and you are not entirely fluent in it, your chances of acceptance will be narrow.

The Spanish Ministry of Education and Culture publishes a document entitled *Pruebas de Acceso a la Universidad (con estudios extranjeros convalidables)* (University Entrance Exams – for students with equivalent foreign qualifications), in which every aspect of *selectividad* is explained. This document may be obtained from one of the two addresses given below. Apart from Spanish candidates with the relevant COU or *bachillerato* qualifications, any foreign student with a qualification equivalent to COU or *bachillerato* (e.g. A levels in the UK) may present themselves for *selectividad*. Students who have previously failed *selectividad* or those who wish to obtain a better grade than the one achieved the previous year are also allowed to present themselves. No candidate without the relevant academic qualifications may present themselves for *selectividad*. These qualifications are:

• COU (*Curso de Orentación Universitaria;* the university guidance course)
OR
• *Bachillerato LOGSE* (the new-style baccalaureate)
OR
• *Bachillerato Experimental* (experimental baccalaureate)
OR
• Students older than 25 years of age
OR
• Students with appropriate overseas qualifications

OR
• Students with Vocational Training qualifications
OR

• Other recognised qualifications (eg anyone with a degree from any faculty and degree holders from Church-affiliated universities, officials from any one of the three armies).

Various documents must be shown prior to presentation for selectividad. These documents include parts one and two of the selectividad matriculation form, to be stamped by the post office *(caja de ahorros)*, a photocopy of the DNI (the Spanish ID card; this will not apply to non-Spanish nationals) or your passport. Also necessary are a certified photocopy proving recognition of your application by the *Ministerio de Educación y Ciencia* (Spanish Ministry of Education and Science), or in its absence, the original of the proof of provisional registration, which proves that you have already applied for the aforementioned certificate or recognition (in the last case, the validity of the tests will rely on the subsequent presentation of the certified proof of recognition). When the candidate is Spanish but has studied abroad, following studies equivalent to COU, the candidate must present a certificate validated by a representative of the Spanish Embassy or Consulate in that country. The certificate must prove that the student possessed resident's status in the Register of Enrolment of the Consular Office or Consular Section of the Spanish Embassy. The presentation of these documents is mandatory. If they are not shown, the application will be deemed invalid. Other documents may be required; consult the Ministry of Education for more information.

The *selectividad* exams themselves must normally be taken at the first choice university itself. Therefore, if you are applying to study at the Universidad Complutense de Madrid, you will usually have to go to Madrid to sit the university entrance exams. Only in exceptional circumstances, and when there are sufficient numbers of students participating from elsewhere, can the exams take place in another part of Spain or in a foreign city where there is a *Consejería de Educación* (Education Council) affiliated to the Spanish Embassy.

The exams take place over two days, twice a year, normally in June and September and consist of two *ejercicios* (exercises). The first exercise has three sections. The first section lasts an hour and a half and involves the summary of, and written commentary on, a Spanish text of no more than 100 lines. The second section of the first exercise, also lasting an hour and a half, requires the examinee to answer questions on the Spanish language in the context of one of two pieces of writing (to be chosen by the candidate). The third and final part of the first exercise involves comprehension of a text in another language (candidates may choose from a number of languages). Comprehension questions are asked in the language that the text is written in and the candidate must reply to these questions in the same language. This test lasts one hour and candidates are not permitted to use a dictionary or any other learning aids. Apart from this last section, all questions must be answered in Spanish. Each section is worth ten points and the average of all three constitutes the overall mark of this first exercise.

For the second exercise, candidates must make three choices from either

the science option (*Opción Ciencias*) or the social sciences-humanities option (*Opción Ciencias Sociales-Humanidades*). From the two, candidates can choose their combination of three from either maths, physics, chemistry, biology, geology and technical drawing, or literature, history of the contemporary world, Latin, Greek, history of art, maths and philosophy, respectively. This exercise requires the candidate to answer two questions (out of four) on each of the three subjects chosen. The time allowed to answer both questions on each topic is one and a half hours (therefore, the total number of hours to answer all six questions is four and a half hours). Each topic is marked out of 10 and the mathematical average of all three will constitute the final mark for this exercise. All questions must be answered in Spanish.

Students are accepted, or not, into their university of choice according to their final marks. For students wishing to undertake a diploma or a degree in technical engineering, a

FURTHER INFORMATION
For an application form or to find out more about university entrance for non-Spanish nationals with qualifications equivalent to COU or *bachillerato*, contact UNED (Universidad Nacional de Educación a Distancia), Sección COU y PAAU, C/Senda del Rey, s/n, Edificio de Humanidades, 28040 Madrid, tel +34 91 398 6612/14/16. There is also a 24 hour information line: +34 91 398 6534 and you can find UNED on **www.uned.es**.

system operates whereby those who are admitted first are those who passed *selectividad* in June in their first choice degree subject. (It is possible to be accepted into your university of choice but not to study your first choice subject.) After these come those who passed *selectividad* in June, though not in their first choice degree subject. Those who are admitted last, if at all, are those who passed COU or *bachillerato* in September, but did not pass *selectividad*, either because they failed it or because they chose not to take it.

You can apply to study at as many universities as you like, and it is necessary to indicate more than one preferred subject of study. You will be given various options and it is advisable to fill each one out (there will be an order of preference) even if you are adamant that there is one subject, and one subject alone, that you wish to study. If you do not, and you fail to gain a place at any of the institutions applied to, you will have to wait an entire year in order to be able to reapply to university.

Spanish students can apply to university in one of two ways. Either they apply by *Distrito único*, which means that they are applying to study within their *comunidad autónoma*, or by *Distrito Compartido*, which means that they are applying to universities outside their own *comunidad autónoma*. Should this be the case, the candidate is limited to only three options. The forms filled out by the candidate varies accordingly.

Admission to state universities depends on several factors: whether the student pertains to the *comunidad autónoma* of the university in question, the date when the university entrance exams were passed or baccalaureate schooling finished and the relationship between the kind of studies applied for and the type of COU or *bachillerato* taken. On an annual basis, universities reserve a fixed amount of places for students from a variety of different backgrounds. For example, there are a certain number of places for students regardless of the university district to which they belong. Provision is also made for university graduates, foreign students (from non-European Union member countries) who passed *selectividad* the previous year (the majority of these will be from South American countries) and finally, for pupils with second level vocational training certificates.

Education in Spanish universities is organised around five ciclos (cycles). These are:

- First cycle education only: vocationally based, this involves three years of training after which a total of 180 to 270 credits may be awarded. There are three possible titles to be earned: diplomado (junior graduate), *ingeniero técnico* (technical engineer) or *arquitecto técnico* (technical architect). Typical subjects in this cycle include library science and documentation, nursing, social work, business science, maritime navigation and a wide range of technical engineering topics including aero-navigation and mining.

- Dual cycle education with no intermediate degree: this involves between four or five years of study. As the name suggests, students study for two academic cycles, but are only awarded a title on completion of the second cycle. A total of between 300 and 450 credits must be earned in order to become either a *licenciado* (holder of a bachelor's degree), *ingeniero* (holder of a degree in engineering) or *arquitecto* (holder of a degree in architecture). Typical subjects in this cycle include fine arts, mathematics, modern languages (known as *filología español* (Spanish philology) or *filología francés* (French philology) or *filología xxxx (*according to the language that you happen to be studying), journalism, medicine, and civil engineering.

- Dual cycle studies with an intermediate degree: students who begin by earning a *diplomado* (junior graduate), *ingeniero técnico* (technical engineer) or *arquitecto técnico* (technical architect) may then go on to study for another year or two to earn the titles of either: *licenciado, ingeniero or arquitecto (see above).*

- Second cycle education only: these two-year courses allow students to earn the titles of either: *licenciado, ingeniero or arquitecto (see above).* Typical subjects in this cycle include linguistics, biochemistry, market research and techniques and electronics.

- Third cycle education: these two year courses, which revolve around seminars, are designed for graduates. To earn the title of *doctor* (doctor) students must, in addition, submit and discuss a thesis based on original research, which they are allowed a maximum of five years to complete.

Universities are entitled to award their own separate degrees and diplomas in addition to the above.

FINANCES

As mentioned above, all students at Spanish universities must pay for their education. However, the amount paid depends on whether the student is attending a state-run (public) university or a private university. Private universities regulate their fees individually. The fees for public universities are state-regulated and are set according to individual credits. In 1996-97, it cost 1,690ptas to take one credit for degrees in medicine or dentistry (Experimental Level 1 – the most expensive credit). Bearing in mind that to gain a degree in either subject it is necessary to gain between 300 and 450 credits, the total cost of a university education (in dentistry or medicine) over the five years of the course would come to between 507,000ptas (about £2,200) and 760,500ptas (about £3,300). The least expensive credit in 1996-7 was Experimental Level 7 (1,065ptas), which covers degrees in social anthropology and culture, administration and political science and advertising and PR.

QUALITY

To date, only one quality assessment test has been carried out with regard to the overall standard in Spanish universities. The research was conducted by Círculo de Progreso in a non-official capacity. Currently, the *Consejo de Universidades* is carrying out an official investigation, the results of which are still not available.

POSTGRADUATE STUDIES

It is possible to study a number of subjects at postgraduate level in Spain, though like the subjects available at undergraduate level, none of these is particularly unusual. However, for those who have studied Spanish in some form at undergraduate level, or who have an interest in Spain and Spanish culture (as well as an excellent command of the language and the relevant qualifications) some of the courses below may be of interest.

Universidad Complutense de Madrid

Magister de Estudios Superiores Iberoamericanos (one year, 325,000ptas) for those with a professional interest in latin america with regard to public administration, private corporations and non-governmental organisations.

Magister in Formación de Especialistas en la Enseñanza del Español come Lengua Extranjera (one year, 395,000ptas), involves the analysis of errors through the influence of English, German, French, Italian, Korean, Japanese, Arabic and Chinese. Master de Radio (one year, 550,000ptas), includes practicals at Radio Nacional de España.

Universidad de Alcalà de Henares

Curso de Lengua y Cultura Española para Extranjeros (one year, 235,000ptas). This course aims to provide an overview with regard to language (grammar, writing, conversation, etc) and culture (history of art, history of Spain, Spanish literature, etc)

Universidad de Barcelona

Master en Formación del Profesorado del Español como Lengua Extanjera (one year, 220,500ptas). For teachers of Spanish as a foreign language.

Universidad del País Vasco

Master Universitario en Formación de Profesorado de Español como Lengua Extranjera (one year). A course aimed at imparting different methods for teaching Spanish as a foreign language. *Master Universitario en Traducción: Especialidad Euskera* (two years), for those intending to use their translating skills on a professional basis, specialising in Euskera.

Escuela de Arte y Antigüedades

C/Conde de Aranda, 4 1ʃ, 28001 Madrid
Tel/Fax: +34 91 577 6713).

Curso de Anticuariado (three years, 1,025,631ptas), offering a specialisation in antiques, with a study of the constructive and decorative techniques of each material.

Curso de Expertización, Tasación y Valoración de Obras de Arte (one year, 217,777ptas), which involves the analysis of different pieces in order to value them correctly.

Curso de Restauración de Muebles y Maderas Antiguas (three years, 1,400,631ptas) a study of the techniques of construction and decoration, discovering 'secrets from the workshop' and learning how to detect and diagnose problems.

Curso de Restauración de Papel, Documentos Gráficos, Grabados y Dibujos (one year, 155,000ptas), analysing paper, its behaviour and its restoration. *Curso de Restauración de Pintura* (three years, 1,204,131ptas), analysing the different processes for restoring canvases, etc.

Centro de Lenguas Modernas de la Universidad de Granada,

Viejo, s/n (Realejo), 18071 Granada,
Tel: +34 958 220 790
Fax: +34 958 220 844:
Curso de Estudio Hipsánicos (eight months, 181,000ptas), a programme for degree holders and professionals who wish to broaden their knowledge of Spanish culture. Subjects include translation, politics, literature and islamic culture in Spain.

CLUNY-ISEIT Instituto Superior de Interpretación y Traducción,

C/Infanta Mercedes, 93, 28020 Madrid
Tel: +34 91 571 0430
Fax: +34 91 571 0458: *Master en Traducción (Interpretación/Terminología)* (18 months, 927,000ptas). With specialities in simultaneous translation and lectures in the fields of economics and the law, this is suitable for both degree holders and overseas students with equivalent qualifications.

Estudio Internacional Sampere,

Castelló, 50, 28001 Madrid
Tel: +34 91 575 9790
Fax: +34 91 576 3910.
Curso de Interprete Jurado (versión presencial o distancia) (nine months, 262,500ptas (learning in situ) or 208,000ptas (distance learning)); *Curso de Traducción General (versión presencial o a distancia)* (nine months, 199,500ptas (learning in situ) or 208,000ptas (distance learning) and *Curso de Traducción Jurídica (versión presecial o a distancia)* (nine months, 141,000ptas (learning in situ) or 208,000ptas (distance learning). These courses are suitable for those whose mother tongue is not Spanish, but who speak it to a very high level (level five of the Escuela Oficial de Idiomas. The material used is based on a selection of texts (general, legal and economic).

Instituto de Estudios de Iberoamérica y Portugal

Diploma de Estudios del Medio Natural en América Latina (one year, 100,000ptas). A study of the environment in Latin America including zoology, botany, the economy and anthropology.
Diploma de Estudios Latinoamericanos (one year, 135,000ptas). General courses on Latin America including some compulsory modules (Latin

American Geography, Latin American Politics) and 34 optional topics (philosophy, reforms, sociology).
Diploma en Estudios Portugueses (one year, 100,000ptas). Portuguese Language and History, Literature and Geography, etc. *Maestría de Estudios Latinoamericanos* (one year, 135,000ptas). A combination of general and more specific courses on the central theme of Latin America.

Instituto de Restauración Oeben,

Serrano, 19 1º izda., 28001 Madrid,
Tel: +34 91 576 5338
Fax: +34 91 431 0759.
Master en Conservación y Restauración para Historiadores del Arte (one year, 850,000ptas). Suitable only for art historians, this course looks at all aspects of the conservation and restoration of works of art, including the history of the collections in the Prado museum. *Master en Conservación y Restauración para Licenciados en Ciencias* (one year, 1,150,000ptas). Suitable for science graduates only, this course examines the scientific processes of the conservation and restoration of works of art.

Escuela de Periodismo UAM/El País,

Miguel Yuste, 40, 28037 Madrid
Tel: +34 91 337 7760
Fax: +34 91 304 8348. *Master en Periodismo* (one year, 1,200,000ptas). Created in 1986, this school - a collaboration between one of Spain's foremost newspapers and one of it's best universities – offers one course, suitable for anyone in possession of a university degree or equivalent. The course includes workshops and lectures. A compulsory period of work experience must be undertaken either on a placement in the Spanish media or abroad.

El Correo Español-El Pueblo Vasco/Universidad del País Vasco, Pintor Losada, 7-1°, 48008 Bilbao Tel: +34 944 870 100 (ext 381-382) Fax: +34 944 733 320. *Master de Periodismo* (title granted by the Universidad del País Vasco itself) (one year, 630,000ptas). This course is structured around various modules including journalistic techniques (reporting, writing up), newspaper design, sports journalism, ethics and language.

European University

As the name suggests, Europe is the campus for this university, which is based in ten countries, often with two or three campuses in each (there are three campuses in Spain – Barcelona, Madrid and Andorra). Students follow bilingual courses (normally in English, and the language of the country in which they are based). The addresses for the European University in Spain are as follows:

EU Barcelona
Ganduxer, 70, 08021 Barcelona
Tel: +34 93 201 8171
Fax: +34 93 201 7935
Email: eubcn@bcn.servicom.es

EU Madrid
Covarrubias, 23, 28010 Madrid
Tel: +34 91 593 4133
Fax: +34 91 593 9232
Email: 104701,1643@compuserve.com

EU Andorra
La Valireta, 2, Encamp, Andorra
Tel: +34 376 832 558
Fax: +34 376 832 780.

You can find the European University on the web on www.euruni.be.

The University of Britain in Spain

If you have two or three A levels, have passed *selectividad* or the International Baccalaureate (IB) or have equivalent qualifications, you will be eligible to study at the University of Britain in Spain. This university has links with 20 or so universities in the UK, which award the degrees taught at UBS. The basic idea is that you can pursue a British degree in Spain, spending your first year in Madrid, the second year either in Madrid or the UK and your third year in the UK. In Madrid, you will be based on the university's campus. Accommodation can be arranged in a university residence or in private accommodation. Subjects taught here are divided into the faculties of Business Studies, Engineering and Health Sciences and students can choose to be taught in Spanish or English.

For more information, contact the admissions office:
Admissions Office, University of Britain in Spain, C/de la Viña, 3, 28003 Madrid, Spain
Tel: +34 91 553 6585
Fax: +34 91 534 5024
Email: jtrainor@acad.suffolk.edu,
Website:
www.ddnet.es/suffolk/ubs.htm.

Spanish Universities Directory

NB: Indented centres are affiliated to the main institution under which they are listed.

ANDALUCÍA
Universidad de Almería
Campus Universitario, Ctra. del Sacramento, s/n, 04120 Cañada de San Urbano
Tel: +34 950 215 000

Fax: +34 950 215 131
Website: www.ualm.es

Universidad de Cádiz, Rectorado,
C/Ancha, 16, 11001 Cádiz
Tel: +34 956 225 706
Fax: +34 956 226 809
Website: www.uca.es

Universidad de Córdoba
Servicio de Información al Estudiante,
Recinto del Colegio Mayor "La
Asunción", Avda Menendez Pidal, s/n,
14071 Córdoba
Tel: +34 957 218 034
Fax: +34 957 218 000
Website: www.uco.es

**ETEA – Facultad de Ciencias
Económicas y Empresariales**
Escritor Castillo Aguayo, 4 – Apdo.
Correos 439, 14004 Córdoba
Tel: +34 957 296 133
Fax: +34 957 203 611

Universidad de Granada
Hospital Real, Cuesta del Hospicio,
s/n, 18071 Granada
Tel: +34 958 243 003 (Information
Office +34 958 243 025/7)
Fax: +34 958 243 071
Website: www.ugr.es

Universidad de Huelva
Servicio de Información, Doctor
Cantero Cuadrado, 6, Huelva 21004
Tel: +34 959 226 550
Website: www.uhu.es

Universidad de Jáen
Paraje "La Lagunillas", s/n, 23071 Jáen
Te:l +34 953 212 121/92
Fax: +34 953 212 239
Email: rg@xauen.ujaen.es

Universidad de Málaga
Campus Univ. de El Ejido, s/n,
29071 Málaga

Tel: +34 95 213 1000
Fax: +34 95 213 2680
Website: www.uma.es

Universidad de Sevilla
San Fernando, 4, 41004 Sevilla
Tel: +34 95 455 1000
Fax: +34 445 1140

ARAGÓN
Universidad de Zaragoza
Ciudad Universitaria, Pedro Cerbuna,
12, 50009 Zaragoza
Tel: +34 976 761 000
Fax: +34 976 761 009
Website: www.unizar.es

ASTURIAS
Universidad de Oviedo
Rectorado, San Francisco, 3, 33003
Oviedo
Tel: +34 98 510 3000
Fax: +34 98 522 6254
Website: www.uniovi.es

BALEARES
Universidad de las Islas Baleares
Servicios Administrativos Centrales,
Son Lledó, Campus Universitario, Ctra
de Valldemossa, Km 7,5, 07071 Palma
de Mallorca
Tel: +34 971 173 000/1
Fax: +34 971 172 852
Website: www.uib.es

CANARIAS
Universidad de la Laguna
Rectorado, Molinos de Agua, s/n,
38207 La Laguna (Tenerife)
Tel: +34 922 603 000
Fax: +34 922 603 090

**Universidad de las Palmas de Gran
Canaria,** Rectorado, Alfonso XIII, 2,
35003 Las Palmas de Gran Canaria
Tel: +34 928 451 000
Fax: +34 928 451 022 Website:
www.ulpgc.es

CANTABRIA

Universidad de Cantabria, Pabellón del Gobierno, Avda de los Castros, s/n, 39005 Santander (Cantabria)
Tel: +34 942 201 017/222
Website: www.unican.es

CASTILLA-LA MANCHA

Universidad de Castilla-La Mancha, Casa-Palacio de Medrano, Paloma, 9, 13001 Ciudad Real
Tel: +34 926 295 300 ext 3622/1
Fax: +34 926 223 894
Website: www.uclm.es

CASTILLA Y LEÓN

Universidad de Burgos
Rectorado, Hospital del Rey, s/n, 09001 Burgos
Tel: +34 947 258 700
Fax: +34 947 258 742

Universidad de León
Rectorado, Avda de la Facultad, 25, 24071 León
Tel: +34 987 291 600/100
Fax: +34 987 291 614
Website: www.193.146.96.2

Universidad Pontificia de Salamanca
Rectorado, Compañía, 5, Apdo. 541, 37002 Salamanca
Tel: +34 923 212 260
Fax: +34 923 262 456

Universidad de Salamanca
Patio de Escuelas, 1, 37008 Salamanca
Tel: +34 923 294 400
Email: sou@arec.usal.es
Website: www.usal.es

Universidad de Valladolid
Palacio de Santa Cruz, Pza de Santa Cruz, 8, 47002 Valladolid
Tel: +34 983 423 000
Fax: +34 983 423 234

CATALUÑA

Universidad Autónoma de Barcelona, Campus Univ de Bellaterra, Edificio A. Rectorado, 08193 Bellaterra (Barcelona)
Tel: +34 93 581 1000
Fax: +34 93 581 2000
Website: www.uab.es

Universidad de Barcelona
Rectorado, Gran Vía de les Corts Catalanes, 585, 08007 Barcelona
Tel: +34 93 403 5546
Fax: +34 93 317 9483

Centro Docente de Enseñanza Superior Abat Oliba
Bellesguard, 30, 08035 Barcelona
Tel: +34 93 418 9893
Fax: +34 93 418 9380

Universidad de Girona
Rectorado, Edificio de les Aligues, Pza San Domènec, s/n, 17004 Girona
Tel: +34 972 418 011
Fax: +34 972 418 031
Website: www.udg.es

Universidad de Lleida
Edifici del Rectorat, Pza Victor Siurana, 1, 25003 Lleida
Tel: +34 973 702 000
Fax: +34 973 702 062

Universidad Politécnica de Cataluña
Rectorado, Avda Doctor Gregorio Marañón, 42, 08028 Barcelona
Tel: +34 93 401 6100/6200
Fax" +34 93 401 6102
Website: www.upc.es

EUNCET – Escola Universidad de Negocios de la Caixa de Terrassa
Rambla d'Egara, 340, 08221 Terrassa (Barcelona)
Tel: +34 93 733 1920
Fax: +34 93 733 1393

UNIVERSITIES

Universidad Pompeu Fabra
Rectorado, Pza de la Mercé, 10-12,
08002 Barcelona
Tel: +34 93 542 2020
Fax: +34 93 542 2002
Website: www.upf.es/cas/index. html

Universidad Ramon Llull
Oficina Central, Sant Joan de la Salle,
8, 08022 Barcelona
Tel: +34 93 253 0450
Fax: +34 93 418 8065
Emai:l urlsc@sec.url.es
Website: www.url.es

ESADE – Escuela Superior de Administración y Dirección de Empresas
Avda de Pedralbes, 60-62, 08034
Barcelona
Tel: +34 93 280 6162
Fax: +34 93 204 8105

Universidad Rovira i Virgilii
Gerenecia y Servicios Centrales,
Rectorado, C/Escorxador, s/n, 43003
Tarragona
Tel: +34 977 558 000
Fax: +34 977 558 022

EXTREMADURA
Universidad de Extremadura
Servicio de Información y Orientación
(SIO), Edificio "La Casa Grande",
Pizarro, 8
Tel: +34 927 243 227
Website: www.unex.es

GALICIA
Universidad de la Coruña
Rectorado, Edif. Maestranza, Rúa de
Maestranza, s/n, 15001 La Coruña
Tel: +34 981 213 344
Fax: +34 981 226 404
Website: www.udc.es

Universidad de Santiago de Compostela
Rectorado, Palacio de San
Jéronimo, Pza del Obradoiro, s/n,
15705 Santiago de Compostela
Tel: +34 981 563 100
Fax: +34 981 588 522
Website: www.usc.es

Universidad de Vigo
Rua Oporto, 1, 36201 Vigo
(Pontevedra)
Tel: +34 986 813 636
Fax: +34 986 813 554
Website: www.uvigo.es

LA RIOJA
Universidad de La Rioja, Rectorado,
C/La Cig͵eña, 60, 26004 Logroño
Tel: +34 941 299 109
Fax: +34 941 299 120

MADRID
Universidad de Alcalá,
Colegio de
San Pedro y San Pablo, Edificio de San
Ildefonso, Pza de San Diego, s/n,
28801 Alcalá de Henares (Madrid)
Tel: +34 91 885 4041/4000
Fax: +34 91 885 4126
Website: www.alcala.es

Centro de Enseñanza Superior Luis Vives
Tutor, 35, 28008 Madrid
Tel: +34 91 559 1221
Fax: +34 91 547 7902

Universidad Alfonso X El Sabio,
Avda Universidad, 1, 28691 Villaneu-
va de la Cañada (Madrid)
Tel: +34 91 810 9100/9200
Fax" +34 91 810 9101

Universidad Antonio de Nebrija,
Campus de la Dehesa de la Villa,
Pirineos, 55, 28040 Madrid
Tel" +34 91 311 6602
Email" ddu@dii.unnet.es
Website" www.unnet.es

Centro Universitario ESTEMA,
Campus del Parque Tecnológico, C/3
Sector Oeste, 46980 Paterna, Valencia
Tel: +34 96 131 8500
Fax: +34 96 131 8189

Universidad Autónoma de Madrid,
Ciudad Universitaria de Cantoblanco,
Ctra de Colmenar Viejo, Km 15,
28049 Madrid
Tel: +34 91 397 5000
Fax: +34 91 397 4123

Universidad Carlos III de Madrid
Edifico Rectorado, Desp. 8.5, Campus
de Getafe, C/Madrid, 126, 28903
Getafe. Tel +34 91 624 9521
Website: www.uc3m.es

Universidad Complutense de Madrid
Rectorado, Avda Séneca, 2, Ciudad
Universitaria, 28040 Madrid
Tel: +34 91 394 1000/01/02
Fax: +34 91 394 3497
Email: infocom@rect.ucm.es
Website: www.ucm.es

Centro de Enseñanza Superior San Pablo (Madrid)
Julian Romea, 23, 28040 Madrid
Tel: +34 91 456 6300
Fax: +34 91 553 8610

Centro de Estudios Superiores Sociales y Jurídicos Ramón Carande
Paseo de los Artilleros, s/n, 28032
Vicálvaro, Madrid
Tel: +34 91 775 1213
Fax: +34 91 775 0342

Centro Universitario Francisco de Vitoria, Crta Pozuelo a Majadahonda,
Km 1,800, 28223 Pozuelo de Alarcón
(Madrid)
Tel: +34 91 351 1566
Fax: +34 91 351 1716

Colegio Universitario "Cardinal Cisneros"
Maldonado, 48, 28006 Madrid
Tel: +34 91 402 9173
Fax: +34 91 309 2099

Colegio Universitario María Cristina
Real Monasterio de El Escorial,
Alamillos, 1, 28200 S.L. de El Escorial
(Madrid)
Tel: +34 91 890 4545
Fax: +34 91 890 6609

Colegio Universitario de Segovia
Trinidad, 3, 40001 Segovia
Tel: +34 921 434 561
Fax: +34 921 443 283

CUNEF – Colegio Universitario de Estudios Financieros
Serrano Anguita, 9 y 13, 28004
Madrid
Tel: +34 91 448 0891
Fax: +34 91 594 1366

Universidad Europea de Madrid (CEES)
Campus Universitario, Tajo, s/n,
Urbanización El Bosque, 28670
Villaviciosa de Odón (Madrid)
Tel: +34 91 616 7142
Fax: +34 91 616 8256
Website: www.uem.es

Universidad Politécnica de Madrid
Rectorado, Avda Ramior de Maetzu,
7, 28040 Madrid
Tel: +34 91 336 6000
Website: www.upm.es

Colegio Universitario CEU – Arquitectura
Camino de las Moreras, s/n, Ciudad
Universitaria, 28040 Madrid
Tel: +34 91 549 3800
Fax: +34 91 549 3850

Universidad Pontificia de Comillas
Sede Cantoblanco, Universidad de
Comillas, 3, 28049 Madrid
Tel: +34 91 734 3950
Fax: +34 91 734 4570
Website: www.upco.es

ICADE – Instituto Universitario de Administración y Dirección de Empresas, Avda Alfonso XIII, 162, 28016 Madrid
Tel: +34 91 350 2070
Fax: +34 91 350 2036

Universidad San Pablo (CEU)
Rectorado, Julián Romea, 18, 28003
Madrid
Tel: +34 91 536 2727
Fax: +34 91 536 0660

MURCIA
Universidad de Murcia
Rectorado, Avenida Teniente Flomesta,
s/n, Edificio Convalescencia, 30003

Murcia
Tel: +34 968 363 000
Fax: +34 968 363 417
Website: www.um.es

NAVARRA
Universidad de Navarra
Rectorado, Edificio Central, Campus
Universitario, 31080 Pamplona
Tel: +34 948 425 600
Fax: +34 948 425 619
Email: jarema@central.unav.es
Website: www.unav.es

Universidad P´blica de Navarra
Rectorado, Campus Arrosadía, s/n,
31006 Pamplona
Tel: +34 948 169 001/000
Fax: +34 948 169 004
Website: www.upna.es

PAÍS VASCO
Universidad de Deusto, Avda de la
Universidades, 24, 48007 Bilbao

FURTHER INFORMATION

For further information about the Spanish education system and university entrance, contact: Ministerio de Educación y Cultura, Oficina de Información, C/Alcalá, 36, 28014 Madrid (Tel: +34 91 701 8000) or Ministerio de Educación y Ciencia Subdirrección General de Cooperación Internacional, Paseo del Prado, 28, 28014 Madrid, (Tel: +34 506 5600). For a comprehensive overview of the Spanish university system you should consult 'Elige tu Futuro: Qué y Dónde Estudiar', a book covering every aspect of the university system, from how to choose your degree to a factual profile of every university in Spain. It even includes a detailed guide as to how much it costs to study every subject. The book itself is not cheap (9,599ptas), so it would be best to consult it in a library, if you can. The book is published by 'Círculo de Progreso', Información Laboral y Académica, C/Serrano, 93 3ʃC, 28006 Madrid, (Tel: +34 91 562 5784, Fax: +34 91 562 3174,Email:circulo@ ibm.net). For those interested in postgraduate studies, Círculo de Progreso also publish a book called 'Masters – Estudios de Progreso' (5,900ptas).

Tel: +34 94 445 3100
Fax: +34 445 2454
Website: www.deusto.es

ESTE – Facultad Ciencias Ecónomicas Empresariales
Universidad de Deusto, Camino de Mundaiz, 50, Apdo de Corrreos, 1359, 20080 Donostia-San Sebastián
Tel: +34 943 273 100
Fax: +34 943 273 932

Universidad del País Vasco
Rectorado, Campus de Leioa, 48940 Leioa (Vizcaya)
Tel: +34 94 464 7700
Fax: +34 94 480 1473

VALENCIA
Universidad de Alicante, Rectorado, Campus de San Vicente del Raspeig, 03690 Alicante
Te:l +34 96 590 3400
Website: www.ua.es

Centro de Estudios Universitarios CEU San Pablo (Elche)
Comissari, 1, 03203 Elche (Alicante)
Tel: +34 96 542 6486
Fax: +34 96 542 6486

Universidad Jaume I
Campus de la Penyeta Roja, 12071 Castellón de la Plana
Tel: +34 964 345 680
Fax: +34 964 345 840
Email: traver@sg.uji.es
Website: www.uji.es

Universidad Politécnica de Valencia
Rectorado, Camino de Vera, s/n, 46071 Valencia
Tel: +34 96 387 7000
Website: www.upv.es

Universidad de Valencia Estudi General
Carrer de la Nau, 2, 46071 Valencia
Tel: +34 96 386 4100

CEU San Pablo
Apdo 68/Edif Seminario Metropolitano, 46113 Moncada (Valencia)
Tel: +34 96 139 1616
Fax: +34 96 139 5272

DISTANCE-LEARNING UNIVERSITIES
Universidad Nacional de Educación a Distancia (UNED)
Bravo Murillo, 38, 28071 Madrid
Tel: +34 91 398 6000/6600
Fax: +34 91 549 6582
General Information +34 91 398 6090/91/92/93 and 6635
Website: www.uned.es

Universidad Oberta de Catalunya
Avda Tibidabo, 39-43, 08035 Barcelona
Tel: +34 93 417 4349
Fax: +34 93 417 6495
Website: www.uoc.es

Index

Abono Transportes (travel card) 19
AC Idiomas 100
Academia Amor de Dios 68
Academia Eureka 128-131
Accommodation 29
ACE Consultores de Idioma . . . . .
. 127-128
Acting courses 204-207
Addresses 32-33
Adult education 27
Aeroclub Ultralijeros 'El Casar'
Guadalajara 229
Aguas Blancas 232
Al-Andalus, S.C. 152
Álava, dance schools in 76
ALBA Language Consulting S.L. . .
. 131-132
Albaicín 17
Alcázar 17
Alicante 17
Alicante, language schools in . . . .
. 92-95
Aliseda - Escuelas Internacionales
de Español 132-133
Altea Cursos (Babel Idiomas) 92-93
Alternative courses 207-209
Amadís de Gaula 162-163
Ambulances, phone number . . .23
Andalucía 5, 16-17
Antonio Gaudí 15
Applying to study 24
Aragón 14
Arcade 45-47
Arriving in Spain 18-23
Art and Design 41-61
Art schools 24, 42, 44-61
Arte Hoy 44
Artestudio, Hermosilla 61
Asturias 5, 14, 40
Asturias, language schools in . . . .
. 95-96
Atocha station, phone number .23
Aula de Música Moderna y Jazz . .
. 218-219
Australia Embassy 18
AVE (high speed train) . . .20, 21
Ávila, language schools in . .96-99
Avinyó Espai Músical 219
Bachillerato 25
Baile de Salon 66
Ballroom dancing associations .67
Barajas airport 19, 23
Barcelona, art schools in 17
Barcelona, dance schools in .76-77
Barcelona, language schools in . . .
. 100-112
Barna House - Centro de Estudio de
Español 100-101
Basque 6, 14

Benidorm 40
Bilbao 16
British and Northern Irish
Consulate 18
Bullfighting 33
Bullfighting courses 203-204
Bureaucracy 33
Buses in Spain 21, 23
Cáceres 17
Canadian Embassy 18
Canary Islands 112-113
Canoeing courses 232
Cantabria 5, 14
Carmen de las Cuevas . . .113-114
Carpe Diem Escuela de Español . .
. 133
Castellano 6, 15
Castila Centro de Estudios
Hispanicos 115-117
Castilla y León 5, 14
Castilla-La Mancha 5, 17
Catalan 6
Cataluña 5, 14-15, 17
CEGRI - Centro Granadí de
Español 120-121
Centre for Cultural Interchange . .
. 134-135
Centro de Arte Moderna Reina
Sofia 11
Centro de Estudios de Castellano .
. 152-154
Centro de Estudios TAME S.L. . . .
. 179-180
Centro de Lenguas Modernas de la
Centro Humboldt 101-102
Centro Internacional de Danza
Carmen Roche 69-70
Centros Nicolá Salmerón .212-213
Ceramics schools 44
Chamartin station, ...23
CILCE Centro Internacional de
Lengua y Cultura Española . . . . .
. 180-181
CLIC - Centro de Lenguas e Inter-
cambio Cultural 175-176
Coffee Consulting 233-234
Colegio Lorca 23, 163-164
Colegio Maravillas 154-155
Colegios Mayores 29-30
Comunidad de Madrid 13
Comunidad Valenciana 17
comunidades autónomas .5, 6, 14,
. 13-17
Consejería de Educacíon 242
Cookery courses 208-210
Córdoba 16, 17
Costa Brava, the 15
Costa del Sol 15
Costa del Sol 17

COU 241
Courses, finding out about . . . . . .
. 234-235
Credit cards, phone number
if lost 23
Cuenca 17
Cultural activities in Madrid . . . . .
. 235-237
Cultural courses 235-237
Cursos Manuel de Falla in Granada
. 224
Dalí 15 . . . .
Dance schools 24, 63-81
Dance schools 67-81
Dance, accreditation and
professionalism 64
Dance, what to wear 64-65
DELE 86
Design 41-61
Design degrees in Barcelona . . .44
Directory of universities . .247-253
Distrito Compartido 243
Distrito/nico 243
Diving courses 232-233
Documento Nacional de Indentidad
(DNI) 6
Don Quijote 165-166
Dressmaking courses 213-217
Education – ciclos 243-244
Education council 242
Education system, structure . . .28
Education, adult 27
Education, primary 26
Education, secondary 26
El Correo Español-El Pueblo
Vasco/Universidad del País Vasco .
. 247
El Escorial 13
El Greco 13
El País 31
El Valle de los Caídos 13
Embassys 18
ENFOREX - Centro de Estudios
internacionales 135-136
Enrolment/payment at language
schools 25
Environmental Education .219-220
Esade Escuela de Idiomas 102-103
Escola D'Arts I Oficis Diputació de
Barcelona 58
Escola d'Arts I Tècniques de la
Moda 216-217
Escola D'Arts Musicals Luthier . .
220
Escola de Música "La Guineu" . .
. 221-222
Escola de Música Joan Llongueres
. 221
Escola de Música Juan Pedro

Carrero 221-222
Escola Oficial d'Idiomas Barcelona
- Drassanes 104
Escuela de Arte no.4 Diseño de
Interiores 61
Escuela de Arte y Antigüedades
. 245
Escuela de Artes Decorativas de
Madrid 47-48
Escuela de Baile de Salón 70
Escuela de Bailes de Salón "Loreto
y José Ignacio" 79-80
Escuela de Dansa Merche
Esmeralda 71
Escuela de Danza Teatro Kainos . .
. 72-73
Escuela de Hostelería Arnadi
(Hofmann) 211
Escuela de Idiomas "Nerja" S.L. . .
. 155-156
Escuela de Música "Chamartín" . .
. 223-224
Escuela de Música de Bellaterra . .
. 222
Escuela de Música de Farré . . .222
Escuela de Música Fundación
Alcalde Zoilo Ruiz-Mateos (guitar
and band instruments) 223
Escuela de Periodismo UAM/EL
País 246-247 . . . .
Escuela de Vela Fuerza Seis . . .231
Escuela Forma 58-59
Escuela Hispalense 178-179
Escuela Mediterráneo 156-157
Escuela Montalbán - Tnadem
Granada 117-118
Escuela Oficial de Cerámica .48-49
Escuela oficial de Idiomas . .85-86
Escuela Oficial de Idiomas - Gener-
alitat Valenciana 181
Escuela Oficial de Idiomas de
Madrid 136
Escuela Oficial de Idiomas de
Salamanca 166-167
Escuela Superior de Dibujo
Profesional 49-50
Escuela Terasa Muñiz 50-52
Escuela ULM 229
Estudi Dibuix I Pintura Dolors Pons
. 61
Estudio de Dansa "Pepa Guerra" .
. 73-74
Estudio de Danza Carmen Cubillo
. 74-75
Estudio Internacional Sampere 246
Estudios de Danza Carmen Senra .
. 75-76
Etiquette 33-34
Eurocentres Madrid 136-138
European University 247
Experiment - Intercambio 66 . . . .
. 138-139
Extremadura 17
Fashion Design courses . .213-217
Festival de Jerez 66
Finances at university 244
Fire brigade, phone number . . .23
Flamenco 16, 63
Flamenco guitar 66
Flamenco outside Spain 65-66
Flying 229-233

Food 34-35
Formación professional 25
Fundació Centre del Vidre de
Barcelona 60
Fundación de Arte y Autores
Contemporáneos - ARAUCO 53-54
Galicia 5, 15, 17, 40
Galician 6
Gaudí 41
Generation gap 35-36
Giralda Center 176-177
Giralda tower 17
Golf 229
Goya41 . . . .
Gran Canaria School of Languages
. 112-113
Granada 16, 17
Granada, language schools in . . .
. 113-124
Guggenheim 16
Hang-gliding 230
Health and welfare 37
Hidden Trails 231
Hispalengua 185 186
Hispalingua - Secreiado
Internacional 95
Hispana Estudio - 2 139
Hispano Continental S.L. .167-168
Homestays 30-31
Horseriding 229-230
Hostales and pensiones 32
IADE (Institución Artistica
de Enseñanza 54-55
Ibiza 37
Inlingua Idiomas 172-173
Instituto Cervantes 87-90
Instituto de Español Picasso . . . .
. 157-158
Instituto de Estudios de
Iberoamérica y Portugal 246
Instituto de Formación Empresarial
de la Cámara Oficial de Comercio e
Industria de Madrid - IFE 140
Instituto de Música y
Tecnología (IMT) 225-227
Instituto de Restauracíon Oeben . .
. 246
Instituto Español "Murallas de
Ávila" - IEMA 96-97
Instituto Español de Granada -
Centre de Estudios y Vacaciones
Almuñecar 121-123
Instituto Hernán Cortés . .140-141
Instituto Mangold . .104-105, 141-
. 142
Instituto Técnico del Vestir
(INTEVE) 218
Instituto Vox 142-143
International House Barcelona . . .
. 105-107
Ireland Embassy 18
Irish pubs in Madrid 12
ISLA-Instituto Salmantina de
Lenguas Aplicadas 169-170
JAÉN Academia de Baile d
Flamenco Conchita Fernández . . .
. 78-79
Jewish in Spain 39
Kenny Roberts Training Ranch . .
. 232
Kingsbrook 107-108

Kroom Dos Diseño 218
La Coruña, language courses in . .
. 126-127
La Latina 10
La Rioja 15
Language schools . . .24, 83-201
Language schools approved by
Ministry of Education and Culture
(private) 191-201
Language schools approved by
Ministry of Education and Culture
(university/state) 186-191
Language schools, choosing a
school 83
Language schools, miscellaneous . .
. 83-201
Language schools, official
recognition 85
Language schools, teachers .86-87
Language schools, what to look for
. 84-85
Language Studies International
(LSI) 143-144
Léon, language courses in 124-126
Learning for Pleasure 211-212
Lengua Viva S.L. 177-178
Lerida, art schools in 61
L'Estudí 59
Letras Castellanas 97-99
Lewis School of Languages,
The 109-110
Lexis Instituto de Idiomas 158-159
Liceo Internacional Agarimo .126-
127
Linguarama Iberica, S.A . .108-109
Living in Spain 29-40
Lottery 37
Málaga, language schools in .152-
161
MADRID 9-13
Madrid 41
Madrid - cultural activities . . . . . .
. 235-237
Madrid Plus S.L. 144-145
Madrid, art schools in 61
Madrid, ceramic schools in . . .44
Madrid, dance schools in . .79-81
Madrid, language schools in . . . . .
. 127,152
Madrileños 10
Málaga 17
Masters courses 42
Masters courses in Spanish .91-92
Max Latino 80-81
Metro in Madrid 19-20
Metro, phone number 23
Mezquite 17
Ministry of Education and Science
. 27
Miscellaneaous schools 24
Miscellaneous courses . .203-204
Miscellaneous sport 229
Monastery of Guadalupe 17
Moorish population 39
Motorcycle racing 232
Mountain sports (walking,
canoeing, white water rafting,
winter sports) 231-232
Mudèjar 14
Murcia 5, 17
Music 37

Music 218-228
Músicaula 227-229
Navarra 15-16
Navarra, language schools in
. 161,162
New Zealand Embassy 18
Nightlife 37
Paella 17
País Vasco 16
Paramo - Academia de Español . . .
. 182-183
Paraninfo 145-146
Parc Güell 15
Parque Nacional de Ordesa 14
Paseo del Prado 10
Pensiones 32
Picasso 41
Picos de Europa 14
Police in Madrid 23
Police, phone numer 23
Politics 38-39
Postal service, phone number . .23
Postal system 33
Postgraduate studies 244-247
Prado, the 11
Press 36, 37, 38
Press, gossip 36-37
Primary school 25
Private universities 239-240
Puerto de Navacerrada 13
Puerto de Navacerrada 13
Quality of university education 244
Rafting courses 232
Regional dances 63
Religion 39
RENFE 21
Renting a flat 31-32
Retiro, the 8
Royal family 39
Sagrada Familia 15
Sailing courses 232, 234
Salamanca 14
Salamanca, language schools in . . .
. 162-172
Salminter - Escuela Salmantina de
Estudios Internacionales .170-171
Saltsan 212
Sampere Estudio Internacional . . .
. 146-147
San Sebastian 16
San Sebastian, language schools in
. 172-173
Santander 14
Santiago de Compostela, language
schools in 173-174
Secondary school 25
Segovia 13
Segovia, language schools in . . . . .
. 174-175
Segundamano 31
Selectividad 24, 25, 240-244
Sevilla 16, 17
Sevilla, dance schools in 81
Sevilla, language schools in . . . . . .
. 175-179
Sierra 13
Sierra Madrileña 13
Sierra Nevada 17
Sierra y Mar 123-124
Skydiving courses 232
Smoking 39
South Africa Embassy 18

Spain and the Spanish 5-17
Spanish education system . . 25-28
Spanorama International .159-160
Sport 229
Stamps 33
State-run universities 239
Structure of the education system .
28 . . . .
TAI - Escuela Superior de Artes y
Espectaulos 206-208
Taller de Musics S.A. 223-224
Taller Fang 55-56
Taller Lingüístico - Instituto Berlin
. 93-94
Taller-Escuela "Camille Cermistas"
. 56-57
Tandem Barcelona 111-112
Tapas 35
Tarifa, language schools in 178-179
Tarragona, dance schools in . . .81
Taxis in Madrid 20
Teachers of Spanish as a foreign
language courses 91
Teaching courses 217-218
Terminology, for art schools . . .42
Thyssen-Bornemisza 11
Time 40
Toledo 13
Torremolinos 17, 40
Torrevieja 17
Tourist offices in Madrid 23
Trains in Spain 20-21
Travel 19-23
Travel discounts 22
Travel etiquette 22-23
Trekking courses 231-232
Trujillo 17
United Kingdom Embassy 18
United States of America Embassy
. 18
Univeridad Antonio de Nebrija . .
. 148-149
Univeridad de Alcalá de Henares .
. 147-148
Universidad Complutense de
Madrid 149-150, 245
Universidad de Alcalà de Henares .
. 245
Universidad de Alcalá, Aula de
Música 224
Universidad de Alicante 94-95
Universidad de Barcelona 245
Universidad de Barcelona/ Universi-
dad de las Islas Baleares, Cátedra
Ramon Llull 99-100
Universidad de Granada - Centro
de Lenguas Modernas (CLM) . . . .
. 118-120
Universidad de Léon - Cursos de
Español Lengua Estranjera 124-126
Universidad de Málaga en Ronda .
. 160-161
Universidad de Navarra . .161-162
Universidad de Salamanca 164-165
Universidad de Santiago de Com-
postela 173-174
Universidad del País Vasco . . .184-
185, 245
Universidad Internacional
Menéndez Pelayo 150-152
Universidad Internacional SEK
. 174-175

Universidad Pontificia de
Salamanca 171-172
Universitat de Valencia Estudi
General 181-182
Universities 239-253
University directory 247-253
University education 25
University entrance exams 240-244
University of Britain in Spain .247
Valdepeñas 17
Valencia 17
Valencia, dance schools in 81
Valencia, language schools in . . . .
. 179-182
Valladolid 14
Valladolid, dance schools in . .81
Valladolid, language schools in . . .
. 182-184
Vélez Per 216-217
Velázquez 41
Viajes Trekking 231-232
Visas and immigration 18-19
Vizcaya, language schools in . . . . .
. 184-185
Vocational training 26
Walking holidays 233
Warwick House 183-184
Watersports - miscellaneous . . . . .
. 232-233
Weather 40
Websites 205
What to study 240
Where to study 239-240
Winchester School of Art (in
Barcelona) 60-61
Windsurfing courses 234
Wine and coffee tasting . .233-234
Youth cards 22
Zaragoza 14
Zaragoza, language schools in
. 185-186